Nashville District
Engineering Division
Relocations Branch

The Asphalt Handbook

THE ASPHALT
HANDBOOK

THE ASPHALT INSTITUTE

April 1965 Edition

Fourth Printing   May 1968

Manual Series No. 4 (MS-4)

FOREWORD

This is a new and completely revised edition of THE ASPHALT HANDBOOK, standard reference work in the field of asphalt technology and construction.

First issued in 1923 as the ASPHALT POCKET REFERENCE FOR HIGHWAY ENGINEERS, the HANDBOOK was reprinted at intervals without material change until 1937. In that year, owing to a rising demand for a more comprehensive volume incorporating design and construction features in related asphalt engineering fields, the first ASPHALT HANDBOOK was published by The Asphalt Institute.

Subsequent editions during the next decade broadened the scope of the book and recognized the continuing advances in asphalt technology. In the aftermath of World War II, however, a new and vigorous interest in asphalt engineering was accompanied by a tremendous forward surge in asphalt technology. This quickening of interest, reflected in vastly increased activity in the field and laboratory, complicated the problem of revising the HANDBOOK. Almost as rapidly as new information could be properly evaluated and accepted, its relative significance was altered appreciably by additional information flowing from carefully controlled investigations.

THE ASPHALT HANDBOOK has kept pace with these changes with new printings and complete revisions when such were deemed necessary. At the same time The Asphalt Institute's program of publishing complete manuals on the various phases of asphalt technology and construction has progressed to the point where it was felt that duplication in the HANDBOOK should be reduced. This new edition, therefore, summarizes, with references, the information contained in other Asphalt Institute technical manuals. Further, it contains additional data not yet found in other Institute publications.

For a list of Asphalt Institute technical publications, see the end papers.

The Asphalt Institute
The Asphalt Institute Building
College Park, Maryland
April, 1965

TABLE OF CONTENTS

LIST OF ILLUSTRATIONS

LIST OF TABLES

Table		Page

Table		Page

Table		Page

Chapter I

USES OF ASPHALT

1.01 OCCURRENCE.—Asphalt is a natural constituent of most petroleums in which it exists in solution. The crude petroleum is refined to separate the various fractions and recover the asphalt. Similar processes occurring in nature have formed natural deposits of asphalt, some practically free from extraneous matter and some in which the asphalt has become mixed with variable quantities of mineral matter, water, and other substances. Natural deposits in which asphalt occurs within a porous rock structure are known as rock asphalts.

1.02 PROPERTIES.—Asphalt is of particular interest to the engineer because it is a strong cement, readily adhesive, highly waterproof, and durable. It is a plastic substance which imparts controllable flexibility to mixtures of mineral aggregates with which it is usually combined. It is moreover highly resistant to the action of most acids, alkalies and salts. Although a solid or semi-solid at ordinary atmospheric temperatures, asphalt may be readily liquefied by the application of heat, or by dissolving it in petroleum solvents of varying volatility, or by emulsification.

1.03 BRIEF HISTORY.—

Prehistoric.—Skeletons of prehistoric animals preserved intact to present day in surface deposits of asphalt, La Brea pit, Los Angeles, Calif.

3200 to 540 B.C.—Recent archaeological excavations show extensive use of asphalt in Mesopotamia and Indus Valley, as cement for masonry and highway construction and as waterproofing layer for temple baths and water tanks.

300 B.C.—Asphalt extensively used for mummification in Egypt.

1802 A.D.—Rock asphalt used in France for floor, bridge, and sidewalk surfacing.

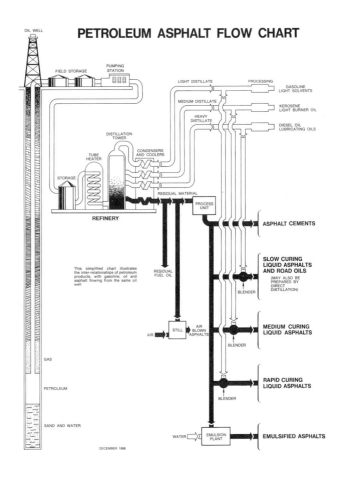

Figure I-1—Petroleum Asphalt Flow Chart

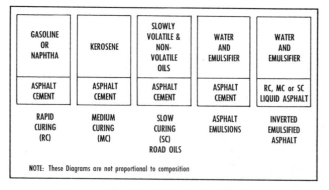

GASOLINE OR NAPHTHA	KEROSENE	SLOWLY VOLATILE & NON-VOLATILE OILS	WATER AND EMULSIFIER	WATER AND EMULSIFIER
ASPHALT CEMENT	ASPHALT CEMENT	ASPHALT CEMENT	ASPHALT CEMENT	RC, MC or SC LIQUID ASPHALT
RAPID CURING (RC)	MEDIUM CURING (MC)	SLOW CURING (SC) ROAD OILS	ASPHALT EMULSIONS	INVERTED EMULSIFIED ASPHALT

NOTE: These Diagrams are not proportional to composition

Figure I-2—Liquid Asphaltic Products

1838 A.D.—Rock asphalt imported and used in sidewalk construction in Philadelphia.

1870 A.D. (circa)—First asphalt pavement laid in Newark, New Jersey by Professor E. J. DeSmedt, a Belgian chemist.

1876 A.D.—First sheet asphalt pavement laid in Washington, D. C., with imported lake asphalt.

1902 A.D.—Approximately 20,000 tons of asphalt refined from petroleum in the United States.

Since 1926—The petroleum asphalt and road oil tonnage produced annually has increased steadily —from 3,000,000 tons in 1926 to over 8,000,000 tons in 1946. Then to more than 24,000,000 tons in 1964.

1.04 ASPHALT FROM PETROLEUM.—Almost all asphalt used in the United States is refined from petroleum. Such asphalt is produced in a variety of types and grades ranging from hard brittle solids to almost water-thin liquids. The semisolid form, known as asphalt cement, is the basic material. Types of products produced by refining are shown in Figure I-1.

Liquid asphaltic products are generally prepared by cutting back or blending asphalt cements with petroleum distillates or by emulsifying them with water. Types of liquid asphaltic products are illustrated in Figure I-2.

Table 1-1—RECOMMENDED USES OF ASPHALT

TYPE OF CONSTRUCTION	References*	Paving 40-50	Paving 60-70	Paving 85-100	Paving 120-150	Paving 200-300	RC 70	RC 250	RC 800	RC 3000	MC 30	MC 70	MC 250	MC 800	MC 3000	SC 70	SC 250	SC 800	SC 3000	RS-1	RS-2	MS-2	SS-1	SS-1h	RS-2K	RS-3K	SM-K	CM-K	SS-K	SS-Kh
ASPHALT CONCRETE AND PLANT MIX, HOT LAID																														
Highways	SS-1		x	x	x										x				x				x						x	x
Airports	MS-11		x	x																										
Parking Areas	MS-4		x	x																										
Driveways	MS-4		x	x																										
Curbs	SS-3		x	x																										
Industrial Floors	MS-4	x	x																											
Blocks	MS-4	x	x																											
PLANT MIX, COLD LAID																														
Graded Aggregate	SS-1													x				x				x	x					x		
ROAD MIX																														
Open-graded Aggregate	MS-14							x	x				x	x							x						x			
Dense-graded Aggregate	MS-14							x	x				x	x			x	x				x		x						
Clean Sand	MS-14							x	x					x			x	x						x			x			
Sandy Soil	MS-14						x	x	x					x				x					x							
PENETRATION MACADAM																														
Large Voids	MS-13					x				x											x					x				
Small Voids	MS-13				x				x																x					
SURFACE TREATMENTS																														
Single, Multiple and Aggregate Seal	MS-13				x			x	x											x	x				x	x			x	x
Sand Seal	MS-13							x	x											x	x				x				x	x

— 4 —

Slurry Seal....................	MS-13																x	x²	x
Fog Seal......................	MS-13																x	x²	x²
Prime Coat, open surfaces......	MS-13			x				x											
Prime Coat, tight surfaces.....	MS-13		x		x	x				x							x	x²	
Tack Coat.....................	MS-13		x		x							x					x²	x²	x
Dust Laying...................	MS-13		x		x	x				x							x²	x²	
PATCHING MIX																			
Immediate Use...............	SS-1						x	x	x										
Stock Pile....................	SS-1						x	x	x						x	x			
HYDRAULIC STRUCTURES																			
Membrane Linings, Canals & Reservoirs..	MS-12	x³																	
Hot Laid, Graded Aggregate Mix for Groins, Dam Facings, Canal & Reservoir Linings........	MS-12	x	x														x⁴	x⁴	x⁴
CRACK FILLING.................	MS-4	x	x								x						x⁴	x⁴	x⁴
MEMBRANE ENVELOPE.............	MS-1	x		Blown asphalts, mineral-filled asphalt cements, and preformed joint compositions															
EXPANSION JOINTS..............	MS-4	x	Blown asphalts																
UNDERSEALING PCC..............	SS-6	Blown asphalts																	
ROOFING.......................	MS-4	Blown asphalts																	
MISCELLANEOUS.................		Specially prepared asphalts for pipe coatings, battery boxes, automobile undersealing, electrical wire coating, insulation, tires, paints, asphalt tile, wall board, paper sizing, waterproofing, floor mats, ice cream sacks, adhesives, phonograph records, tree grafting compounds, grouting mixtures, etc.																	

In northern areas where rate of curing is slower, a shift from MC to RC or from SC to MC may be desirable. For very warm climates, a shift to next heavier grade may be warranted.

1 In combination with powdered asphalt.
2 Diluted with water.
3 Also 50-60 penetration blown asphalt and prefabricated panels.
4 Slurry mix.
*Publications of The Asphalt Institute where specifications or additional information may be found.

Table I-2—SUGGESTED GRADES OF ASPHALT CEMENT FOR DIFFERENT CLIMATES

PAVING USES	CLIMATE	
	Hot and Temperate	Cold
Airfields		
Runways.................	60–70	85–100
Taxiways.................	60–70	85–100
Parking Aprons...........	60–70	85–100
Highways		
Heavy Traffic.............	60–70	85–100
Medium to Light Traffic.....	85–100	120–150
Streets		
Heavy Traffic.............	60–70	85–100*
Medium to Light Traffic.....	85–100	85–100
Driveways		
Industrial................	60–70	85–100
Service Station............	60–70	85–100
Residential...............	85–100	85–100
Parking Lots		
Industrial................	60–70	60–70
Commercial..............	60–70	85–100
Recreational		
Tennis Courts.............	85–100	85–100
Playgrounds..............	85–100	85–100
Curbing..................	60–70	85–100

* 60–70 penetration normally used for sheet asphalt.

Chapter II

TERMS RELATING TO ASPHALT AND ITS USES

A.—*Asphaltic Materials*

2.01 ASPHALT.—"A dark brown to black cementitious material; solid, semisolid, or liquid in consistency; in which the predominating constituents are bitumens which occur in nature as such or which are obtained as residue in refining petroleum." (ASTM Designation D8.)

Asphalt is a constituent in varying proportions of most crude petroleums.

2.02 ASPHALT BLOCKS.—Asphalt concrete molded under high pressure. The type of aggregate mixture composition, amount and type of asphalt, and the size and thickness of the blocks may be varied to suit usage requirements.

2.03 ASPHALT, BLOWN OR OXIDIZED.—Asphalt that is treated by blowing air through it at elevated temperature to give it characteristics desired for certain special uses such as roofing, pipe coating, undersealing portland cement concrete pavements, membrane envelopes, and hydraulic applications.

2.04 ASPHALT, CATALYTICALLY BLOWN.—An air-blown asphalt produced by using a catalyst during the blowing process.

2.05 ASPHALT CEMENT.—Asphalt that is refined to meet specifications for paving, industrial, and special purposes. (See Table IV-1.) Its penetration is usually between 40 and 300. The term is often abbreviated A.C.

2.06 ASPHALT JOINT FILLER.—An asphaltic product used for filling cracks and joints in pavement and other structures.

2.07 ASPHALT JOINT FILLERS, PREFORMED. —Premolded strips of asphalt mixed with fine mineral substances, fibrous materials, cork, sawdust, etc.; manufactured in dimensions suitable for construction joints.

2.08 ASPHALT, LIQUID.—An asphaltic material having a soft or fluid consistency that is beyond the range of measurement by the normal penetration test, the limit of which is 300 maximum. Liquid asphalts include (A) Cutback Asphalts and (B) Emulsified Asphalts.

A. Cutback Asphalt.—Asphalt cement which has been liquefied by blending with petroleum solvents (also called diluents), as for the RC and MC liquid asphalts (see a and b below). Upon exposure to atmospheric conditions the diluents evaporate, leaving the asphalt cement to perform its function.

a. Rapid-Curing (RC) Asphalt.—Liquid asphalt composed of asphalt cement and a naphtha or gasoline-type diluent of high volatility. (See Table IV-2.)

b. Medium-Curing (MC) Asphalt.—Liquid asphalt composed of asphalt cement and a kerosene-type diluent of medium volatility. (See Table IV-3.)

c. Slow-Curing (SC) Asphalt.—Liquid asphalt composed of asphalt cement and oils of low volatility (see Table IV-4).

d. Road-Oil.—A heavy petroleum oil, usually one of the Slow-Curing (SC) grades of liquid asphalt. (See Table IV-4.)

B. Emulsified Asphalt.—An emulsion of asphalt cement and water which contains a small amount of an emulsifying agent, a heterogeneous system containing two normally immiscible phases (asphalt and water) in which the water forms the continuous phase of the emulsion, and minute globules of asphalt form the discontinuous phase. (See Tables IV-5 and IV-6.) Emulsified asphalts may be of either the anionic, electro-negatively charged asphalt globules, or cationic, electro-positively charged asphalt globules types, depending upon the emulsifying agent.

An emulsified asphalt in which the continuous phase is asphalt, usually an RC or MC liquid asphalt, and the discontinuous phase is minute globules of water in relatively small quantities is called an inverted emulsified asphalt. This type emulsion may also be either anionic or cationic.

2.09 ASPHALT, MINERAL FILLED.—Asphalt containing finely divided mineral matter passing No. 200 sieve.

2.10 ASPHALT, NATURAL (NATIVE).—Asphalt occurring in nature which has been derived from petroleum by natural processes of evaporation of volatile fractions leaving the asphalt fractions. The native asphalts of most importance are found in the Trinidad and Bermudez Lake deposits. Asphalt from these sources often is called LAKE ASPHALT.

2.11 ASPHALT PAINT.—A liquid asphaltic product sometimes containing small amounts of other materials such as lampblack, aluminum flakes, and mineral pigments.

2.12. ASPHALT PANELS, PREMOLDED.—Generally made with a core of asphalt, minerals, and fibers, covered on each side by a layer of asphalt-impregnated felt or fabric, coated on the outside with hot applied asphalt. The panels are made under pressure and heat to a width of three to four feet by one-eighth to one inch thick, and to any desired length.

2.13 ASPHALT, PETROLEUM.—Asphalt refined from crude petroleum.

2.14 ASPHALT PLANKS.—Premolded mixtures of asphalt fiber and mineral filler, sometimes reinforced with steel or fiberglass mesh. They are usually made in three- to eight-foot lengths and six to twelve inches wide. Asphalt planks may also contain mineral grits which maintain a sandpaper texture throughout their life.

2.15 ASPHALT, POWDERED.—Solid or hard asphalt crushed or ground to a fine state of subdivision.

2.16 ASPHALT PRIMER.—A liquid asphalt of low viscosity which penetrates into a non-bituminous surface upon application.

2.17 ASPHALT, ROCK.—Porous rock such as sandstone or limestone that has become impregnated with natural asphalt through geologic process.

2.18 ASPHALT, SEMI-SOLID.—Asphalt which is intermediate in consistency between liquid asphalts and solid or hard asphalt—that is, normally has a penetration between 10 and 300.

2.19 ASPHALT, SOLID OR HARD.—Asphalt having a normal penetration of less than 10.

2.20 BITUMEN.—A mixture of hydrocarbons of natural or pyrogenous origin, or a combination of both; frequently accompanied by nonmetallic derivatives which may be gaseous, liquid, semisolid, or solid; and which are completely soluble in carbon disulfide.

2.21 FLUX OR FLUX OIL.—A thick, relatively nonvolatile fraction of petroleum which may be used to soften asphalt to a desired consistency; often used as base stock for manufacture of roofing asphalts.

2.22 GILSONITE.—A form of natural asphalt, hard and brittle, occurring in rock crevices or veins from which it is mined.

B.—*Asphalt Pavements and Surface Treatments*

2.23 AGGREGATE.—Any hard, inert, mineral material used for mixing in graduated fragments. It includes sand, gravel, crushed stone, and slag.

2.24 AGGREGATE, COARSE.—That retained on the No. 8 sieve.

2.25 AGGREGATE COARSE-GRADED.—One having a continuous grading in sizes of particles from coarse through fine with a predominance of coarse sizes.

2.26 AGGREGATE, FINE.—That passing the No. 8 sieve.

2.27 AGGREGATE, FINE-GRADED.—One having a continuous grading in sizes of particles from coarse through fine with a predominance of fine sizes.

2.28 AGGREGATE, MACADAM.—A coarse aggregate of uniform size usually of crushed stone, slag, or gravel.

2.29 AGGREGATE, OPEN-GRADED.—One containing little or no mineral filler or in which the void spaces in the compacted aggregate are relatively large.

2.30 AGGREGATE, WELL-GRADED.—Aggregate that is graded from the maximum size down to filler with the object of obtaining an asphalt mix with a controlled void content and high stability.

2.31 ASPHALT BASE COURSE.—A foundation course consisting of mineral aggregate, bound together with asphaltic material.

2.32 ASPHALT BLOCK PAVEMENTS.—Pavements in which the surface course is constructed of asphalt blocks. These blocks are laid in regular courses as in the case of brick pavements.

2.33 ASPHALT CONCRETE.—High quality, thoroughly controlled hot mixture of asphalt cement and well-graded, high quality aggregate, thoroughly compacted into a uniform dense mass typified by Asphalt Institute Type IV Mixes. (See Asphalt Institute Specification Series No. 1.)

2.34 ASPHALT EMULSION SLURRY SEAL.—A mixture of slow-setting emulsified asphalt, fine aggregate and mineral filler, with water added to produce slurry consistency.

2.35 ASPHALT FOG SEAL.—A light application of liquid asphalt without mineral aggregate cover. Slow setting asphalt emulsion diluted with water is the preferred type.

2.36 ASPHALT INTERMEDIATE COURSE (sometimes called Binder Course.)—A course between a base course and an asphalt surface course.

2.37 ASPHALT LEVELING COURSE.—A course (asphalt aggregate mixture) of variable thickness used to eliminate irregularities in the contour of an existing surface prior to superimposed treatment or construction.

2.38 ASPHALT MACADAM.—A type of pavement construction using a course, open-graded aggregate that is usually produced by crushing and screening stone, slag or gravel. Such aggregate is called macadam aggregate. Asphalt may be incorporated in macadam construction either by penetration or by mixing.

2.39 ASPHALT MASTIC.—A mixture of asphalt and fine mineral material in such proportions that it may be poured hot or cold into place and compacted by troweling to a smooth surface.

2.40 ASPHALT OVERLAY.—One or more courses of asphalt construction on an existing pavement. The overlay generally includes a leveling course, to correct the contour of the old pavement, followed by uniform course or courses to provide needed thickness. When overlaying rigid-type pavements the overlay should be not less than 4 inches thick to minimize reflection of cracks and joints through the overlay. Greater thickness of overlay may be required depending upon conditions of old pavement and traffic to be served.

2.41 ASPHALT PAVEMENTS.—Pavements consisting of a surface course of mineral aggregate coated and cemented together with asphalt cement on supporting courses such as asphalt bases; crushed stone, slag, or gravel; or on portland cement concrete, brick, or block pavement. (See Figure II-1.)

2.42 ASPHALT PAVEMENT STRUCTURE (sometimes called Flexible Pavement Structure).—Courses of asphalt-aggregate mixtures, plus any non-rigid courses between the asphalt construction and the foundation or subgrade. The term "flexible" sometimes used in connection with asphalt pavements denotes the ability of such a pavement structure to conform to settlement of the foundation.

2.43 ASPHALT PRIME COAT.—An application of low viscosity liquid asphalt to an absorbent surface. It is used to prepare an untreated base for an asphalt surface. The prime penetrates into the base and plugs the voids, hardens the top and helps bind it to the overlying asphalt course. It also reduces the necessity of maintaining an untreated base course prior to placing the asphalt pavement.

2.44 ASPHALT, SAND.—A mixture of sand and asphalt cement or liquid asphalt prepared with or without special control of aggregate grading with or without mineral filler. Either mixed-in-place or plant-mix construction may be employed. Sand-asphalt is used in construction of both base and surface courses.

2.45 ASPHALT SEAL COAT.—A thin asphalt surface treatment used to waterproof and improve the texture of an asphalt wearing surface. Depending on the purpose, seal coats may or may not be covered with aggregate. The main types of seal coats are aggregate seals, fog seals, emulsion slurry seals and sand seals.

2.46 ASPHALT, SHEET.—A hot mix of asphalt cement with clean angular, graded sand and mineral filler. Its use is ordinarily confined to surface course, usually laid on an intermediate or leveling course.

2.47 ASPHALT SOIL STABILIZATION (SOIL TREATMENT).—Treatment of naturally occurring non-plastic or moderately plastic soil with liquid asphalt at normal temperatures. After mixing, aeration and compaction provide water resistant base and subbase courses of improved load bearing qualities.

2.48 ASPHALT, STONE-FILLED SHEET.—A sheet asphalt containing up to 25 percent coarse aggregate.

2.49 ASPHALT SURFACE COURSE.—The top course of an asphalt pavement, sometimes called asphalt wearing course.

2.50 ASPHALT SURFACE TREATMENTS.—Applications of asphaltic materials to any type of road or pavement surface, with or without a cover of mineral aggregate, which produce an increase in thickness of less than one inch.

2.51 ASPHALT TACK COAT.—A very light application of liquid asphalt applied to an existing asphalt or portland cement concrete surface. Asphalt emulsion diluted with water is the preferred type. It is used to insure a bond between the surface being paved and the overlying course.

2.52 BASE COURSE.—The layer of material immediately beneath the surface or intermediate course. It may be composed of crushed stone, crushed slag, crushed or uncrushed gravel and sand, or combinations of these materials. It also may be bound with asphalt. (See *Asphalt Base Course.*)

2.53 COLD-LAID PLANT MIXTURE.—Plant mixes which may be spread and compacted at atmospheric temperature.

2.54 A DEEP-LIFT ASPHALT PAVEMENT is one in which the asphalt base course is placed in one or more lifts of 4 or more inches compacted thickness.

2.55 DEEP-STRENGTH® is a term registered by The Asphalt Institute with the U.S. Patent Office. The term DEEP-STRENGTH (also called "mark") certifies that the pavement is constructed of asphalt with an asphalt surface on an asphalt base and in accordance with design concepts established by the Institute. (See latest edition of *Thickness Design* manual (MS-1)).

2.56 A FULL-DEPTH ASPHALT PAVEMENT is an asphalt pavement in which asphalt mixtures are employed for *all* courses above the subgrade or improved subgrade. A FULL-DEPTH asphalt pavement is laid directly on the prepared subgrade. (The mathematical symbol T_A denotes Full-Depth or Total Asphalt.)

RENEWABLE, SKID-RESISTANT ASPHALT SURFACE

ASPHALT BASE
(one or more courses)

PREPARED SUBGRADE

2.57 HOT-LAID PLANT MIXTURE.—Plant mixes which must be spread and compacted while at an elevated temperature. To dry the aggregate and obtain sufficient fluidity of the asphalt (usually asphalt cement), both must be heated prior to mixing—giving origin to the term "hot mix."

2.58 MINERAL DUST.—The portion of the fine aggregate passing the No. 200 sieve.

2.59 MINERAL FILLER.—A finely divided mineral product at least 65 percent of which will pass a No. 200 sieve. Pulverized limestone is the most commonly manufactured filler, although other stone dust, hydrated lime, portland cement, and certain natural deposits of finely divided mineral matter are also used.

2.60 MIXED-IN-PLACE (ROAD-MIX).—An asphalt course produced by mixing mineral aggregate and

—14—

liquid asphalt at the road site by means of travel plants, motor graders, drags, or special road-mixing equipment.

2.61 MULTIPLE SURFACE TREATMENTS.—Commonly two or three successive applications of asphaltic material and mineral aggregate. (Treatments designated "Armor Coat," "Multiple Lift," and "Inverted Penetration" are essentially multiple surface treatments.)

2.62 PAVEMENT STRUCTURE.—All courses of selected material placed on the foundation or subgrade soil, other than any layers or courses constructed in grading operations.

2.63 PAVEMENT STRUCTURE COMBINATION- OR COMPOSITE-TYPE.—When the asphalt pavement is on an old portland cement concrete pavement, a portland cement concrete base, or other rigid-type base, the pavement structure is referred to as a combination- or composite-type pavement structure.

2.64 PLANT MIX.—A mixture, produced in an asphalt mixing plant, which consists of mineral aggregate uniformly coated with asphalt cement or liquid asphalt.

2.65 ROAD-MIX.—See MIXED-IN-PLACE.

2.66 ROCK ASPHALT PAVEMENTS.—Pavements constructed of rock asphalt, natural or processed 'and treated with asphalt or flux as may be required for construction.

2.67 SUBBASE.—The course in the asphalt pavement structure immediately below the base course is called the subbase course. If the subgrade soil is of adequate quality it may serve as the subbase.

2.68 SUBGRADE.—The uppermost material placed in embankments or unmoved from cuts in the normal grading of the roadbed. It is the foundation for the asphalt pavement structure. The subgrade soil sometimes is called Basement Soil or Foundation Soil.

2.69 SUBGRADE IMPROVED.—Any course or courses of select or improved material between the foundation soil and the subbase is usually referred to as the Improved Subgrade. The improved subgrade can be made up of two or more courses of different quality materials.

Chapter III

TESTS

A.—Asphalts

3.01 GENERAL.—Asphalt is available in a wide variety of standard types and grades (see Figure I-1). Standard specifications for the types and grades of asphalt used in pavement construction and other engineering applications are given in Chapter IV (see Tables IV-1 through IV-8). Laboratory tests required to determine conformance of asphalts with these specifications are described briefly in the following paragraphs and references are given to standard test methods. For convenience, tests applicable to each type of asphalt are grouped together and appear in the order as listed in specification tables referred to above.

Correct sampling procedures must be used to obtain representative test samples of asphalt. Sampling is discussed in *Specifications and Construction Methods for Asphalt Concrete and Other Plant Mix Types*, Specification Series No. 1 (SS-1) and *Asphalt Plant Manual*, Manual Series No. 3 (MS-3), The Asphalt Institute. Procedures for sampling asphalt are described in AASHO Method of Test T40 and ASTM Method of Test D140.

Asphalt Cement

3.02 PENETRATION.—The penetration test determines the relative hardness or consistency of an asphalt cement by measuring the distance that a standard needle will penetrate vertically into a sample of asphalt under known conditions of temperature, loading, and time. When other conditions are not specifically mentioned, it is understood that a penetration value or measurement is made at 77°F (25°C); that the needle is loaded to 100 grams and that the load is applied for 5 seconds. (See Figure III-1.) This is known as standard penetration. The unit of penetration is 1/10 millimeter, about 1/254

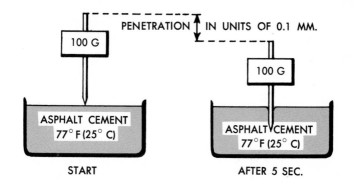

Figure III-1—Standard Penetration Test

inch. It is evident that the softer the asphalt cement the greater will be its number of penetration units.

By means of penetration limits, asphalt cements are classified into grades on the basis of hardness or consistency. The Asphalt Institute has adopted four grades of asphalt cement for paving, having penetration ranges as follows: 60-70, 85-100, 120-150, and 200-300. In addition, the Institute has specifications for a 40-50 penetration grade which is used for paving in some circumstances and also for special and industrial purposes. Standard equipment and procedures for making the Penetration Test are prescribed in AASHO Method of Test T49 and ASTM Method of Test D5.

3.03 VISCOSITY.—The purpose of the viscosity test is to determine the flow characteristics of asphalts in the range of temperatures used during application. The viscosity or consistency of asphalt cement is measured by either the kinematic viscosity test or the Saybolt Furol viscosity test.

Kinematic viscosity of asphalt cement at higher temperatures, such as 275°F (135°C) is usually measured with gravity flow capillary viscometers. For this test, because of the wide range of viscosities of asphalts, several calibrated viscometers differing in the size of capillary are necessary. The basis of the test is the

measure of time required for the constant volume of
material to flow under rigidly controlled test conditions,
such as temperature and the head of flowing liquid.
Using the measured time in seconds and the viscometer
calibration constant, it is possible to compute the viscosity of the material in the fundamental units, stokes,
or centistokes.

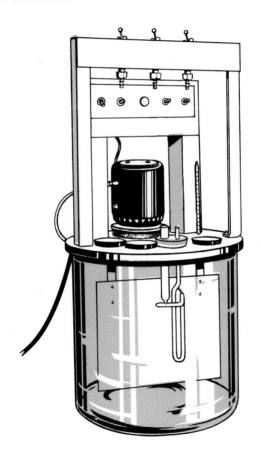

Figure III-2—Kinematic Capillary Viscosity Test

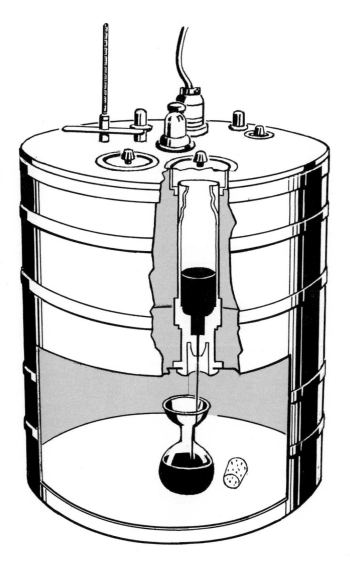

Figure III-3—Saybolt Furol Viscosity Test

The test procedure and apparatus for kinematic viscosity are described in AASHO Method of Test T201 and ASTM Method of Test D2170.

The relationship of centistokes, kinematic viscosity, to seconds, Saybolt Furol viscosity, is approximately 2-1. Conversion factors for converting kinematic viscosities to Saybolt Furol seconds for limited range of temperatures are given in ASTM Designation D2161, *Method for Conversion of Kinematic Viscosity to Saybolt Universal Viscosity or to Saybolt Furol Viscosity.*

For the Saybolt Furol test the Saybolt viscometer equipped with a Furol orifice is used. A specified volume of asphalt cement is placed in a standard tube closed with a cork stopper. Since the temperature of viscosity determination for the asphalt cements is often above 212°F (100°C), oil is used as a medium for the constant temperature bath of the viscometer. After the asphalt reaches a prescribed temperature the stopper is withdrawn and the time in seconds is measured for 60 ml. of material to flow through the Furol orifice. More viscous materials require longer times to flow through the orifice. Figure III-3 illustrates the test procedure. Test values are expressed in terms of seconds, Saybolt Furol (SSF). Equipment and procedures for this test are detailed in ASTM Method of Test E102.

Another test, determining absolute viscosity in poises, can be used to measure viscosity of asphalt cements at lower temperatures [140°F (60°C) for instance] with vacuum capillary viscometers. The test is described in AASHO Method of Test T202 and ASTM Method of Test D2171.

3.04 FLASH POINT.—The flash point of asphalt cement indicates the temperature to which the material may be safely heated without danger of instantaneous flash in the presence of an open flame. This temperature, however, is usually well below that at which the material will burn. This latter temperature is called the "fire point" but is seldom included in specifications on asphalt cements.

The flash point of an asphalt cement is measured by

the Cleveland Open Cup Flash Point Test under standard conditions prescribed in AASHO Method of Test T48 and ASTM Method of Test D92. A schematic illustration of the test is shown in Figure III-4. A brass cup is partly filled with asphalt cement and heated at a prescribed rate. A small flame is played over the surface of the sample periodically, and the temperature at which sufficient vapors are released to produce an instantaneous flash is designated as the flash point.

The Pensky-Martens Flash Point Test is sometimes used for asphalt cements. It serves the same general

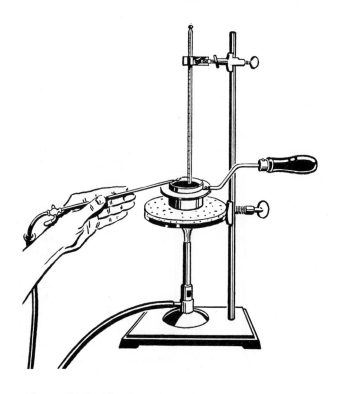

Figure III-4—Cleveland Open Cup Flash Point Test

purpose as the Cleveland Open Cup Flash Point described above. Equipment and procedures, however, are somewhat different in that provisions are made for continuous stirring of the sample during the testing period. Equipment and procedures for this test are prescribed in AASHO Method of Test T73 and ASTM Method of Test D93. Equipment for this test is illustrated in Figure III-5.

3.05 THIN FILM OVEN TEST.—The Thin Film Oven Test is used to obtain a general indication of the

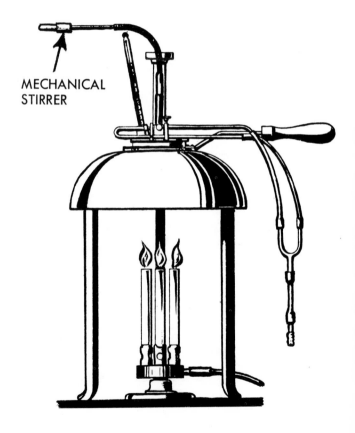

MECHANICAL
STIRRER

Figure III-5—Pensky-Martens Flash Point Test

amount of hardening which may be expected to occur in an asphalt cement during the plant mixing operation. This hardening tendency is measured by penetration tests, made before and after the Thin Film Oven Test. The penetration of the asphalt cement after the Thin Film Oven Test is expressed as a percentage of the penetration prior to the test. Specifications then prescribe minimum values for the percent of retained penetration (see Table IV-1), which vary for the different grades of asphalt cement. The Asphalt Institute considers that the change in weight of the asphalt cement during the Thin Film Oven Test is of no real significance and therefore such requirements are not included in its specifications.

The Thin Film Oven Test is conducted by placing a 50 cc sample of asphalt cement in a cylindrical pan 5.5 inches in inside diameter and ⅜-inch deep, with a flat bottom. This provides a test sample of asphalt approximately ⅛-inch deep. The sample and container are placed on a rotating shelf in a well-ventilated oven and maintained at a temperature of 325°F (162.8°C) for a period of five hours. The asphalt cement is then poured into a standard container used for the penetration test. Procedures for the Thin Film Oven Test are fully explained in AASHO Method of Test T179 (ASTM Method of Test D1754).

The Thin Film Oven Test has replaced the Loss on Heating Test (AASHO Method of Test T47 and ASTM Method of Test D6) in the specifications of many agencies, including The Asphalt Institute.

3.06 DUCTILITY.—In many applications, ductility is an important characteristic of asphalt cements. The presence or absence of ductility, however, is usually of more significance than the actual degree of ductility. Asphalt cements possessing ductility are normally more adhesive than asphalt cements lacking this characteristic. On the other hand, asphalt cements having an exceedingly high degree of ductility are usually more temperature susceptible. In some applications, such as paving mixes, ductility and adhesion are more important; while in others, such as slab undersealing and crack filling, the more essential property is low-temperature susceptibility.

Ductility of an asphalt cement is measured by an "extension" type of test illustrated in Figure III-6. A briquette of asphalt cement is molded under standard conditions and dimensions. It is then brought to standard test temperature and pulled or extended at a specified rate of speed until the thread connecting the two ends breaks. The elongation (in centimeters) at which the thread of material breaks is designated as ductility. Standard conditions for this test are fully prescribed in AASHO Method of Test T51 and ASTM Method of Test D113.

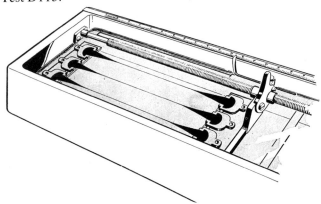

Figure III-6—Ductility Test

3.07 SOLUBILITY.—The solubility test determines the bitumen content in asphalt cement. The portion of asphalt cement that is soluble in carbon disulfide represents the active cementing constituents.

Most asphalt cements are equally soluble in carbon disulfide and carbon tetrachloride. Because carbon tetrachloride is not flammable, it is the solvent most commonly used.

The determination of solubility is simply a process of dissolving the asphalt cement in a solvent and separating out the insoluble matter. The test equipment and procedure are fully prescribed in AASHO Method of Test T44 and ASTM Method of Test D4.

3.08 SPECIFIC GRAVITY.—Although not normally specified, it is desirable to know the specific gravity of the asphalt cement being used. This information is of value for making volume corrections when volume measurements are made at elevated temperatures. It is also used as one of the factors for the determination of voids in compacted asphalt paving mixes. Specific gravity is the ratio of weight of any volume of material to the weight of an equal volume of water both at a specified temperature. Thus, a specific gravity of 1.05 means that the material is 1.05 times as heavy as water at the indicated temperature. All liquids and most solids undergo changes in volume with changes in temperature. They expand when heated and contract when cooled. In order to indicate definite conditions applicable to a given specific gravity value, the temperature of the material and the temperature of the water should be shown. Thus, Sp.Gr. at 60/60°F (15.6/15.6°C) indicates that the determination has been made with both materials at a temperature of 60°F (15.6°C) [usually the specific gravity of asphaltic materials is determined at 77°F (25°C) and converted to specific gravity at 60°F (15.6°C)]. The specific gravity of asphalt cement is normally determined by the pycnometer method as prescribed in AASHO Method of Test T43 and ASTM Method of Test D70.

3.09 SOFTENING POINT.—Different grade asphalts soften at different temperatures. The softening point is usually determined by the ring and ball test method. Although this test is not included in the specification tests for the paving grade asphalts, it is often used to characterize the harder materials used in applications other than paving. It indicates the temperatures at which these harder asphalts reach an arbitrary degree of softening. In this test the heated asphalt is poured into a brass ring of specified dimensions. The sample thus prepared is suspended in a water bath and a steel ball of specified dimensions and weight is placed in the center of the sample. The bath is heated at a controlled rate and the temperature at the instant the steel ball reaches the bottom of the glass vessel is recorded. This temperature is termed the softening point of asphalt.

The test procedures and apparatus are fully described in AASHO Method of Test T53 and ASTM Method of Test D36.

Rapid-Curing (RC) and Medium-Curing (MC) Liquid Asphalt

3.10 VISCOSITY.—The consistency or resistance to flow of liquid asphalts is measured by a viscosity test essentially the same as described for the asphalt cements. Glass, gravity-flow capillary viscometers are used to measure kinematic viscosity at 140°F (60°C) for all types and grades of liquid asphalt. The apparatus and test procedure for kinematic viscosity are described in AASHO Method of Test T201 and ASTM Method of Test D2170.

The Saybolt Furol test can be used if capillary viscometers are not available. Equipment and procedures for this test are detailed in AASHO Method of Test T72 and ASTM Method of Test D88.

3.11 FLASH POINT.—The flash point of rapid-curing and medium-curing asphalts is measured by the Tag Open Cup Flash Point Test. The purpose of the test is the same as described for asphalt cements. The equipment, however, is modified to provide for indirect heating of the liquid asphalt (Figure III-7). Equipment and procedures for the test are prescribed in AASHO Method of Test T79 and ASTM Method of Test D1310.

3.12 DISTILLATION.—The distillation test is used to determine the relative proportions of asphalt and diluent present in RC and MC liquid asphalts. It is also used to measure the amount of diluent that distills off at various temperatures denoting its evaporation characteristics. This, in turn, indicates the relative rate at which the material will "cure" after application. Asphalt recovered in the test may also be used for other tests as described for asphalt cements.

The test is made by placing a specified amount of asphalt in a distillation flask connected to a condenser. The asphalt is gradually heated to a specified temperature and the amount of diluent driven off at various temperatures is recorded. After a temperature of 680°F (360°C) is reached, the amount of asphalt remaining is measured and expressed as a percent by volume of the original sample.

Equipment and procedures for the distillation test on liquid asphalts are detailed in AASHO Method of Test T78 and ASTM Method of Test D402. The test is illustrated diagrammatically in Figure III-8.

3.13 TESTS ON RESIDUE FROM DISTILLATION.
—The asphalt remaining from the distillation test is usually tested for penetration, ductility, and solubility.

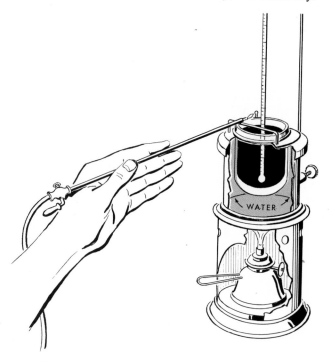

Figure III-7—Tag Open Cup Flash Point Test

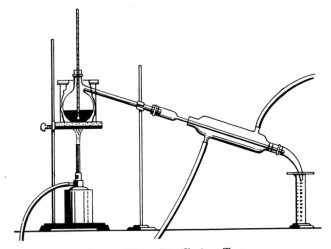

Figure III-8—Distillation Test

3.14 WATER IN ASPHALT.—A measured volume of asphalt is placed in a metal still and thoroughly mixed with a petroleum naphtha solvent. The still is provided with a reflux condenser, which discharges into a graduated trap. Heat is applied to the still and water present in the sample is collected in the trap. The volume of water is measured and calculated on the basis of percent by volume of the original sample. Equipment and procedure for this test are detailed in AASHO Method of Test T55 and ASTM Method of Test D95.

3.15 SPECIFIC GRAVITY.—Although not normally specified, it is desirable to know the specific gravity of liquid asphalts being used. This information may be used for making volume corrections when volume measurements are made at elevated temperatures. The specific gravity is normally determined by the pycnometer method as prescribed in AASHO Method of Test T43 and ASTM Method of Test D70.

Slow-Curing (SC) Liquid Asphalt

3.16 VISCOSITY.—Equipment, procedures, and purpose of this test are the same as described for rapid-curing and medium-curing asphalts.

3.17 FLASH POINT.—Equipment, procedures, and purpose of this test are the same as described for asphalt cements.

3.18 DISTILLATION.—Equipment, procedures, and purpose of this test are the same as described for RC and MC liquid asphalts except that diluent distilled off only at 680°F (360°C) is measured, rather than at several temperatures. This is because the diluent in SC liquid asphalts is oily in nature and these products are not intended to cure in the same manner as RC and MC liquid asphalts.

3.19 FLOAT.—The float test is made on the residue from distillation of SC liquid asphalts. This is a consistency test and is used because the residue is usually too soft for the penetration tests or too small in quantity for the Saybolt Furol Viscosity test. It significance, therefore, is confined to an interpretation of consistencies of products within these limitations.

In the test illustrated in Figure III-9, a "plug" of asphaltic residue is solidified into the bottom orifice of the Float Cup by cooling to 41°F (5°C). The Float Cup is then placed in water at 122°F (50°C) and the time required for the water to break through the plug is determined. Values are limited by specifications for the various grades of SC liquid asphalt. The test is prescribed in AASHO Method of Test T50 and ASTM Method of Test D139.

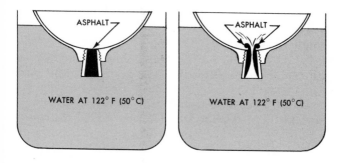

Figure III-9—Float Test

3.20 ASPHALT RESIDUE OF 100 PENETRA-TION.—This test is made on SC products. Because the rate of curing of an SC material is slow, it may or may not reach a penetration of 100 during its service life. The principal value of the test is that it provides a residue upon which standard tests for asphalt cements may be run.

A sample of SC liquid asphalt is heated to a tempera-ture of 480°-500°F (249°-260°C), and maintained at this temperature until it loses sufficient oils to reach a penetration of 100. The proportionate quantity, by weight, of asphaltic residue remaining is then determined. Specifications prescribe minimum proportions of such residue for each grade of SC liquid asphalt. The test procedure is prescribed in AASHO Method of Test T56 and ASTM Method of Test D243.

3.21 DUCTILITY.—Ductility of the asphalt residue of 100 penetration usually is determined for slow-curing liquid asphalts.

3.22 SOLUBILITY.—Equipment, procedures, and purpose of the solubility test for SC liquid asphalts are the same as described for asphalt cements.

3.23 WATER IN ASPHALT.—Equipment, proce-dures, and purpose of this test are the same as described for rapid-curing and medium-curing liquid asphalts.

3.24 SPECIFIC GRAVITY.—The procedures and the purpose of the specific gravity test for slow-curing liquid asphalts are the same as those described for rapid-curing and medium-curing liquid asphalts.

Emulsified Asphalt

3.25 VISCOSITY.—The purpose of the viscosity test on emulsified asphalts is the same as described for other liquid asphalts. Equipment and procedures for the vis-cosity test on emulsified asphalts, however, are prescribed in AASHO Method of Test T59 and ASTM Method of Test D244.

3.26 RESIDUE FROM DISTILLATION.—A distil-lation test on emulsified asphalts is made to determine the relative proportions of asphalt and water and to provide asphalt which may be further tested. The test procedure is essentially the same as illustrated for other liquid asphalts in Figure III-8, except that an iron still and ring burners are used in place of the glass flask and Bunsen burner. Equipment and procedures for the test are prescribed in AASHO Method of Test T59 and ASTM Method of Test D244.

3.27 SETTLEMENT.—The settlement test detects the tendency of asphalt globules to settle during storage of an emulsified asphalt. A sample is allowed to stand in a graduated cylinder for five days after which a difference in asphalt content between the top and bottom of the sample is determined. The procedures and equipment are prescribed in AASHO Method of Test T59 and ASTM Method of Test D244.

3.28 DEMULSIBILITY.—The demulsibility test indicates the relative rate at which the colloidal asphalt globules in the rapid and medium setting types of anionic emulsified asphalts will coalesce (or "break") when spread in thin films on soil or aggregate. Calcium chloride will coagulate or flocculate the minute asphalt globules present in these emulsified asphalts. In the test, a solution of calcium chloride and water is thoroughly mixed with emulsified asphalt and poured over a sieve to determine the degree of coalescence of the asphalt globules.

In testing rapid-setting (RS) emulsions, a very weak solution of calcium chloride and water is employed; specifications prescribe the concentration of the solution and the minimum amount of asphalt to be retained on the sieve. A high degree of "demulsibility" is required of this type of emulsified asphalt as it is expected to "break" almost immediately upon contact with the aggregate on which it is applied.

The testing of medium-setting (MS) emulsified asphalt requires a stronger solution of calcium chloride than that used in testing rapid-setting types. In applications where the MS type is specified, rapid coalescence of the asphalt is not desired and specifications normally place a maximum limit of "demulsibility" for these products and prescribe the concentration of the solution. Equipment and procedures for this test are prescribed in AASHO Method of Test T59 and ASTM Method of Test D244.

3.29 SIEVE TEST.—The sieve test complements the settlement test and has a somewhat similar purpose. It is used to determine quantitatively the percent of asphalt present in the form of relatively large globules. Such globules do not provide thin and uniform coatings of asphalt on the aggregate particles and may or may not be detected by the settlement test.

In the sieve test, a representative sample of emulsified asphalt is poured through a Number 20-mesh sieve. For anionic emulsions the sieve and retained asphalt are then rinsed with a mild sodium oleate solution and finally with distilled water. For cationic emulsions distilled water is used instead of sodium oleate solution. After rinsing, the sieve and asphalt are dried in an oven and the amount of retained asphalt determined. The procedure and equipment for this test are prescribed in AASHO Method of Test T59 and ASTM Method of Test D244.

3.30 CEMENT MIXING.—The cement mixing test serves a similar purpose for slow-setting (SS) emulsified asphalts as the demulsibility test for the rapid- and medium-setting grades. The SS grades are prepared for use with fine materials and dusty aggregates and are normally unaffected by calcium chloride solutions as used in the demulsibility test.

In the cement mixing test, a sample of emulsified asphalt is mixed with finely-ground portland cement and the mixture washed over Number 14 sieve. Specifications usually limit the amount of material which may be retained on the sieve. Equipment and procedures for the test are prescribed in AASHO Method of Test T59 and and ASTM Method of Test D244.

3.31 TESTS ON RESIDUE.—The penetration, solubility and ductility tests, as made on asphalt cements, are usually made on the residue from distillation.

3.32 COATING TEST.—The coating test determines the ability of an asphalt emulsion to coat an aggregate thoroughly, to withstand a mixing action while remaining as a film on the aggregate, and to resist the washing action of water after completion of the mixing.

The job aggregate and asphalt emulsion are mixed by hand with a mixing blade for a prescribed period. Limestone aggregate is coated with calcium carbonate dust before mixing. About half of the mixture is then placed on absorbent paper for visual evaluation of the surface area of the aggregate coated by the asphalt. The remainder of the mixture in the pan is sprayed with water and rinsed until the water runs clear from the pan. Then it is placed on absorbent paper and evaluated for coating. Equipment and detailed procedures for the test are prescribed in ASTM Method of Test D244-61T.

3.33 PARTICLE CHARGE TEST.—The particle charge test is made to identify cationic emulsions. It is performed by immersing a positive electrode (anode) and a negative electrode (cathode) into a sample of emulsion and connecting them to a controlled direct-current electrical source. At the end of a specified period the electrodes are observed to determine which pole has an appreciable layer of asphalt deposited on it. Cationic emulsions will be attracted by the cathode. Equipment and procedures for the test are detailed in AASHO Interim Method of Test T59A-63I and ASTM Method of Test D244 (Tentative Revision, 1963).

3.34 pH Test.—The pH test determines the acidity of cationic asphalt emulsions. The test is performed with a standard pH meter as described in AASHO Method of Test T200 and ASTM Method of Test E70.

3.35 OIL DISTILLATE.—The oil distillate, percent by volume of the original emulsion sample, is obtained from the amount of oil in the graduated cylinder at the end of the test for residue by distillation, AASHO Method of Test T59 (ASTM Method of Test D244).

3.36 SPECIFIC GRAVITY.—The procedures and purpose of the specific gravity test for emulsified asphalts are the same as those described for other liquid asphalts.

B.—*Mineral Aggregates*

3.37 GENERAL.—Mineral aggregates are used in combination with asphalts to prepare mixes for a wide variety of purposes. As the aggregates normally constitute 90 percent or more by weight of such mixes, their properties have a very important effect upon the finished

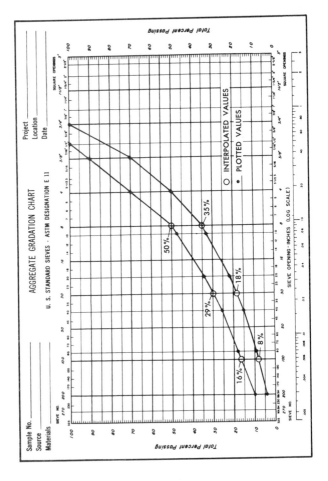

Figure III-10—Aggregate Grading Chart

product. The most commonly used mineral aggregates are crushed stone and slag, crushed or uncrushed gravel, sand, and mineral filler. In asphalt pavement construction the control of properties of mineral aggregates is just as important as the control of asphalt properties. Tests commonly employed with mineral aggregates are described briefly in the following paragraphs and references are given to standard procedures for these tests.

Correct sampling procedures must be used to obtain representative test samples of mineral aggregates. Sampling is fully described in Asphalt Institute Manual Series No. 3, *Asphalt Plant Manual*. Procedures for aggregate sampling are detailed in AASHO Method of Test T2 and ASTM Method of Test D75.

3.38 SIEVE ANALYSIS.—There are two methods of determining the relative proportions of various particle sizes in a mineral aggregate: Dry Sieve Analysis, and Washed Sieve Analysis.

(1) **Dry Sieve Analysis.**—A weighed quantity of thoroughly dried aggregate is shaken over a set of sieves having selected sizes of square openings. The sieves are nested together such that the one having the largest opening is on top and those of successively smaller openings are placed beneath. A pan is placed below the bottom sieve to collect all material passing through it. The shaking is normally accomplished with a mechanical sieve shaker.

The weight of material retained on each sieve size is determined and expressed as a percent of the weight of the original or total sample. For convenience, these data are usually plotted on a chart, as illustrated in Figure III-10. On such charts, total percent by weight of material passing each sieve size may be plotted. Such plots provide a means of readily visualizing the gradation characteristics of the mineral aggregate.

Commonly used with asphalt paving mixes are the 2½, 2, 1½, 1, ¾, ½, and ⅜ inch square opening sieves and the No. 4, 8, 16, 30, 50, 100, and 200 sieves.

Specifications for testing sieves are contained in AASHO Specification M92 and ASTM Specification E 11. Standard procedures for making dry sieve analysis of coarse and fine aggregates are given in AASHO Method of Test T27 and ASTM Method of Test C136. For mineral fillers, such procedures are given in AASHO Method of Test T37 and ASTM Method of Test D546.

(2) **Washed Sieve Analysis.**—This method of test covers a procedure for determining the particle size distribution of fine and coarse aggregates by washing procedures. Such procedures should always be used where the aggregate contains extremely fine dust, or clay, which may cling to the coarser aggregate particles. In such instances, results obtained from the dry sieve analysis will obviously be in error.

For details of this test, see The Asphalt Institute's *Asphalt Plant Manual,* Manual Series No. 3.

3.39 SAND EQUIVALENT.—The sand-equivalent test, developed by the California Division of Highways, indicates the relative proportion of detrimental fine dust or clay-like materials in mineral aggregates used for asphalt paving mixtures and mineral aggregates or soils used for base courses. The test is applied to the fraction passing a No. 4 sieve.

A sample of material is placed in a transparent, graduated cylinder containing a prepared solution of calcium chloride, glycerine, and formaldehyde in water. The sample and solution are vigorously shaken in a prescribed manner. The same solution passed through an irrigator tube, under pressure, is used to wash the clayey material upward and out of the sample as the cylinder is gradually filled. After a 20-minute settling period, the top level of the clay suspension is read. A metal weighted foot is then lowered into the cylinder and allowed to come to rest on top of the clean sand. The level of the bottom of the foot is read. The sand-equivalent value is the ratio, multiplied by 100, of the reading at the top of the sand, divided by the reading at the top of the clay. Equipment and procedures for this test are detailed in AASHO Method of Test T176.

3.40 ABRASION (WEAR).—The Los Angeles Abrasion Test is used to measure wear or abrasion resistance of mineral aggregate.* The Los Angeles abrasion machine is diagrammatically illustrated in Figure III-11. The drum is charged with a standard weight of aggregate particles conforming to one of seven standard sieve gradings which most nearly approximates the grading of material proposed for use. A standard weight of steel spheres is also placed in the drum as an abrasive charge. The drum is then rotated for 500 revolutions after which the material is removed and sieved on a No. 12 sieve. The percentage passing this sieve is reported as percent of wear.

Relatively high resistance to wear, as indicated by a low percent of abrasion loss, is a desirable characteristic of aggregates to be used in asphalt pavement construction. Equipment and procedures for this test are detailed in AASHO Method of Test T96 and ASTM Method of Test C131.

3.41 SOUNDNESS TEST.—The soundness test is an indication of the resistance to weathering of fine and coarse aggregates. The test is made for aggregates that have not been proven sound through an adequate record of service. It measures the resistance of aggregate to disintegration by saturated solutions of either sodium or magnesium sulfate.

The test is made by immersing containers of sized fractions of an aggregate sample in a saturated solution of sodium or magnesium sulfate. The sample containers are

---

* Percent of wear as measured by the Los Angeles Test does not necessarily have any relationship to polishing of aggregate under traffic wear.

Note: The Deval machine is still used by a few agencies for determining abrasion of aggregate. See AASHO Methods of Test T3 and T4 ASTM Methods of Test D2 and D289.

constructed to allow free access to and drainage of the solution from the sample without loss of aggregate. Samples are oven dried after immersion. After the required number of immersion and drying cycles, the percent weight loss of the sized fractions is determined by sieving. Weighted average percent losses for each size fraction, based upon the gradation of the original sample, are determined. The total of these values is the percent loss test value. Equipment and procedures for this test are detailed in AASHO Method of Test T104 and ASTM Method of Test C88.

Figure III-11—Los Angeles Abrasion Test

3.42 SPECIFIC GRAVITY.—The specific gravity of aggregates is usually determined for two reasons:

(1) To permit a calculation of voids of compacted asphalt paving mixes.

(2) To adjust quantities of aggregate components of a paving mix, where such components vary appreciably in specific gravity.

Equipment and procedures for determining apparent and bulk specific gravities of coarse aggregates are detailed in AASHO Method of Test T85 and ASTM Method of Test C127. For fine aggregates, see AASHO Method of Test T84 and ASTM Method of Test C128. A method for measuring asphalt lost by absorption into the aggregate particles is given in the appendixes of The Asphalt Institute publication, *Mix Design Methods for Asphalt Concrete and Other Hot-Mix Types,* Manual Series No. 2.

3.43 UNIT WEIGHT.—The unit weight of an aggregate may be determined on either a loose or compacted basis. A cylindrical container of known volume is used for the test. Volumes are usually 0.1, 0.5 or 1.0 cu. ft., depending upon the size of aggregate to be tested. For measurement of loose unit weight, the container is filled by a specified procedure and the weight of aggregate in the filled container is determined. For measurement of compacted weight, the container is filled in three approximately equal layers and "rodding" or "jigging" procedures are applied to each layer, depending upon the size of aggregate being used for the test. Equipment and procedures for these tests are detailed in AASHO Method of Test T19 and ASTM Method of Test C29.

The compacted unit weight generally is used as an indication of quality of crushed slag. The heavier slags tend to be less porous and structurally stronger than those having lower unit weight. On the basis of experience, a minimum compacted unit weight of 70 lbs. per cu. ft. is normally specified for slag less than two inches to be used in asphalt paving mixes and 65 lbs. per cu. ft. for a slag two inches or larger in size. The slag should be tested in the gradation proposed for use.

3.44 MOISTURE.—The determination of moisture in mineral aggregates is made by weighing a sample of the material, drying it to constant weight in an oven maintained at about 230°F (110°C), and then determining the dry weight of the sample. The difference between the original and final weights is considered to be moisture loss during drying. The loss in weight, expressed as a percent of the final or dry weight, is the moisture content of the aggregate.

C.—Asphalt Paving Mixtures

3.45 GENERAL.—Not only is it important to test the asphalts and mineral aggregate separately, but tests should also be made on combinations of these materials to establish proper proportions and characteristics for such mixtures. Tests commonly employed for asphalt paving mixtures are described briefly in the following paragraphs and references are given to standard procedures for such tests.

3.46 MARSHALL TEST.—The Marshall Test for asphalt paving mixtures may be used for laboratory design and field control of mixtures containing asphalt cement and aggregates not exceeding one inch in maximum size. Principal features of the test are density-voids analysis and stability-flow tests on specimens of compacted asphalt paving mixtures.

Test specimens approximately 2½ inches high and 4 inches in diameter are prepared by prescribed procedures and compacted by drop-hammer method compaction procedures. The density and voids of the compacted specimen are established and the specimen then heated to 140°F (60°C) for the Marshall stability and flow tests. The specimen is placed in a split breaking head for these tests as illustrated in Figure III-12. Load is applied to the specimen at a rate of two inches per minute. The maximum load registered during the test, in pounds, is designated as the Marshall Stability of the specimen. The amount of movement, or strain, occurring between no load and the maximum load, in units of 0.01 inch is the

Figure III-12—Marshall Stability and Flow Test

flow value of the specimen. Specimens are prepared at a range of asphalt contents, above and below the estimated optimum, and tested by the procedures just described. Usually, specimens at each asphalt content are made in triplicate.

Test data thus derived are used to establish the optimum asphalt content of the mixture and to determine certain physical characteristics of the mixture. Equipment and procedures for these tests are described in detail in *Mix Design Methods for Asphalt Concrete and Other Hot-Mix Types,* Manual Series No. 2, published by The Asphalt Institute. Suggested criteria (see .Table IV-12) for the evaluation of paving mixes are also included in this publication. Equipment and procedures for the Marshall tests are also outlined in ASTM Method of Test D1559.

3.47 HVEEM METHOD.—The Hveem Method of designing and testing asphalt mixtures involves three principal tests as follows:

    (1) The Stabilometer Test
    (2) The Cohesiometer Test
    (3) The Centrifuge Kerosene Equivalent (CKE) Test

All are used for designing mixes in the laboratory. The CKE is also used as a field test.

The stabilometer and cohesiometer tests are suitable for mixtures containing either asphalt cement or liquid asphalt and aggregates not exceeding one inch in maximum size. Test specimens of asphalt mixture 2½ inches high and 4 inches in diameter are compacted by specified procedures in a kneading compactor as shown in Figure III-13.

The density and voids of the compacted specimen are established and the specimen then heated to 140°F (60°C) and tested in the Hveem Stabilometer. The stabilometer is a type of triaxial test in which vertical loads are applied and resulting lateral pressures read at several increments of vertical load. The test is illustrated in Figure III-14.

The specimen is enclosed in a rubber membrane, surrounded by a liquid that transmits the lateral pressure developed during the test. Values derived from the test are relative in nature. The scale has been established on the basis that if the specimen were a liquid, the lateral pressure would equal the vertical pressure and for this case the relative stability is considered to be zero. At the other end of the scale, an incompressible solid that trans-

Figure III-13—Mechanical Kneading Compactor for the Preparation of Test Specimens

mits no lateral pressure is considered to have a relative stability value of 90. Tests on asphalt paving mixes yield values within this 0-90 range. Relative stability of the specimen is calculated by an established formula.

A cohesiometer test is usually made on the test specimen upon completion of the stabilometer test. This is the flexural type of test in which the specimen fails in tension as illustrated in Figure III-15.

In this test, the specimen is also heated to 140°F (60°C), and maintained at this temperature during the testing period in a temperature-controlled cabinet. The specimen is clamped in the testing device, as shown in Figure III-15, and load is applied at a constant rate at the end of a lever arm. When the end of the lever arm

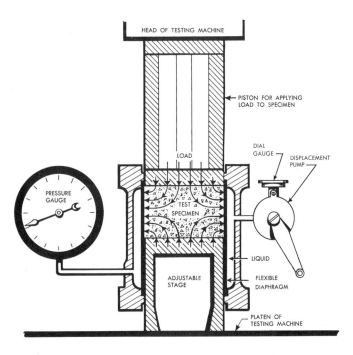

Figure III-14—Hveem Stabilometer Test

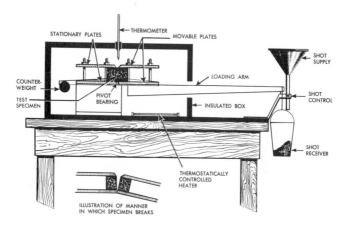

Figure III-15—Hveem Cohesiometer Test

has traveled one-half inch, the flow of shot used for applying load is automatically cut off and their weight is determined. The cohesiometer value is determined by an established formula.

Another feature of the Hveem Method, sometimes employed, is a determination of the estimated optimum asphalt content of the mix by a procedure known as the Centrifuge Kerosene Equivalent (CKE) Test. The portion of aggregate in the mix which passes the No. 4 sieve is saturated with kerosene and then centrifuged. The ⅜ inch to No. 4 size aggregate, considered to represent the coarse aggregate portion of the mix, is saturated in lubricating oil and allowed to drain for 15 minutes at 140°F (60°C). Weights of kerosene and oil retained by these aggregates are used in the prescribed procedure for calculating and estimating the optimum asphalt content of the mix. Normally, stabilometer and cohesiometer tests will be run at the asphalt content indicated by the CKE test and at greater and lesser asphalt contents, in order to establish the optimum asphalt content and to determine certain other physical characteristics of the compacted mixture. Suggested criteria (see Table IV-12) for the evaluation of highway paving mixes are included in this publication. Equipment and procedures for the tests summarized above are described in detail in *Mix Design Methods for Asphalt Concrete and Other Hot-Mix Types,* Manual Series No. 2, published by The Asphalt Institute. Equipment and procedures for making the stabilometer and cohesiometer tests are also detailed in ASTM Method of Test D1560. Equipment and procedures for preparing the test specimens with the kneading compactor are also detailed in ASTM Method of Test D1561.

3.48 HUBBARD-FIELD METHOD.—The Hubbard-Field Method is a procedure employed for the laboratory design of asphalt paving mixes. The procedure was developed originally for the design of sand and sheet asphalt paving mixes with asphalt cements, wherein all of the aggregate passes the No. 4 sieve and at least 65 percent passes the No. 10 sieve. Principal features of the test are a density-voids analysis and a stability test.

Test specimens of asphalt paving mixture two inches in diameter and one inch high are prepared by specified compaction procedures. Density and voids of the compacted specimen are determined and the specimen is then subjected to the Hubbard-Field Stability Test as illustrated in Figure III-16. In this test the specimen is first heated to 140°F (60°C), and placed in the testing mold. Load is applied, as indicated, at a rate of 2.4 inches per minute. The two-inch diameter specimen is forced through a restricted orifice, 1.75 inches in diameter. The maximum load in pounds thus sustained is the Hubbard-Field Stability.

Two or three such specimens are prepared and tested at each of several asphalt contents, usually in ½ percent increments above and below an estimated "optimum" asphalt content. The average values for each asphalt content are plotted on charts and used to establish an optimum asphalt content for the mix. These data are also used to determine if the mixture meets established criteria at the optimum asphalt content (see Table IV-12).

Equipment and procedures for the Hubbard-Field Method are described in detail in *Mix Design Methods for Asphalt Concrete and Other Hot-Mix Types,* Manual Series No. 2, published by The Asphalt Institute. Suggested criteria for evaluation of asphalt paving mixes are also included in this publication. Equipment and procedures for making these tests are also prescribed in AASHO Method of Test T169 and ASTM Method of Test D1138.

3.49 DENSITY.—The density, or unit weight, of a compacted asphalt paving mixture is determined for the following purposes:

(1) On laboratory compacted specimens to:

a. Provide a basis for computing the percent of air voids and voids in the mineral aggregate in the compacted mixtures; an integral part of some asphalt paving mixture design procedures.

b. Provide an indication of the optimum asphalt content in some mix design procedures.

c. Establish a basis for controlling compaction during construction of the asphalt pavement.

d. Provide a basis for calculating the spread required for a given thickness of pavement.

(2) On specimens obtained from pavements to check density of pavement and effectiveness of rolling operations.

The usual procedure for determining density is to weigh the specimen, determine its volume, and calculate the weight-volume relationship in terms of some convenient unit (e.g., pounds per cubic foot). The specimen is first weighed in air, then in water, and the difference in weight provides a measure of the volume of the specimen.

This procedure is satisfactory if the specimen is practically impermeable to water. Where specimens are water permeable, however, they should first be coated with paraffin before immersion. Calculation of density must then allow for the weight and volume of the paraffin coating.

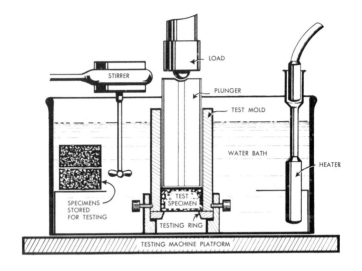

Figure III-16—Testing Hubbard Field Specimens

In some instances, the volume of a specimen is determined by measurements. Generally, however, it is difficult to obtain proper accuracy by this method.

A detailed discussion of weight-volume relationship and methods for determining the density of compacted specimens may be found in an Appendix of *Mix Design Methods for Asphalt Concrete and Other Hot-Mix Types,* Manual Series No. 2, published by The Asphalt Institute. Equipment and details for such procedures may also be found in AASHO Method of Test T166 and ASTM Method of Test D1188.

3.50 VOIDS AND EFFECTIVE ASPHALT CONTENT.—As noted under mix design method discussed previously the determination of voids in the compacted specimen of paving mixture is included as a part of the design method. The data required before a sample of compacted paving mixture can be analyzed for air voids, voids in the mineral aggregate (VMA), and the effective asphalt content are:

(1) Composition of the mixture in terms of percent by weight of aggregate and total asphalt content.

(2) Bulk specific gravity of the aggregate.

(3) Apparent specific gravity of the asphalt cement.

(4) Asphalt lost by absorption into the aggregate particles.

(5) Bulk specific gravity of the compacted paving mixture.

(6) Measured or calculated theoretical maximum specific gravity of the paving mixture.

Procedures are outlined in detail in Appendices B and C, *Mix Design Methods for Asphalt Concrete and Other Hot-Mix Types,* Manual Series No. 2, published by The Asphalt Institute.

3.51 EXTRACTION.—Extraction is the procedure used for separating the asphalt from the mineral aggregates in an asphalt paving mixture. The purpose of extraction is to provide a basis for determining the asphalt content of a mixture and to provide asphalt-free aggregates which may be used for a gradation analysis and such other tests on the aggregate as may be desired. Where further tests on the extracted asphalt are desired a "Recovery" is made.

The centrifugal method is a widely used extraction method for determining asphalt content and for obtaining asphalt-free aggregates. The asphaltic mixture is heated, broken apart, and placed in a centrifuge bowl. Then, a solvent is added which dissolves the asphalt. Solvents commonly used are trichloroethylene, benzene, or ethylene dichloride.* The dissolved asphalt is then separated from the mineral aggregate by a special type of centrifuge. Solvent must be added several times during the centrifuging procedure before all of the asphalt is extracted.

The difference between the original weight of the asphaltic mixture and the weight of the dry aggregate

---

* Carbon tetrachloride, also used as a solvent, is not recommended because of its toxicity.

after extraction is used as the basis for determining the proportions of asphalt and aggregate in a mixture. Corrections must be made for the small amount of fine mineral matter passing through the centrifuge bowl filter ring during the extraction. This is done by evaporating and ashing an aliquot portion of the solvent-asphalt solution. Corrections must also be made for water, if present in the asphaltic mixture.

Alternate extraction methods, using extractors of several different designs, are described along with the centrifugal method in ASTM Method of Test D2172. All of the alternate extraction methods utilize a perforated sample container, a condenser, and an external heat source. AASHO Method of Test T164 describes equipment and procedures for the centrifugal method.

3.52 RECOVERY OF ASPHALT.—Where further tests are desired for asphalt extracted from paving mixtures, recovery of asphalt must be made without changing its properties.

The asphalt may be extracted from the mixture by the standard procedures described in Article 3.51, provided nitration grade benzene or reagent grade trichloroethylene solvents are used. Solutions from the extraction are first centrifuged to remove most of the fine mineral matter. The asphalt then is recovered by distillation. Procedures include the introduction of a controlled flow of carbon dioxide gas into the contents of the distillation flask to remove the last traces of the solvent. Equipment and procedures are detailed in AASHO Method of Test T170, and ASTM Method of Test D1856.

3.53 MOISTURE AND VOLATILE DISTILLATES. —It is sometimes desirable to know the amount of moisture and/or volatile distillates in an asphalt paving mixture, especially where liquid asphalts are used. Such measurements are usually made by some type of distillation procedure, such as the one outlined in ASTM Method of Test D255. Some agencies use procedures detailed in AASHO Method of Test T110 and ASTM Method of Test D1461.

3.54 SWELL.—Asphaltic mixtures containing fines of doubtful quality are sometimes measured for swell as a basis for judging the possible detrimental effects of water on the pavement. This test is more frequently used with dense-graded mixtures using liquid asphalts. A sample of paving mix is compacted in a metal cylinder, usually four inches in diameter, and cooled to room temperature. The specimen and mold are then placed in a pan of water and

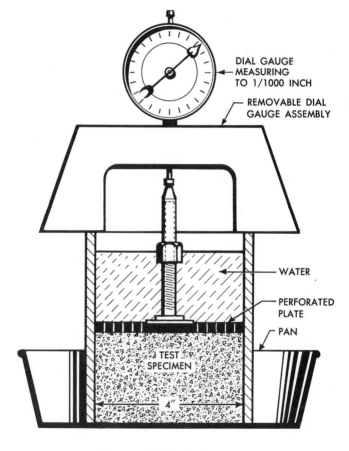

DIAL GAUGE MEASURING TO 1/1000 INCH

REMOVABLE DIAL GAUGE ASSEMBLY

WATER

PERFORATED PLATE

PAN

TEST SPECIMEN

4"

Figure III-17—Swell Test

a dial-gauge assembly mounted above the sample as illustrated in Figure III-17. The initial reading of the dial gauge is recorded and additional readings are taken after a specified period of time, usually 24 hours, or until there is no further swelling in the specimen. Equipment and procedures for the test as used by the California Division of Highways are described in *Mix Design Methods for Asphalt Concrete and Other Hot-Mix Types,* Manual Series No. 2, published by The Asphalt Institute. Equipment and procedures for such a test are also detailed in AASHO Method of Test T101.

3.55 REFERENCES.—The following Asphalt Institute publications contain details of many of the tests described in this chapter:

(1) *Mix Design Methods for Asphalt Concrete and Other Hot-Mix Types,* Manual Series No. 2 (MS-2)

(2) *Asphalt Plant Manual,* Manual Series No. 3 (MS-3)

TABLE III-1—AUTHORITATIVE METHODS OF TEST AS COMMONLY SPECIFIED

A. ASPHALTS

Art.		AASHO	ASTM
	Asphalt Cement		
3.02	Penetration........................	T49	D5
3.03	Viscosity	T201	D2170
	(*See also Saybolt Furol Test, at High Temperatures, or ASTM Method of Test E102*)		
3.04	Flash Point........................	T48	D92
	(*See also Pensky-Martens Flash Point Test, AASHO Method of Test T73 and ASTM Method of Test D93*)		
3.05	Thin Film Oven Test	T179	D1754
3.06	Ductility	T51	D113
3.07	Solubility	T44	D4
3.08	Specific Gravity...................	T43	D70
3.09	Softening Point	T53	D36

Rapid-Curing and Medium-Curing Asphalt

3.10	Viscosity .... *(See also Saybolt Furol Test, AASHO Method of Test T72 or ASTM Method of Test D88)*	T201	D2170
3.11	Flash Point........................	T79	D1310
3.12	Distillation	T78	D402
3.13	Tests on Residue (*See Asphalt Cements, Articles 3.02 thru 3.09*)		
3.14	Water in Asphalt	T55	D95
3.15	Specific Gravity....................	T43	D70

Slow-Curing Asphalt

3.16	Viscosity (See RC and MC Asphalts)..	T201	D2170
3.17	Flash Point (See Asphalt Cements)....	T48	D92
3.18	Distillation	T78	D402
3.19	Float Test	T50	D139
3.20	Asphalt Residue of 100 Penetration ..	T56	D243
3.21	Ductility	T51	D113
3.22	Solubility (*See Asphalt Cements and RC and MC Asphalts*)	T44	D4
3.23	Water in Asphalt	T55	D95
3.24	Specific Gravity....................	T43	D70

Emulsified Asphalt

3.25	Viscosity	T59	D244
3.26	Residue from Distillation	T59	D244
3.27	Settlement	T59	D244
3.28	Demulsibility	T59	D244
3.29	Sieve Test	T59	D244
3.30	Cement Mixing	T59	D244
3.31	Tests on Residue (*See Asphalt Cements, Articles 3.02 thru 3.09*)		
3.32	Coating Test	—	D244-61T
3.33	Particle Charge Test	T59A	D244
3.34	pH Test	T200	E70
3.35	Oil Distillate	T59	D244
3.36	Specific Gravity....................	T43	D70

B. Mineral Aggregates

Art.		AASHO	ASTM
3.38	Sieve Analysis		
	Dry Sieve Analysis		
	Coarse and Fine Aggregates	T27	C136
	Mineral Filler....................	T37	D546
	Wash Sieve Analysis.............	—	—
	(*See* Asphalt Plant Manual, *Asphalt Institute, MS-3*)		
3.39	Sand Equivalent	T176	—
3.40	Abrasion (Wear)	T96	C131
3.41	Soundness Test	T104	C88
3.42	Specific Gravity		
	Coarse Aggregate	T85	C127
	Fine Aggregate	T84	C128
3.43	Unit Weight	T19	C29
3.44	Moisture..........................	—	—

C. Asphalt Paving Mixtures

Art.		AASHO	ASTM
3.46	Marshall Test*	—	D1559
3.47	Hveem Method*		
	Stabilometer and Cohesiometer		
	Tests	—	D1560
	Kneading compactor	—	D1561
3.48	Hubbard-Field Method*	T169	D1138
3.49	Density*	T166	D1188
3.50	Voids*............................	—	—
3.51	Extraction	T164	D2172
3.52	Recovery of Asphalt...............	T170	D1856
3.53	Moisture and/or Volatile Distillates..	—	D255
	Alternate Methods	T110	D1461
3.54	Swell*	T101	

---

* *See* Mix Design Methods for Asphalt Concrete and Other Hot-Mix Types, *Asphalt Institute Manual Series No. 2.*

Chapter IV

SUMMARY OF SPECIFICATIONS AND PRINCIPAL RECOMMENDATIONS

4.01 GENERAL.—This chapter contains a summary of Asphalt Institute specifications on asphalt and aggregates for pavement construction. In addition, the chapter includes principal recommendations by the Institute for this type of work. Specifically, the following parts, extracted from various publications by The Asphalt Institute, are included:

A. Specifications for Asphalts
B. Grading Specifications for Mineral Aggregates
C. Recommendations for the Classification and Gradation of Asphalt Paving Mixtures
D. Recommendations for the Design of Asphalt Paving Mixtures
E. Recommendations for the Control of Asphalt Application Temperatures

A.—Specifications for Asphalts

4.02 ASPHALT TABLES.—Specifications for asphalt cements and liquid asphalts appear in Tables IV-1 through IV-8.

IMPORTANT

The Asphalt Institute, ASTM, AASHO, and most user agencies have adopted new specification grades for liquid asphalts (Tables IV-2, IV-3, and IV-4). Former specifications for these materials are included in Appendix B.

In the new grade designations, the number signifies the lower limit of the kinematic viscosity for the grade. The upper viscosity limit is twice the lower limit. For example, MC-70 denotes a Medium-Curing liquid asphalt having a kinematic viscosity within the range of 70-140 centistokes at 140°F, (60°C).

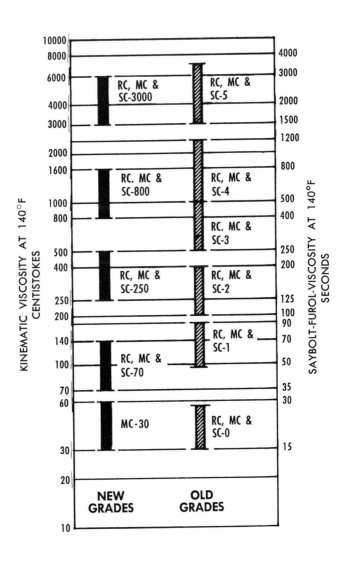

Figure IV-1—Comparison of New and Old Liquid
Asphalt Grades at 140°F (60°C)

Table IV-1—SPECIFICATIONS FOR ASPHALT CEMENTS

As of December 1967*

CHARACTERISTICS	AASHO Test Method	ASTM Test Method	GRADES				
			40-50¹	60-70	85-100	120-150	200-300
Penetration, 77° F., 100 g., 5 sec.	T49	D5					
Viscosity at 275° F. Kinematic, Centistokes	T201	D2170	240+	200+	170+	140+	100+
Saybolt Furol, SSF	....	E102	120+	100+	85+	70+	50+
Flash Point (Cleveland Open Cup), °F.	T48	D92	450+	450+	450+	425+	350+
Thin Film Oven Test Penetration After test, 77° F., 100 g., 5 sec., % of Original	T179	D1754	55+	52+	47+	42+	37+
Ductility: At 77° F., cms.	T51	D113	100+	100+	100+	60+	......
At 60° F., cms.							60+
Solubility in Carbon Tetrachloride, %²	T44	D2042	99.0+	99.0+	99.0+	99.0+	99.0+
General Requirements			The asphalt shall be prepared by the refining of petroleum. It shall be uniform in character and shall not foam when heated to 350° F.				

¹ Also special and industrial uses.
² Alternatively, trichloroethylene (not trichloroethane) may be used as the solvent for determining solubility. In case of dispute, however, carbon tetrachloride will be used as the referee solvent.

* See Specifications for Asphalt Cements and Liquid Asphalts, SS-2, The Asphalt Institute, for latest revisions.

Table IV-2—SPECIFICATIONS FOR RAPID-CURING (RC) LIQUID ASPHALTS

CHARACTERISTICS	AASHO Test Method	ASTM Test Method	GRADES			
			RC-70	RC-250	RC-800	RC-3000
Kinematic Viscosity at 140°F., cs.	T201	D2170	70-140	250-500	800-1600	3000-6000
Flash Point (Open Tag.), °F.	T79	D1310	....	80+	80+	80+
Distillation						
Distillate (percent of total distillate to 680°F.):						
to 374°F.	T78	D402	10+	....	....	....
to 437°F.			50+	35+	15+	....
to 500°F.			70+	0+	45+	25+
to 600°F.			85+	80+	75+	70+
Residue from distillation to 680°F., percent by volume			55+	65+	75+	80+
Tests on Residue from Distillation						
Penetration, 77°F., 100 g., 5 sec.	T49	D5	80-120	80-120	80-120	80-120
Ductility, 77°F., cms.	T51	D113	100+	100+	100+	100+
Solubility in Carbon Tetrachloride, %[1]	T44	D2042	99.5+	99.5+	99.5+	99.5+
Water,%	T55	D95	0.2-	0.2-	0.2-	0.2-

General Requirement—The material shall not foam when heated to application temperature recommended by The Asphalt Institute.

Note: When the Heptane-Xylene Equivalent Test is specified by the consumer, a negative test with 35 percent xylene after 1 hour will be required, AASHO Method T102.

[1] Alternatively, trichloroethylene (not trichloroethane) may be used as the solvent for determining solubility. In case of dispute, however, carbon tetrachloride will be used as the referee solvent.

* See Specifications for Asphalt Cements and Liquid Asphalts, SS-2, The Asphalt Institute, for latest revisions.

CHARACTERISTICS	AASHO Test Method	ASTM Test Method	GRADES				
			MC-30	MC-70	MC-250	MC-800	MC-3000
Kinematic Viscosity at 140°F., cs.	T201	D2170	30-60	70-140	250-500	800-1600	3000-6000
Flash Point (Open Tag.), °F.[1]	T79	D1310	100+	100+	150+	150+	150+
Distillation Distillate (per cent of total distillate to 680°F.):		T78					
To 437°F.		D402	25-	20-	0-10	....	....
To 500°F.			40-70	20-60	15-55	35-	15-
To 600°F.			75-93	65-90	60-87	45-80	15-75
Residue from distillation to 680°F., per cent by volume			50+	55+	67+	75+	80+
Tests on Residue from Distillation Penetration, 77°F., 100 g., 5 sec.	T49	D5	120-250	120-250	120-250	120-250	120-250
Ductility, 77°F., cms.[2]	T51	D113	100+	100+	100+	100+	100+
Solubility in Carbon Tetrachloride, %[3]	T44	D2042	99.5+	99.5+	99.5+	99.5+	99.5+
Water, %	T55	D95	0.2-	0.2-	0.2-	0.2-	0.2-

General Requirement—The material shall not foam when heated to application temperature recommended by The Asphalt Institute.

Note: When the Heptane-Xylene Equivalent Test is specified by the consumer, a negative test with 35 percent xylene after 1 hour will be required, AASHO Method T102.

[1] Flash Point by Cleveland Open Cup may be used for products having a flash point greater than 175°F.
[2] If penetration of residue is more than 200 and its ductility at 77°F. is less than 100, the material will be acceptable if its ductility at 60°F. is 100+.
[3] Alternatively, trichloroethylene (not trichloroethane) may be used as the solvent for determining solubility. In case of dispute, however, carbon tetrachloride will be used as the referee solvent.

* See *Specifications for Asphalt Cements and Liquid Asphalts*, SS-2, The Asphalt Institute, for latest revisions.

Table IV-4—SPECIFICATIONS FOR SLOW-CURING (SC) LIQUID ASPHALTS AND ROAD OILS

As of December 1967*

CHARACTERISTICS	AASHO Test Method	ASTM Test Method	GRADES					
			SC-70	SC-250	SC-800	SC-3000		
Kinematic Viscosity at 140°F., cs.	T201	D2170	70-140	250-500	800-1600	3000-6000		
Flash Point (Cleveland Open Cup), °F.	T48	D92	150+	175+	200+	225+		
Distillation Total Distillate to 680°F., % by volume Kinematic Viscosity at 140°F., Stokes	T78 T201	D402 D2170	10-30 4-70	4-20 8-100	2-12 20-160	5— 40-350		
Asphalt Residue of 100 Penetration, % Ductility of 100 Penetration Asphalt Residue at 77°F., cms.	T56 T51	D243 D113	50+ 100+	60+ 100+	70+ 100+	80+ 100+		
Solubility in Carbon Tetrachloride, %[1]	T44	D2042	99.5+	99.5+	99.5+	99.5+		
Water, %	T55	D95	0.5—	0.5—	0.5—	0.5—		

General Requirement—The material shall not foam when heated to application temperature recommended by The Asphalt Institute.

Note: When the Heptane-Xylene Equivalent Test is specified by the consumer, a negative test with 35 percent xylene after 1 hour will be required, AASHO Method T102.

[1] Alternatively, trichloroethylene (not trichloroethane) may be used as the solvent for determining solubility. In case of dispute, however, carbon tetrachloride will be used as the referee solvent.

* See Specifications for Asphalt Cements and Liquid Asphalts, SS-2, The Asphalt Institute, for latest revisions.

Table IV-5—SPECIFICATIONS FOR ANIONIC EMULSIFIED ASPHALTS

As of December 1967*

CHARACTERISTICS	AASHO Test Method	ASTM Test Method	GRADES				
			Rapid Setting		Medium Setting	Slow Setting	
			RS-1	RS-2	MS-2	SS-1	SS-1h
TESTS ON EMULSION[1]							
Furol Viscosity at 77°F., sec.			20-100	......	......	20-100	20-100
Furol Viscosity at 122°F., sec.			......	75-400	100+	......	......
Residue from Distillation, % by weight	T59	D244	57+	62+	62+	57+	57+
Settlement, 5 days, % difference			3−	3−	3−	3−	3−
Demulsibility:							
35 ml. of 0.02 N CaCl$_2$, %			60+	50+	......	......	......
50 ml. of 0.10 N CaCl$_2$, %			......	......	30−	......	......
Sieve Test (Retained on No. 20), %			0.10−	0.10−	0.10−	0.10−	0.10−
Cement Mixing Test, %			......	......	......	2.0−	2.0−
TESTS ON RESIDUE							
Penetration, 77°F., 100 g., 5 sec.	T49	D5	100-200	100-200	100-200	100-200	40-90
Solubility in Carbon Tetrachloride, %	T44	D2042	97.5+	97.5+	97.5+	97.5+	97.5+
Ductility, 77°F., cms.	T51	D113	40+	40+	40+	40+	40+

[1] All tests shall be performed within 30 days from the date of emulsion shipment.

[2] Alternatively, trichloroethylene (not trichloroethane) may be used as the solvent for determining solubility. In case of dispute, however, carbon tetrachloride will be used as the referee solvent.

* See Specifications for Asphalt Cements and Liquid Asphalts, SS-2, The Asphalt Institute, for latest revisions.

Table IV-6—SPECIFICATIONS FOR CATIONIC EMULSIFIED ASPHALTS

As of December 1967*

CHARACTERISTICS	AASHO Test Method	ASTM Test Method	GRADES[2]					
			Rapid Setting		Medium Setting		Slow Setting	
			RS-2K	RS-3K	SM-K	CM-K	SS-K	SS-Kh
TESTS ON EMULSION[1]								
Furol Viscosity at 77°F., sec.	T59	D244			50-500	50-500	20-100	20-100
Furol Viscosity at 122°F., sec.	T59	D244	20-100	100-400				
Settlement, 5 days,[3] % difference	T59	D244	5—	5—	5—	5—	5—	5—
Sieve Test (Retained on No. 20), %[4]	T59	D244	0.10—	0.10—	0.10—	0.10—	0.10—	0.10—
Aggregate Coating—Water Resistance Test[5]		D244						
Dry Aggregate (Job), % Coated	T59	D244			80+	80+		
Wet Aggregate (Job), % Coated	T59A	D244			60+	60+		
Cement Mixing Test, %							2—	2—
Particle Charge Test			Positive	Positive	Positive	Positive		
pH	T200	E70					6.7+	6.7+
Distillation: Residue, % by weight	T59	D244	60+	65+	60+	65+	57+	57+
Oil Distillate,[6] % by Volume of Emulsion	T59	D244	3—	3—	20—	12—		
TESTS ON RESIDUE								
Penetration, 77°F., 100 g., 5 sec.	T49	D5	100-250	100-250	100-250	100-250	100-200	40-90
Solubility in Carbon Tetrachloride, %[7]	T44	D2042	97.0+	97.0+	97.0+	97.0+	97.0+	97.0+
Ductility, 77°F., cm.	T51	D113	40+	40+	40+	40+	40+	40+

[1] All tests shall be performed within 30 days from the date of emulsion shipment.

[2] K signifies cationic type. RS signifies rapid setting grade, SM indicates mixing grade, CM indicates coarse aggregate mixing grade.

[3] The test requirement for settlement may be waived when the emulsified asphalt is used in less than 5 days; or when the purchaser may require that the settlement test be run from the time the sample is received until it is used, if the elapsed time is less than 5 days.

[4] Except that distilled water is used instead of sodium oleate solution.

[5] Calcium carbonate shall not be added to the job aggregate when making the aggregate coating—water resistance test.

[6] Volume of oil distillate may be determined by reading on the graduated cylinder which is used to collect total distillate.

[7] Alternatively, trichloroethylene (not trichloroethane) may be used as the solvent for determining solubility. In case of dispute, however, carbon tetrachloride will be used as the referee solvent.

Table IV-7—SPECIFICATIONS FOR ASPHALT FOR UNDERSEALING PORTLAND CEMENT CONCRETE PAVEMENTS

As of December 1967*

CHARACTERISTICS	AASHO Test Method	ASTM Test Method	GRADES [1]	
			160°-180°F.	180°-200°F.
Softening Point (Ring and Ball), °F.	T53	D36	160°-180°F.	180°-200°F.
Penetration of Original Sample				
At 32°F., 200 g., 60 sec.			15+	10+
At 77°F., 100 g., 5 sec.	T49	D5	25-40	15-30
At 115°F., 50 g., 5 sec.			90-	60-
Ductility at 77°F., cms.	T51	D113	3+	2+
Flash Point (Cleveland Open Cup) °F	T48	D92	425+	425+
Solubility in Carbon Tetrachloride, % [2]	T44	D2042	99.0+	99.0+
Loss on Heating, 325°F., 5 hrs., %	T47	D6	1.0-	0.5-
Penetration After Loss on Heating, % of Original	T49	D5	70+	70+
General Requirements			The asphalt shall be prepared by the refining of petroleum. It shall be uniform in character and shall not foam when heated to 350°F.	

[1] Asphalt for undersealing portland cement concrete is available in a special 140°-160°F. grade but is intended to be used only rarely and where the average atmospheric temperatures are very low.

[2] Alternatively, trichloroethylene (not trichloroethane) may be used as the solvent for determining solubility. In case of dispute, however, carbon tetrachloride will be used as the referee solvent.

* See Specifications for Asphalt Cements and Liquid Asphalts, SS-2, The Asphalt Institute, for latest revisions.

Table IV-8—SPECIFICATIONS[1] FOR ASPHALT FOR HYDRAULIC MEMBRANE CONSTRUCTION
As of December 1967*

CHARACTERISTICS	AASHO Test Method	ASTM Test Method	GRADE
Softening Point (Ring and Ball), °F.	T53	D36	175-200
Penetration of Original Sample:			
At 32°F., 200 g., 60 sec.			30+
At 77°F., 100 g., 5 sec.	T49	D5	50-60
At 115°F., 50 g., 5 sec.			120—
Ductility at 77°F., cms.	T51	D113	3.5+
Flash Point (Cleveland Open Cup), °F	T48	D92	425+
Solubility in Carbon Tetrachloride, %[2]	T44	D2042	97.0+
Loss on Heating, 325°F., 5 hrs., %	T47	D6	1.0—
Penetration After Loss on Heating, % of Original	T49	D5	60+
General Requirements	The asphalt shall be prepared by the refining of petroleum. It shall be uniform in character and shall not foam when heated to 400°F.		

[1] The above specifications should be considered tentative.
[2] Alternatively, trichloroethylene (not trichloroethane) may be used as the solvent for determining solubility. In case of dispute, however, carbon tetrachloride will be used as the referee solvent.

* See *Specifications for Asphalt Cements and Liquid Asphalts,* SS-2, The Asphalt Institute, for latest revisions.

Table IV-9—SIZES OF COARSE AGGREGATES

Amounts finer than each laboratory sieve (square openings), percentage by weight

Size number	Nominal size square openings (1)	4	3½	3	2½	2	1½	1	¾	½	⅜	No. 4	No. 8	No. 16	No. 50	No. 100
1	3½ to 1½	100	90 to 100		25 to 60		0 to 15		0 to 5							
2	2½ to 1½			100	90 to 100	35 to 70	0 to 15		0 to 5							
24	2½ to ¾			100	90 to 100		25 to 60		0 to 10		0 to 5					
3	2 to 1				100	90 to 100	35 to 70	0 to 15		0 to 5						
357	2 to No. 4				100	95 to 100		35 to 70		10 to 30		0 to 5				
4	1½ to ¾					100	90 to 100	20 to 55	0 to 15		0 to 5					
467	1½ to No. 4					100	95 to 100		35 to 70		10 to 30	0 to 5				
5	1 to ½						100	90 to 100	20 to 55	0 to 10	0 to 5					
56	1 to ⅜						100	90 to 100	40 to 85	10 to 40	0 to 15	0 to 5				
57	1 to No. 4						100	95 to 100		25 to 60		0 to 10	0 to 5			
6	¾ to ⅜							100	90 to 100	20 to 55	0 to 15	0 to 5				
67	¾ to No. 4							100	90 to 100		20 to 55	0 to 10	0 to 5			
68	¾ to No. 8							100	90 to 100		30 to 65	5 to 25	0 to 10	0 to 5		
7	½ to No. 4								100	90 to 100	40 to 70	0 to 15	0 to 5			
78	½ to No. 8								100	90 to 100	40 to 75	5 to 25	0 to 10	0 to 5		
8	⅜ to No. 8									100	85 to 100	10 to 30	0 to 10	0 to 5		
89	⅜ to No. 16									100	90 to 100	20 to 55	5 to 30	0 to 10	0 to 5	
9	No. 4 to No. 16										100	85 to 100	10 to 40	0 to 10	0 to 5	
10	No. 4 to 0 (2)										100	85 to 100			0 to 5	10 to 30

(1) In inches, except where otherwise indicated. Numbered sieves are those of the United States Standard Sieve Series.
(2) Screenings.

Reprinted from AASHO Designation M43 - Standard Sizes of Coarse Aggregate For Highway Construction

Table IV-10—MIX COMPOSITIONS

Mix[1] Type	2½ in.	1½ in.	1 in.	¾ in.	½ in.	⅜ in.	#4	#8	#16	#30	#50	#100	#200	Percent[2] Asphalt
I a	100	35-70		0-15				0-5						0-3	3.0-4.5
II a						100	40-85	5-20						0-4	4.0-5.0
II b					100	70-100	20-40	5-20						0-4	4.0-5.0
II c				100	70-100	45-75	20-40	5-20						0-4	3.0-6.0
II d			100	70-100		35-60	15-35	5-20						0-4	3.0-6.0
II e		100	70-100	50-80		25-60	10-30	5-20						0-4	3.0-6.0
III a					100	75-100	35-55	20-35		10-22	6-16	4-12	2-8	3.0-6.0
III b				100	75-100	60-85	35-55	20-35		10-22	6-16	4-12	2-8	3.0-6.0
III c				100	75-100	60-85	30-55	20-35		5-20	3-12	2-8	0-4	3.0-6.0
III d			100	75-100		45-70	30-50	20-35		5-20	3-12	2-8	0-4	3.0-6.0
III e		100	75-100	60-85		40-65	30-50	20-35		5-20	3-12	2-8	0-4	3.0-6.0
IV a					100	80-100	55-75	35-50		18-29	13-23	8-16	4-10	3.5-7.0
IV b				100	80-100	70-90	50-70	35-50		18-29	13-23	8-16	4-10	3.5-7.0
IV c			100	80-100		60-80	48-65	35-50		19-30	13-23	7-15	0-8	3.5-7.0
IV d		100	80-100	70-90		55-75	45-62	35-50		19-30	13-23	7-15	0-8	3.5-7.0
V a					100	85-100	65-80	50-65	37-52	25-40	18-30	10-20	3-10	4.0-7.5
V b				100	85-100	85-100	65-80	50-65	37-52	25-40	18-30	10-20	3-10	4.0-7.5
VI a					100	85-100		65-78	50-70	35-60	25-48	15-30	6-12	4.5-8.5
VI b				100	85-100	85-100		65-80	47-68	30-55	30-55	10-25	3-8	4.5-8.5
VII a						100	85-100	80-95	70-89	55-80	30-60	10-35	4-14	7.0-11.0
VIII a						100	100	95-100	85-98	70-95	40-75	20-40	8-16	7.5-12.0

[1] See article 4.0.7
[2] By weight as a percentage of total mix.

Table IV-11—SUITABILITY OF LABORATORY DESIGN METHODS[1]

PAVING MIX TYPE AND DESCRIPTION [2]	HUBBARD-FIELD	MARSHALL	HVEEM
I Macadam	X	X	X
II Open Type	X	X	D
III Coarse Graded	X	D	A
IV Dense Graded.............	X	A	A
V Fine Graded	X	A	A
VI Stone Sheet	A	A	A
VII Sand Sheet (Sand Asphalt)...	A	A	A
VIII Fine Sheet (Sheet Asphalt)....	A	A	A

A—Suitable
D—Doubtful
X—Unsuitable

[1] See Chapter III for description of methods.
[2] See Article 4.07.

B.—*Grading Specifications for Mineral Aggregates*

4.03 COARSE AGGREGATE.—Coarse aggregate is all mineral material retained on the No. 8 sieve. It consists of crushed stone, crushed slag, or crushed or uncrushed gravel.

Suggested specifications and test criteria for coarse aggregates are contained in The Asphalt Institute publication, *Specifications and Construction Methods for Asphalt Concrete and Other Plant-Mix Types*, Specification Series No. 1. Chapter III of this handbook summarizes the recommended test requirements and briefly describes each test. Table IV-9 gives the gradation requirements for various sizes of coarse aggregates.

4.04 FINE AGGREGATE.—Fine aggregate is all mineral matter passing the No. 8 sieve. It consists of natural sand or manufactured material derived by crushing stone, slag, or gravel and it includes mineral filler and mineral dust.

Suggested specifications and test criteria for fine aggregate are contained in *Specifications and Construction*

Methods for Asphalt Concrete and Other Plant-Mix Types, Specification Series No. 1. Chapter III of this handbook summarizes the test requirements and briefly describes each test.

4.05 SPECIAL LOCAL AGGREGATES.—There are a number of local types of aggregate which often do not pass the standard tests but which make excellent asphalt mixtures because of certain inherent qualities. In areas where aggregates meeting standard tests are scarce, it often will be possible to use substandard materials if experience has shown them to be satisfactory or where research and testing warrant such use.

4.06 COMBINED MINERAL AGGREGATE.— Many specifications require that the Sand Equivalent test be performed on the combined mineral aggregate. *Specifications and Construction Methods for Asphalt Concrete and Other Plant-Mix Types*, Specification Series No. 1, has this requirement and suggested test criteria. Chapter III of this handbook briefly describes the test.

C.—Classification of Asphalt Paving Mixes

4.07 DESCRIPTION.—Asphalt paving mixes may be produced from a wide range of aggregate combinations, each having its own particular characteristics and suited to specific design and construction uses. Aside from the asphalt content, the principal characteristics of the mix are determined, in the main, by the relative amounts of:

(1) Coarse Aggregate (retained on No. 8 sieve)
(2) Fine Aggregate (passing No. 8 sieve)
(3) Mineral Dust (passing No. 200 sieve)

The aggregate composition may vary from a coarse-textured mix having a predominance of coarse aggregate to a fine-textured mix having mostly fine aggregate.

To assort these variables, The Asphalt Institute classifies hot-mix asphalt paving according to mix type, based on the relative amounts of coarse aggregate, fine aggregate, and mineral dust.

This method was developed to classify the terms and designations for hot-mix asphalt paving used locally throughout the country. The terms and limits included agree in general with overall practice but may be at variance with the practice of a given local area. Aside from the advantages of standardizing terms, this method of paving mix classification permits a logical subdivision of each mix type into a series of mix compositions having specific design uses, such as *surface course, plant-mix surface treatment, intermediate course, leveling course,* or *base course.* The description, principal usage, and paving applications for the complete series of mix compositions are outlined in detail in *Specifications and Construction Methods for Asphalt Concrete and Other Plant-Mix Types* (SS-1), published by The Asphalt Institute. Table IV-10 contains a summary of these recommended mix compositions.

D.—*Design of Asphalt Paving Mixes*

4.08 GENERAL.—The three best known design methods for asphalt paving mixes are the Marshall, the Hubbard-Field, and the Hveem. They have been widely used for construction design with satisfactory results. For each method, criteria have been developed by correlating results of laboratory tests on the compacted paving mixes under service conditions.

Table IV-11 grades the suitability of the design methods for different types of mixes. Suggested criteria are given in Table IV-12. The design of asphalt paving mixes is discussed in detail in The Asphalt Institute publication *Mix Design Methods for Asphalt Concrete and Other Hot-Mix Types*, Manual Series No. 2 (MS-2).

4.09 JOB-MIX FORMULA.—The term job-mix formula is generally used in the singular but actually three or more job-mix formulas may be involved by the time a project is well under way. These are:

(1) The Design Job-Mix Formula which is used in the preliminary stages of the project design when the specifications are prepared, the preliminary investigation of materials is made, and the preliminary mix designs are studied in the laboratory.

(2) The Preliminary Job-Mix Formula is tentatively determined on the basis of tests of samples taken (a) from the aggregate delivered and stockpiled on the project or (b) from the hot bins of the asphalt plant.

(3) The Final Job-Mix Formula is determined after the asphalt plant is in regular operation and the characteristics of the mix have been determined from samples of the production mix, including its workability performance and other characteristics, on the roadbed.

E.—Control of Asphalt Application Temperatures

4.10 GENERAL.—Asphalt is a thermoplastic material that decreases in viscosity with increasing temperature. The relationship between temperature and viscosity, however, may not be the same for different sources or types and grades of asphaltic material.

4.11 APPLICATION TEMPERATURES.—Application temperatures are normally specified for various uses of asphaltic materials but, because of these viscosity variations, the specification of temperature *alone* is inadequate for their most effective use. Therefore, The Asphalt Institute recommends that the temperature-viscosity relationship* for each asphaltic material be taken into consideration to arrive at the proper temperature to give the desired viscosity for the construction operation being used.

The most suitable application viscosity will depend upon such factors as:

    (1) Type of application (mixing or spraying)
    (2) Characteristics and gradation of aggregate
    (3) Weather conditions (spraying application)

---

* *A chart,* Asphalt Institute Form No. TV-1, *is available from the Institute for plotting these data (see Figure IV-4).*

Because of these variables, the proper viscosity for a specific application must be established by trial, within ranges specified below.

The most effective temperature for plant mixing of dense graded mixes is that at which the viscosity of the asphalt is in the range of 150-300 centistokes kinematic viscosity (75-150 seconds, Saybolt Furol). Mixing and placing of more open graded mixes can often be adequately accomplished at higher viscosities—300-1600

Table IV-12—SUGGESTED CRITERIA FOR TEST LIMITS[1]

DESIGN METHOD [2]	HEAVY TRAFFIC [2]		MEDIUM TRAFFIC [2]		LIGHT TRAFFIC [2]	
	Min.	Max.	Min.	Max.	Min.	Max.
MARSHALL						
Number of compaction blows, each end of specimen......	75		50		35	
Stability, lbs................	750	—	500	—	500	—
Flow, units of 0.01 in.........	8	16	8	18	8	20
% Air Voids						
Surfacing or Leveling	3	5	3	5	3	5
Sand or Stone Sheet	3	5	3	5	3	5
Base....................	3	8	3	8	3	8
%Voids in Mineral Aggregate						
Surfacing or Leveling						
Sand or Stone Sheet			See Figure IV-2			
Base..................						
HUBBARD-FIELD						
Original Method						
Stability, lbs..............	2000	—	1200	2000	1200	2000
% Air Voids	2	5	2	5	2	5
HVEEM						
Stabilometer value..........	37	—	35	—	30	—
Cohesiometer value	50	—	50	—	50	—
Swell, in..................	—	.03	—	.03	—	.03
% Voids [3]................	4	—	4	—	4	—

[1] *Criteria applicable only when testing is done in conformance with methods outlined in Asphalt Institute Publication, Mix Design Methods for Asphalt Concrete and other Hot-Mix Types, MS-2. All criteria, not stability value alone, must be considered in designing an asphalt paving mix.*

[2] *See Thickness Design, Asphalt Pavement Structures for Highways and Streets, Manual Series No. 1 (MS-1) for details of traffic classifications.*

[3] *Although not a routine part of the design method, an effort is made to provide a minimum of 4 percent air voids in the total mix.*

centistokes (150-800 seconds, Saybolt Furol)—to prevent drainage of the asphalt during transit. However, no mixes should be made at temperatures below 225°F.

These temperature-viscosity relationships are based on the use of dry aggregate—the temperature of which controls the mix temperature. It should be recognized that a temperature sufficient to dry the aggregate is the prime consideration, provided the maximum mix temperature —measured immediately after dropping from the pugmill—does not exceed 350°F. Therefore, the aggregate should be controlled within the temperature range of the asphalt that will provide a viscosity within the ranges recommended in the paragraph above. Occasionally, however, it may be necessary to heat the aggregate above the temperature corresponding to the recommended viscosity mixing range to dry it sufficiently to obtain a satisfactory mix.

The recommended distributor spraying viscosity is normally in the range of 40-120 centistokes (20-60 seconds, Saybolt Furol). The higher viscosities in this range are generally used for sealing and penetration of

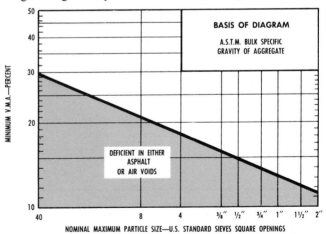

Figure IV-2—Relationship Between Minimum Voids in Mineral Aggregate (V.M.A.) and Nominal Maximum Particle Size of the Aggregate for Compacted Dense-Graded Paving Mixtures

open surfaces. The lower viscosities are normally used for sealing and penetration of dense surfaces.

In the absence of suitable temperature-viscosity data, the following tabulation provides a guide for use in

Table IV-13—SUGGESTED TEMPERATURES FOR USES OF ASPHALT

Type and Grade of Asphalt	Pugmill Mixing Temperature of Aggregates*	Distributor Spraying Temperature
Asphalt Cements		
(For Open-Graded Mixes, Types I & II)**		
40-50	225-310°F	
60-70	225-305°F	
85-100	225-300°F	
120-150	225-300°F	
200-300	225-300°F	
(For Dense-Graded Mixes, Types III-VIII)**		
40-50	275-350°F	
60-70	265-330°F	
85-100	255-325°F	
120-150	245-325°F	
200-300	225-300°F	
(For Distributor Spray Applications)		
40-50***		300-410°F
60-70***		295-405°F
85-100		290-400°F
120-150		285-395°F
200-300		275-385°F
Liquid Asphalts		
RC, MC, and SC Grades		
30	60-105°F	
70	95-140°F	See
250	135-175°F	Figure
800	165-205°F	IV-3
3000	200-240°F	
Asphalt Emulsions		
RS-1	****	75-130°F
RS-2	****	110-160°F
MS-2	50-140°F	100-160°F
SS-1	50-140°F	75-130°F
SS-1h	50-140°F	75-130°F
RS-2K	****	75-130°F
RS-3K	****	110-160°F
CM-K	50-140°F	100-160°F
SM-K	50-140°F	100-160°F
SS-K	50-140°F	75-130°F
SS-Kh	50-140°F	75-130°F

*The temperature of the aggregates and asphalt immediately before mixing should be approximately that of the completed batch.

**Mix Type III is intermediate between dense- and open-graded mixes. As the gradation of the mix changes from dense-graded to open-graded the mixing temperature should be lowered accordingly.

***Not normally used for spray applications in pavement construction.

****Not used for mixing.

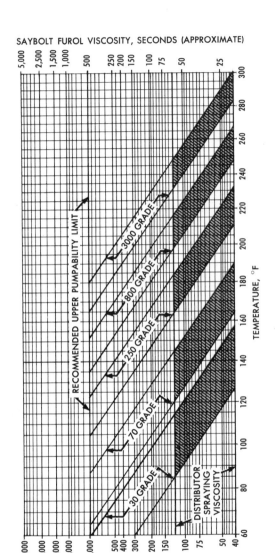

SAYBOLT FUROL VISCOSITY, SECONDS (APPROXIMATE)

KINEMATIC VISCOSITY, CENTISTOKES

Figure IV-3—Temperature-Viscosity of Liquid Asphalts

Kinematic viscosity, centistokes = $\dfrac{\text{Absolute viscosity, centipoises}}{\text{density}}$

Saybolt Furol viscosity $\cong$ 0.5 centistokes viscosity

CAUTION

The purpose of Table IV-13 and Figure IV-3 is to indicate temperature ranges necessary to provide proper asphalt viscosity for spraying and mixing applications for the grades of asphalt shown. It *must* be recognized, however, that temperature ranges indicated generally are above the minimum flash point for the RC, MC and SC liquid asphaltic materials as specified by The Asphalt Institute and other agencies. In fact, some of these liquid asphalts will "flash" at temperatures below these indicated ranges. Accordingly, suitable safety precautions are mandatory at all times when handling these liquid asphalts. These safety precautions include, but are not limited to, the following:

(1) Open flames or sparks must not be permitted close to these materials. Controlled heat should be applied in heating kettles, mixers, distributors, or other equipment designed and approved for the purpose.

(2) Open flames must not be used to inspect or examine drums, tank cars, or other containers in which these materials have been stored.

(3) All vehicles transporting these materials must be properly vented.

(4) Only experienced personnel must be permitted to supervise the handling of these materials.

(5) All applicable intra- and interstate commerce requirements must be met.

determining application temperatures for asphalt cements and asphalt emulsions.

Figure IV-3 is for use in determining distributor spraying application temperatures for liquid asphalts.

4.12 REFERENCES—The following Asphalt Institute publications contain additional information concerning specifications and use recommendations for asphalts, aggregates, and paving mixtures:

(1) *Specifications and Construction Methods for Asphalt Concrete and Other Plant-Mix Types*, Specification Series No. 1 (SS-1)

(2) *Mix Design Methods for Asphalt Concrete and Other Hot-Mix Types,* Manual Series No. 2 (MS-2)

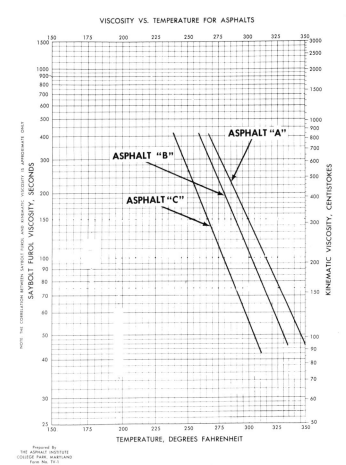

VISCOSITY VS. TEMPERATURE FOR ASPHALTS

Prepared By
THE ASPHALT INSTITUTE
COLLEGE PARK, MARYLAND
Form No. TV-1

Figure IV-4—Viscosity vs. Temperature for Asphalts

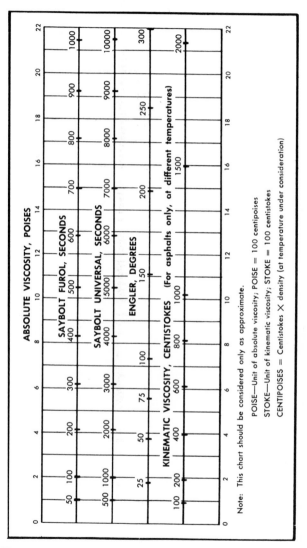

Figure IV-5—Viscosity Conversions for Various Methods of Measurement

Chapter V

DESIGN OF ASPHALT PAVEMENT STRUCTURES

A.—*Thickness Design of Highways and Streets*

5.01 GENERAL.—An asphalt pavement structure can be designed and constructed to support the heaviest traffic density and axle loads. It does so by distributing downward and outward the imposed high-intensity pressures and stresses, reducing them in magnitude until they may be carried safely by the native or subgrade soil. The thickness of the pavement structure, however, must reflect the conditions of traffic, subgrade, and construction materials to assure continued good performance. This usually involves the use of materials of successively higher strength and bearing value from the subgrade soil to the pavement surface. The characteristics of the materials used will influence the designed thickness of each component layer and, thus, the total thickness.

The Asphalt Institute method of design is presented in detail in *Thickness Design—Asphalt Pavement Structures for Highways and Streets*, Manual Series No. 1 (MS-1). Also discussed is the substitution of various materials for high quality asphalt concrete, similar to Asphalt Institute dense-graded Type IV mixes. Thickness ratios are recommended for the substitution of these materials. With them the most economical and durable combinations of materials can be selected for the pavement structure.

Asphalt pavement construction is so versatile that several types of asphalt mixtures often are suitable for certain traffic and climatic conditions. There are times when mix types other than those similar to Asphalt Institute Type IV mixes may also provide excellent service. However, the substitution ratios and service period for these mixes have not as yet been firmly established. State highway engineers and Asphalt Institute engineers are experienced in the use of these types and are familiar with the thicknesses required for local conditions of traffic and climate. They should be consulted by designers considering the use of other types of asphalt mixes.

5.02 PROCEDURE.—The Asphalt Institute procedure for determining the thickness of an asphalt pavement structure depends on the anticipated traffic, the strength value of the supporting or foundation material (CBR, R-Value, Plate Bearing Value), the quality of the materials selected and the construction procedures.

(1) *Traffic Analysis.* The anticipated traffic is calculated as a *Design Traffic Number,* which is the average number of equivalent 18,000-pound single-axle loads per day expected in the heaviest traffic or truck lane(s) during the design period, normally 20 years. There are several methods of calculating the design traffic number. Figure V-1 and Figure V-2 are simplified charts for determining this value.

(2) *Evaluation of Subgrade, Subbase, and Base Materials.* Materials selected for use in the construction of an asphalt pavement structure must be evaluated to provide information for an adequate and economical design (see Appendix A). The materials must also be checked to determine quality and to establish compaction requirements. The following mechanical strength tests are the most frequently used and are recommended by The Asphalt Institute:

    a. California Bearing Ratio (CBR)

    b. Bearing Value (Plate Bearing Test), psi, 12 inch plate, 0. 2 inch deflection, 10 repetitions

    c. Resistance Value (R-Value)

The methods for determining the strength value of the foundation materials are provided in detail in *Soils Manual for the Design of Asphalt Pavement Structures,* Manual Series No. 10 (MS-10), The Asphalt Institute.

(3) *Design Procedures.* After the strength value(s) of the foundation material and the Design Traffic Number have been determined, the thickness of the pavement structure is established by use of the appropriate thickness design chart, see Figures V-3 and V-4. Because of the differences in procedures and numerical values in the CBR and R-Value tests, separate thick-

ness charts are provided for each. As the plate bearing values can be correlated with CBR values from laboratory tests on undisturbed samples, the same thickness chart is used for both tests.

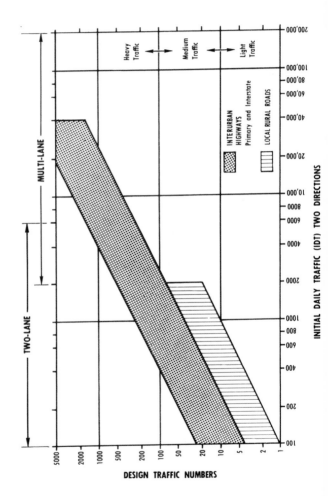

Figure V-1—Traffic Analysis Chart, Inter-urban Highways and Rural Roads

When there is a choice of available materials that can be used in the construction of an asphalt pavement structure, alternate designs should be made incorporating various combinations of these materials to determine the most economical pavement.

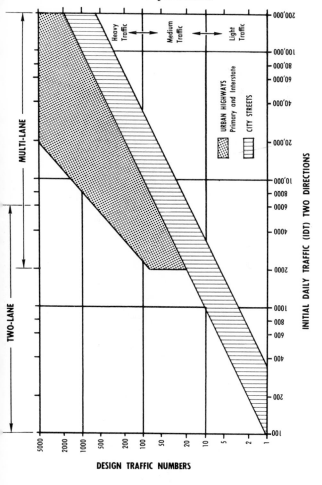

Figure V-2—Traffic Analysis Chart, Urban Highways and City Streets

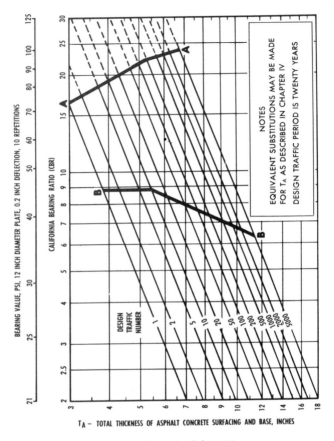

A-line determines required minimum thickness of asphalt concrete.

B-line determines minimum thickness of base and surface required to permit use of granular subbase material.

Figure V-3—Thickness Requirements for Asphalt Pavement Structures Using Subgrade Soil CBR or Plate Bearing Values

(4) *Economic Analysis and Selection of Design.* Following the establishment of alternate designs, the estimated cost for each pavement section is determined, including other factors such as average annual maintenance costs, climatic conditions, and service record of asphalt pavements built with the local materials. Detailed procedures for computing annual costs of high-

ways or of highway pavements are contained in Chapter VI.

In certain areas, local experience and conditions may justify a modification of the design thicknesses. The thicknesses derived by the Asphalt Institute procedure are conservative and are adequate for severe conditions. However, standard chemical and physical tests

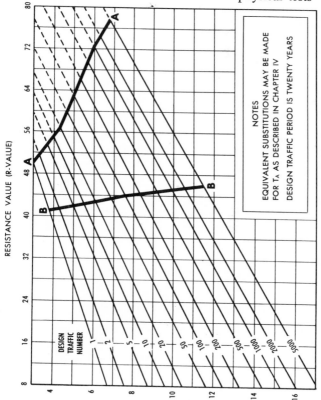

NOTES

EQUIVALENT SUBSTITUTIONS MAY BE MADE FOR T_A AS DESCRIBED IN CHAPTER IV

DESIGN TRAFFIC PERIOD IS TWENTY YEARS

RESISTANCE VALUE (R-VALUE)

DESIGN TRAFFIC NUMBER

T$_A$ - TOTAL THICKNESS OF ASPHALT CONCRETE SURFACING AND BASE, INCHES

A-line determines required minimum thickness of asphalt concrete.

B-line determines minimum thickness of base and surface required to permit use of granular subbase material.

Figure V-4—Thickness Requirements for Asphalt Pavement Structures Using Subgrade Soil Resistance Value

may not always anticipate the behavior of soils. Where there is reason to believe that such circumstances exist, the engineer should consult the nearest office of The Asphalt Institute.

5.03 DESIGN PERIOD.—The design period is the number of years until the first major resurfacing of the new asphalt pavement structure is anticipated. The procedures outlined in *Thickness Design, MS-1*, are based on a design period of 20 years. However, methods are given which can be used for other design periods, either longer or shorter than 20 years. The end of the design period is calculated to be that time when the pavement reaches a Present Serviceability Index of 2.5.*

5.04 PLANNED STAGE CONSTRUCTION.—Quite often stage construction can be planned for better overall pavement performance. One method of planned stage construction is to design for relatively short periods, for example, 5 years or less, with provision for overlays as needed. Another method is to design for a full period of, for example, 20 years and then reduce the design by 1 or 2 inches with plans to add the reduced thickness when the serviceability index approaches 2.5. Both methods are presented in *Thickness Design, MS-1*. Chapters VI and IX of this handbook also contain discussions of stage construction.

5.05 DRAINAGE AND COMPACTION.—Good drainage and thorough preparation and compaction of subgrade and base materials are essential features of a properly designed and constructed pavement. Information on drainage of asphalt pavement structures is included in *Thickness Design* (MS-1) and in Chapter VIII of this handbook. Details relating to compaction of courses in the asphalt pavement structure also are given

---

* The Present Serviceability Index is a number between 0 and 5 used to classify a pavement's present riding quality. A pavement rated less than 2.5 may need to be resurfaced.

in *Thickness Design* (MS-1). Supplemental compaction information is included in Chapter VIII of this handbook.

5.06 FROST EFFECTS.—Frost susceptibility is closely related to susceptibility to water. Hence, either selection of materials or treatment of materials for resistance to the one will take care of the other. In localities where freezing weather occurs, subbase and improved subgrade materials should be selected which are not susceptible to detrimental behavior upon freezing and thawing. Asphalt membranes should be considered for controlling moisture in highway embankments with high volume change soils.

Frost problems and recommended treatments, including asphalt membranes, are discussed in *Thickness Design* (MS-1).

5.07 ASPHALT OVERLAY PAVEMENTS.—Existing pavements may be improved by overlaying with asphalt surfacing or with a combination of asphalt surfacing and asphalt base. Under some conditions a high quality non-asphalt base may be included in the overlay. Overlays may be considered in two categories:

(1) To provide smooth, skid- and water-resistant surfaces or to make improvements in grade or cross-section.

(2) To strengthen existing pavements to handle heavier loads or increased traffic.

In the first case, the overlay is usually constructed entirely of asphalt concrete and the design thickness is determined by factors other than an increase in pavement strength.

In the second case, where increased strength is required, the design procedure is based on the concept that the old and new layers will form a composite pavement structure having the strength and performance characteristics necessary for the new condition.

Procedures for determining the thickness of overlay pavements are included in *Thickness Design* (MS-1).

B.—Thickness Design of Airport Pavements

5.08 GENERAL.—As in highways, the design of an airport pavement structure must start with an analysis and classification of the existing subgrade or soil foundation. The properties that affect the performance of the soil, such as grain sizes, moisture content, and bearing capacity, must be determined. Then to determine the total thickness of the pavement structure, the maximum anticipated wheel load must be estimated. Thicknesses of component layers depend upon the construction materials used.

5.09 PAVEMENT STRUCTURE DESIGN METHODS.—At the present time there are three methods in common use for determining total thickness requirements for asphalt pavement structures for airports. These methods are the CBR, the Plate Bearing, and the FAA. These three methods differ basically in the procedures employed to determine the strength of the subgrade. The CBR method evaluates subgrade strength by the CBR (California Bearing Ratio) test. The Plate Bearing method uses a plate bearing test to determine subgrade supporting value. The FAA method establishes the subgrade bearing strength on the basis of subgrade classes (F values) which are dependent upon soil texture, climate, and drainage.

Organizations employing CBR, Plate Bearing, and classification methods for rating the subgrade have developed corresponding charts of design curves. These curves indicate the thicknesses of pavement structures needed to carry various wheel loads or gross aircraft weights over subgrades having a range of supporting values. *Asphalt Pavements for Airports,* Manual Series No. 11 (MS-11), The Asphalt Institute, contains design curves developed by The Asphalt Institute for a wide range of both single and multiple wheel assemblies. While generally similar to the curves of other organizations, they are not the same in all respects.

5.10 ASPHALT OVERLAYS FOR AIRPORT PAVEMENTS.—Some of the earlier airport pavement structures were not designed or built to carry the increased traffic and loads imposed by today's larger and heavier airplanes. Other airports were poorly constructed and are deteriorating, and some are suffering from a long lack of maintenance. Overlaying with asphalt concrete can effectively improve and strengthen such pavement structures. *Asphalt Pavements for Airports,* MS-11, discusses evaluation, design methods, and construction practices leading to overlaying airport pavements.

C.—Design of Asphalt Mixes

5.11 GENERAL.—The design of asphaltic hot mixtures to carry heavy traffic should be based on the following considerations:

(1) When thoroughly compacted, the mixture should develop not less than the minimum stability value specified.

(2) When thoroughly compacted, dense graded aggregate surface mixtures should contain not more than five nor less than three percent air voids. The maximum limit insures impermeability and the minimum limit prevents overfilling of voids in the aggregate. Overfilling of voids may result in bleeding and possible loss of stability under traffic in excessive summer heat, as well as slipperiness in the following wet weather.

(3) The mixture should contain as high a percentage of asphalt as possible, commensurate with requirements one and two. Maximum durability of the pavement under service conditions is thus obtained, and ravelling, due to a deficiency of asphalt, is prevented.

(4) The mixture should be readily workable when heated to the temperature specified for spreading in order to facilitate uniform spreading and compaction during construction of the pavement. There is no test for determining workability but a little experience will enable the laboratory operator or construction inspector

to tell when a mixture is undesirably harsh, stiff, or gummy. Harshness may often be reduced by using a lower percentage of coarse aggregate. Stiffness may be reduced by using a lower percentage of fine sand and filler. Gumminess may sometimes be reduced by lowering the percentage of asphalt and filler. Change should not be made without testing for effect on stability, because either reducing coarse aggregate (especially if crushed) or sand and filler, may reduce stability.

5.12 MIX DESIGN METHODS.—Refer to Chapter IV and to *Mix Design Methods for Asphalt Concrete and Other Hot-Mix Types,* Manual Series No. 2 (MS-2), The Asphalt Institute, for details of mix design methods.

5.13 REFERENCES.—Details of designing asphalt pavement structures are covered thoroughly in the following Asphalt Institute publications:

(1) *Thickness Design—Asphalt Pavement Structures for Highways and Streets,* Manual Series No. 1 (MS-1).

(2) *Mix Design Methods for Asphalt Concrete and Other Hot-Mix Types,* Manual Series No. 2 (MS-2).

(3) *Soils Manual for Design of Asphalt Pavement Structures,* Manual Series No. 10 (MS-10).

(4) *Asphalt Pavements for Airports,* Manual Series No. 11 (MS-11).

Chapter VI

HIGHWAY PAVEMENT ECONOMICS

6.01 INTRODUCTION.—In selecting a pavement design, the structural section having the best combination of engineering qualities and cost is the one that should be chosen. First, comparable alternate thickness designs should be made considering all materials available to the project. Then an economic analysis should follow to determine which of these designs should be selected.

The analysis usually is made on the basis of annual cost per mile during the period selected to amortize the investment in the pavement, normally 40 years. If there is no clear choice between two or more designs, they should be placed in the bidding proposal as alternates.

6.02 ECONOMICS OF PLANNED STAGE CONSTRUCTION.—Often, designing a pavement to be completed by stage construction will be more economical on an annual cost basis than by requiring the entire job in the initial contract. The savings accrue mainly from longer life of the pavement structure for approximately the same expenditure of funds.

Another economic advantage of stage construction stems from the amount of traffic using the pavement. Traffic volume must be estimated for the initial design, so deferring the final stage of construction makes it possible to secure a true count of the traffic using the highway. Then adjustments to the design may be made, either decreasing or increasing the thickness of the second stage of construction. If it can be decreased because of less traffic than anticipated, money is saved in construction. If thickness must be increased because of higher than expected traffic volume, money may be saved by preventing failures caused by overloading.

6.03 DETERMINATION OF ANNUAL COSTS OF HIGHWAYS.

—This discussion is based on a paper by R. H. Baldock* in which he examined existing methods available for determining the annual cost of highways. He found that all of these methods are similar in that each considers a highway to be a capital investment of public or private funds and each presents a procedure for determining annual cost which includes many factors in addition to construction cost. Mr. Baldock proposed an additional procedure which more conclusively describes the total costs involved.

This procedure for evaluation of highways includes all factors affecting the annual cost with respect to a reasonable period of analysis. To avoid obsolescence due to major technological changes affecting transportation, an analysis period of 40 years was selected. The entire investment is amortized during this period although the highway will almost undoubtedly continue to serve as a portion of the original or some lesser system. This procedure follows the general accounting practice usually applied to capital investments.

Two methods are proposed for analysis of annual cost. The first involves *all* costs pertaining to the complete highway and is used to evaluate the whole facility. The second analyzes only those costs pertaining to the traveled way or mainline section, including pavement structure, shoulders, and when appropriate, structural drainage features. Only the latter method is needed to evaluate and compare alternate pavement designs to determine the most appropriate design for a specific highway.

6.04 BASIC FACTORS REQUIRED FOR DETERMINING ANNUAL COST.

—The basic factors involved in computing the annual cost per mile of highway are as follows:

---

* R. H. Baldock, "Determination of the Annual Cost of Highways," Highway Research Board Record 12, Highway Research Board, Washington, D. C., 1963. (Mr. Baldock, Consulting Engineer-Economist, formerly was State Highway Engineer of the Oregon State Highway Commission.)

(1) **First Cost (Per Mile).** First cost should include construction and right-of-way. Construction costs should be divided between the pavement structure and shoulders, and all other construction expenses. This division makes it easier to compare the annual costs of alternate pavement designs.

(2) **Maintenance Cost (Per Mile).** The total per mile maintenance cost should be divided into pavement structure and shoulder maintenance expense and the expense of all other maintenance. The sum of these represents maintenance in determining total annual cost per mile but only the former, which represents the cost of pavement maintenance, is used in comparing alternate designs.

(3) **Operation Cost (Per Mile).** Operation costs should include the expense, other than maintaining the capital investment, of providing service to the road user. This includes snow removal, sanding, signs, signals, striping and marking, and similar services. Many states charge some of the above items to maintenance and for determining annual highway costs the separation of these items is not necessary.

(4) **Administration and Overhead Costs (Per Mile).** The administration and overhead costs, including field surveys and office design, are considerable and must be charged. It is suggested that they be prorated over the miles on the system on the basis of first cost of construction.

(5) **Cost of Resurfacing and Resurfacing Frequency (Per Mile).** Resurfacing costs are estimated on the basis of past experience. Pavement structural design presented in this manual is based upon resurfacing after 20 years of service life. This period should be used for resurfacing frequency.

(6) **Salvage Value (Per Mile).** This procedure amortizes the entire investment in a highway over the analysis period of 40 years. For this reason, the salvage value at the end of the analysis life of the project may

be considered as having a zero value and does not enter into the computation.

(7) **Interest Rate.** Money has a definite rental value and interest on the investment in a highway must be charged to enable economic evaluation of the project. If constructed with borrowed funds, interest payments accrue to the security holder. If, on the other hand, the project is funded from the owners' revenues, interest is in the nature of a fixed charge against the project to compensate for the loss of earning power of the funds "frozen" therein. In the case of public funds derived from taxes, these funds, if not so captured, could have been invested by the public to yield a safe and reasonable return and, therefore, the interest charge represents a cost.

Economists have used interest rates varying from 5 to 10 percent in studies of highway economics. It is recommended that the interest rate used in determination of the annual highway cost be 6 percent annually.

(8) **Annual Costs of Traveled Way or Mainline Pavement Only (Per Mile).** When economic studies are made to determine the most appropriate of the several alternate pavement designs being considered, initial construction and maintenance costs of the traveled way, or mainline section, only should be used. Right-of-way, Administration and Overhead, Operation, and other costs may be disregarded because they apply equally to all alternates.

6.05 DETERMINATION OF THE ANNUAL COST OF HIGHWAYS.—Two formulas are presented in Mr. Baldock's paper for determining the annual cost of highways. Formula No. 1 includes all costs of building, maintaining, operating and administrating the highway. This formula is used to calculate the total cost.

(1) **Formula No. 1.**
Formula No. 1 calculates the total annual cost as follows:

$$C = CRF_n [A + E_1 PWF_{n_1} + E_2 PWF_{n_1} - \left(1 - \frac{Y}{X}\right)$$
$$(E_1 \text{ or } E_2) PWF_n] + M + O + D$$

where:

C = the complete annual cost per mile of highway

CRF = the Capital Recovery Factor = $\dfrac{r(1 + r)^n}{(1 + r)^n - 1}$

PWF = Present Worth Factor, for a single payment = $\dfrac{1}{(1 + r)^{n1}}$

r = the interest rate (6 percent)

n = the analysis period (40 years)

n_1 = the number of years after construction that future work is performed
(Note by The Asphalt Institute: n_1 will have different values in the same analysis depending upon whether it is used with E_1 or E_2)

A = total construction and right-of-way costs per mile

E_1 = first resurfacing costs per mile

E_2 = second resurfacing costs per mile

Y = number of years between the last resurfacing and the end of analysis period

X = estimated service life, in years, of last resurfacing

M = total annual maintenance cost per mile

O = annual operation cost per mile

D = annual administration and overhead cost per mile

(2) Formula No. 2.

Formula No. 2 includes only costs necessary to compare alternate pavement designs. This one calculates the annual cost per mile of the traveled way, or mainline section.

$$C_1 = CRF_n [A_1 + E_1 PWF_{n_1} + E_2 PWF_{n_1} - \left(1 - \frac{Y}{X}\right)$$
$$(E_1 \text{ or } E_2) PWF_n] + M_1$$

where:

C_1 = annual cost of traveled way, or mainline section, per mile

A_1 = initial construction cost of traveled way, or mainline section, per mile

M_1 = annual maintenance cost of traveled way, or mainline section, per mile

All other terms are defined under Formula No. 1.

6.06 EXAMPLES.—

Example 1.

Annual Cost of Traveled Way—Complete Construction

All Asphalt Concrete Section

Cost Elements

Analysis Period, n............................40 years
Interest Rate, r..............................6.0 percent
Initial Cost, A $70,710
Resurfacing, E $11,705
Estimated Life of Resurfacing, X ....20 years
Annual Maintenance Cost, N_1 ....$190
Time Between Last Resurfacing and
  End of Analysis Period, Y ....20 years
Capital Recovery Factor, CRFn—40 yrs.........0.06646
Present Worth Factor, PWFn—40 yrs...........0.09722
Present Worth Factor, PWFn$_1$—20 yrs. 0.31180

$C_1 = 0.06646 [70,710 + (11,705) (0.31180) + 0 - 0] + 190$
$C_1 = 0.06646 [70,710 + 3650] + 190$
$C_1 = 0.06646 [74,360] + 190$
$C_1 = 4,942 + 190$
$C_1 = \$5,132$ Annual Cost per mile

Example 2.

Annual Cost of Traveled Way—Stage Construction

All Asphalt Concrete Section

Cost Elements

Analysis Period, n............................40 years
Interest Rate, r ....6.0 percent
Initial Cost, A_1 ($1\frac{1}{2}$ inch asphalt concrete
  withheld for future) $61,980
Second Stage Cost, E_1 (Place $1\frac{1}{2}$ inch
  at 5th year)................................$8,810
Resurfacing, E_2 (Place 2″ at 25th year).........$11,705
Estimated Life of Second Stage and Resurfacing..20 years
Annual Maintenance Cost, M_1 ....$190
Time Between Last Resurfacing and End
  of Analysis Period, Y ....15 years
Capital Recovery Factor, CRFn—40 yrs.........0.06646

Present Worth Factor, PWFn—40 yrs.........0.09722
Present Worth Factor, PWFn₁—5 yrs.........0.74726
Present Worth Factor, PWFn₁—25 yrs. 0.23300

$$C_1 = 0.06646 \, [61{,}980 + (8{,}810)(0.74726) + (11{,}705)(0.23300) - (1 - \frac{15}{20})(11{,}705)(0.09722)] + 190$$

$C_1 = 0.06646 \, [61{,}980 + 6{,}583 + 2{,}727 - 284] + 190$

$C_1 = 0.06646 \, [71{,}066] + 190$

$C_1 = 4{,}719 + 190$

$C_1 = \$4{,}909$ Annual Cost per Mile

6.07 REFERENCES.—The following Asphalt Institute publications contain additional information on highway pavement economics:

(1) *Thickness Design—Asphalt Pavement Structures for Highways and Streets,* Manual Series No. 1 (MS-1)

(2) "The Annual Cost of Highways," by R. H. Baldock, Information Series No. 128 (IS-128), reprinted from *Highway Research Record No. 12,* Highway Research Board, Washington, D. C., 1963.

Chapter VII

ASPHALT CONSTRUCTION EQUIPMENT

7.01 INTRODUCTION.—With modern equipment, any type of asphalt construction may be essentially a mechanical process. As it is the intent of specifications to provide for the various steps to uniformly good results they should encourage new development and take advantage of the improvements as rapidly as made.

This chapter is not intended to cover every type of equipment but rather to draw attention to some of the principal items in most common use. Drawings of certain types of equipment are used to show only the essential parts and their general relationship rather than to convey an exact picture. Occasionally, where drawings are not feasible, illustrations of a particular manufacturer are shown but this is not to be construed as an endorsement by The Asphalt Institute or recommendation of the particular make.

7.02 RAILROAD TANK CARS.—Railroad tank cars are made in several sizes, the most common being of 10,000 gallons capacity, or approximately 40 tons. Smaller sizes of 8,000 and 6,500 gallons capacity are sometimes available. The cars are equipped with coils for heating when necessary. Insulated cars may be used, so that when loaded with hot asphalt at the refinery, unloading may be accomplished with little or no heating.

7.03 MOTOR TRANSPORT TRUCKS.—Transport trucks have steel or aluminum tanks with baffle plates to prevent surging. They may be insulated and often contain heating flues. Pumping equipment also is desirable. Tanks are made in several sizes, 2,400 to 5,000 gallons being most common. A tandem trailer combination thus may haul approximately the same amount as the railroad tank car.

7.04 STEEL DRUMS.—Steel drums are usually of 50 to 55 gallons capacity. Asphalt cements may be shipped in friction-top drums constructed of 24 to 28 gauge metal. Steel drums of 28 gauge metal are usually strong enough for asphalt cement of 85-100 penetration or lower. Asphalt cements softer than 85-100 penetration and liquid asphaltic products require a heavier drum, usually of 18 gauge, equipped with bungs. Asphalt is also transported in bulk, in barges, and ships.

7.05 ASPHALT HEATERS.—Asphalt heaters use fuel oil, gas or electricity and are of the following principal types:

(1) Tank heaters which heat the asphalt by circulating steam or hot oil through coils in the tank.

(2) Combination tank heater and booster may heat the asphalt in the tanks to pumping viscosity only; then the amount of asphalt required for immediate use may be heated to the desired use viscosity by the booster. This effects savings in heating costs and subjects the asphalt to the higher use temperatures for the minimum possible time.

(3) Asphalt kettles are used for maintenance and repairs. They come in several sizes, 75 to 225 gallons being the most common. Some have a derrick attachment for hoisting steel drums when supplies are so delivered. They preferably should be equipped with pump and hand spray.

7.06 BROOMS AND CLEANING EQUIPMENT.— Prior to surface treatment, or the construction of a new surface course on an old pavement, it is necessary to thoroughly clean the existing surface and cracks. Surface cleaning brooms vary from small towed revolving cylindrical drum brooms to elaborate self-propelled combination flusher brooms with vacuum and magnetic debris lifters.

Crack cleaning equipment consists of
(1) a hand-propelled machine with a motor-driven vertical cleaning device similar to a router by which

the operator can follow the crack and not increase its width

(2) a plow attached to tractor or motor grader

(3) grinders for truing and shaping fracture cracks for proper filling

(4) a compressed air jet. Some machines are equipped with a steel wire brush for cleaning the crack and for blowing the area clean of any dust resulting from the cleaning operation.

Areas not accessible to power equipment should be swept with hand brooms. Steel, rattan, fibre or plastic are used for bristles in the brooms.

7.07 SCARIFIERS.—In maintenance and reconstruction it is sometimes desirable to break up the old surface, reshape to proper grade, and add new material. This breaking up is called scarifying and there are special tools for the purpose. The scarifiers may be attached to the blade frame of a motor grader or to the frame of a roller. For deeper and more difficult scarifying, tractor-towed scarifiers which consist of a heavy steel frame with large curved steel teeth are used. They can be adjusted for depth, and as the tractor moves forward tend to dig to the full depth below the frame. (See Figure VII-1.)

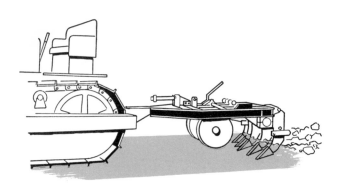

Figure VII-1—Scarifier

7.08 PULVERIZERS.—After scarifying, the old surface material is broken down to approximately the original
aggregate particle sizes by rotary type pulverizers similar
to those used in mixed-in-place construction, by traveling
hammer mills, or by grid rollers. When the hammer mill
or grid roller type pulverizer is used, the material may
be broken into as small particles as desired by repeated
passes of the equipment. Generally, when using this
equipment it is necessary to windrow the scarified material.

7.09 THE ASPHALT DISTRIBUTOR.—This is the
key piece of equipment in the construction of surface
treatments, road mixes, and penetration macadams. It
consists of a truck, or a trailer, on which is mounted an
insulated tank with a heating system, usually oil burning,
with direct heat from the flue passing through the tank.
It also has a power driven pump which will handle
products ranging from light cold application liquid
asphalt to heavy asphalt cement heated to spraying viscosity.* At the back end of the tank is a system of spray
bars and nozzles through which the asphalt is forced under
pressure onto the construction surface. Most new spray
bars are constructed for full circulation of the asphalt
through the bar when not spraying. These spray bars
will cover widths from 6 feet to 30 feet in one pass, depending upon the pump capacity. A thermometer is installed in the tank for quickly checking the temperature of
the contents. A connection is available to attach a hose,
for single or double outlet, to cover areas not reached by
the spray bar. It also is used in subsealing rigid slab
pavements.

Distributors are made in sizes from 800 to 5,500 gallon
capacity. Some maintenance distributors as small as 400
gallon size are made. Figure VII-2 is a cutaway drawing
showing the essential parts of a distributor. The asphalt

---

* See Chapter IV for Temperature-Viscosity of Various Asphaltic Materials.

TABLE VII-1—ASPHALT DISTRIBUTOR DATA*

Distributor	Nozzle Size	Nozzle Spacing	Nozzle Slot Angle	Nozzle Height Above Road	Pump Discharge—Gals. per Min.—or Pump Speed	Pump Pressure	Application Rate Gal. per Sq. Yd.	Coverage
CHAUSSE	$\frac{1}{16}$ in.	4 in. 6 in.	45° with Spray Bar	6 in. to 15 in.	95 gals. per min. at 420 RPM	5 to 15 lbs. per sq. in.	Varies with size of Bar and speed of truck	4 in. Center—Triple Lap 6 in. Center—Double Lap
	$\frac{1}{8}$ in.	4 in. 6 in.	45° with Spray Bar	6 in. to 15 in.	95 gals. per min. at 420 RPM	5 to 15 lbs. per sq. in.	Varies with size of Bar and speed of truck	4 in. Center—Triple Lap 6 in. Center—Double Lap
	$\frac{3}{32}$ in.	4 in. 6 in.	45° with Spray Bar	6 in. to 15 in.	45 gals. per min. at 420 RPM	5 to 15 lbs. per sq. in.	Varies with size of Bar and speed of truck	4 in. Center—Triple Lap 6 in. Center—Double Lap
	$\frac{3}{16}$ in.	4 in. 6 in.	45° with Spray Bar	6 in. to 15 in.	45 gals. per min. at 420 RPM	5 to 15 lbs. per sq. in.	Varies with size of Bar and speed of truck	4 in. Center—Triple Lap 6 in. Center—Double Lap
ETNYRE	$\frac{1}{16}$ in.	4 in.	30° with Spray Bar	12 in.	5 to 7 gals. per ft. of Spray Bar	—	0.03 gal. to 3.0 gals.	Triple Lap
	$\frac{3}{32}$ in.	4 in.	30° with Spray Bar	12 in.	7 to 10 gals. per ft. of Spray Bar	—	0.03 gal. to 3.0 gals.	Triple Lap
	$\frac{1}{8}$ in.	4 in.	30° with Spray Bar	12 in.	10 to 15 gals. per ft. of Spray Bar	—	0.03 gal. at 3.0 gals.	Triple Lap
	$\frac{3}{16}$ in.	4 in.	30° with Spray Bar	12 in.	12 to 20 gals. per ft. of Spray Bar	—	0.03 gal. to 3.0 gals.	Triple Lap
	S36-5	4 in.	30° with Spray Bar	12 in.	10 to 15 gals. per ft. of Spray Bar	—	0.06 gal. to 3.0 gals.	Quadruple Lap
GRACE—200 Series	$\frac{1}{16}$ in.	6 in.	60° with Spray Bar	11 in.	100 gals. per min.	35 lbs. per sq. in.	0.05 gal. to 1.0 gal.	Double Lap
	$\frac{3}{32}$ in.	6 in.	60° with Spray Bar	11 in.	100 gals. per min.	35 lbs. per sq. in.	0.05 gal. to 1.0 gal.	Double Lap

300 Series							
⅛ in.	4 in.	60° with Spray Bar	9 in.	325 gals. per min.	35 lbs. per sq. in.	0.05 gal. to 1.0 gal.	Triple Lap
3⁄16 in.	4 in.	60° with Spray Bar	9 in.	325 gals. per min.	35 lbs. per sq. in.	0.05 gal. to 1.0 gal.	Triple Lap
LITTLEFORD							
⅛ in. Square Slot	4 in.	15° with Spray Bar	10 in. min. 12 in. max.	12½ gals. per ft. of Spray Bar	—	0.05 gal. to 3.3 gals.	Triple Lap
⅛ in. "V" Slot	4 in.	15° with Spray Bar	10 in. min. 12 in. max.	12½ gals. per ft. of Spray Bar	—	0.05 gal. to 3.3 gals.	Triple Lap
ROSCO							
No. 0	4 in.	25° with Spray Bar	10 in.	—	10 to 50 lbs. per sq. in.	0.05 gal. to 2.0 gals.	Triple Lap
No. 1	4 in.	25° with Spray Bar	10 in.	—	10 to 50 lbs. per sq. in.	0.05 gal. to 2.0 gals.	Triple Lap
No. 2	4 in.	25° with Spray Bar	10 in.	—	10 to 50 lbs. per sq. in.	0.05 gal. to 2.0 gals.	Triple Lap
SEAMAN-GUNNISON							
⅛ in.	4 in.	15° with Spray Bar	9 in.	375 gals. per min. at 375 RPM	—	0.1 gal. to 3.0 gals.	Triple Lap
3⁄16 in.	4 in.	15° with Spray Bar	9 in.	375 gals. per min. at 375 RPM	—	0.1 gal. to 3.0 gals.	Triple Lap
SOUTH BEND (Municipal)							
1⁄16 in.	4 in. 6 in.	22° with Spray Bar	9 in. min. 11 in. max.	90 gals. to 375 gals. per min.	20 to 40 lbs. per sq. in.	0.1 gal. to 3.0 gals.	Triple Lap
⅛ in.	4 in. 6 in.	22° with Spray Bar	9 in. min. 11 in. max.	90 gals. to 375 gals. per min.	20 to 40 lbs. per sq. in.	0.1 gal. to 3.0 gals.	Triple Lap
3⁄16 in.	4 in. 6 in.	22° with Spray Bar	9 in. min. 11 in. max.	90 gals. to 375 gals. per min.	20 to 40 lbs. per sq. in.	0.1 gal. to 3.0 gals.	Triple Lap
STANDARD							
1⁄16 in.	4 in.	45° with Spray Bar	9 in.	375 gals. per min. at 675 RPM	50 lbs. per sq. in.	0.1 gal. to 1.0 gal.	Triple Lap
5⁄32 in.	4 in.	45° with Spray Bar	9 in.	375 gals. per min. at 675 RPM	50 lbs. per sq. in.	0.1 gal. to 1.0 gal.	Triple Lap

* Furnished by the manufacturers.

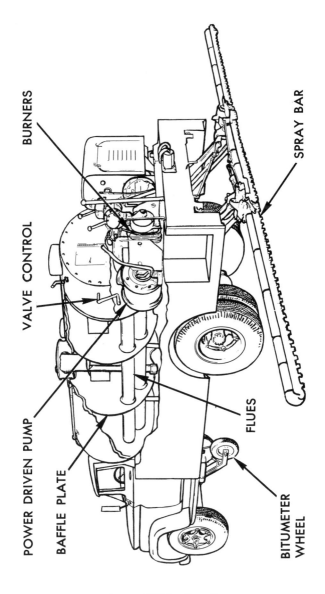

BURNERS

SPRAY BAR

VALVE CONTROL

POWER DRIVEN PUMP

BAFFLE PLATE

FLUES

BITUMETER WHEEL

Figure VII-2—Distributor

distributor is discussed in detail in *Asphalt Surface Treatments,* Manual Series No. 13 (MS-13), The Asphalt Institute.

7.10 AGGREGATE SPREADER.—Aggregate spreaders are of four general types:

(1) The revolving disc whirl type which attaches to or is built on to the aggregate truck and normally is used for sanding. The aggregate is fed on to the spreader disc through an adjustable opening and the speed of the disc is usually adjustable to control the width of spread. (See Figure VII-3.)

(2) A box with adjustable opening which attaches to and is suspended from the tail gate of the dump truck. Some are equipped with vanes which tend to aid in the spread of the aggregate from one end of the box to the other. (See Figure VII-4.)

(3) A spreader box mounted on its own wheels which is attached to and pushed by the dump truck. (See Figure VII-5.) Some of this type have:

a. Baffles or vanes and spreader screw or spiral or auger agitator which aid in the distribution of the aggregate throughout the length of the box.

b. Spread or feed roll and adjustable gate to facilitate the control of the aggregate spread.

(4) The self-propelled aggregate spreader. Some of the features of a modern, self-propelled aggregate spreader are:

a. Receiving hopper on the rear and spread hopper on the front.

b. The spreader is steered by the operator and pulls the dumping truck facilitating proper alignment of spread.

c. The width of spread is adjustable.

d. Independently operated belt conveyors and baffles.

e. Screw-type auger, baffle plates, and an adjustable deflector to prevent segregation of the aggregate.

f. A rod screen or grizzly to reject all over-size and foreign objects.

g. An adjustable hand-actuated control gate.

h. A spreader roll.

i. An adjustable screen to place the larger aggregate in the asphalt first and the finer aggregate on top.

j. A self-propelled spreader usually operates at full throttle in a desired gear, working against the governor to assure constant speed.

Recently combination asphalt distributor and aggregate spreader units have been developed which spray the asphalt and spread the cover aggregate in one pass of the machine.

Figure VII-3—Whirl Spreader

Figure VII-4—Vane Spreader

Figure VII-5—Hopper Spreader (mounted on wheels)

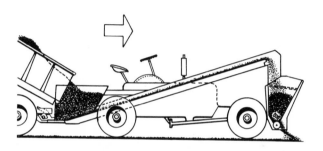

Figure VII-6—Self-Propelled Spreader

7.11 EQUIPMENT FOR MIXED-IN-PLACE (ROAD-MIX) CONSTRUCTION.—Equipment for mixed-in-place construction—also called road mixing—is of the following principal types:

(1) The rotary type with transverse shafts, mixes the asphalt and aggregate by revolving tines under a hood; most are now equipped with a spray system which applies the asphalt while mixing. Most makes have only one rotor but others have up to four rotors all under a long hood.

(2) Power graders and various kinds of plows are still used extensively for small projects.

(3) Intermediate between the mixed-in-place equipment and the stationary asphalt plant is a type of mixer known as a travel plant. It contains many of the parts

found in the usual asphalt plant with exception of dryer and screens. Travel plants are of two types:

a. Receives the aggregate into a hopper from trucks, mixes the aggregate with asphalt, and spreads the mixture; all in one pass of the machine.

b. Takes the aggregate from windrows, mixes the aggregate and asphalt and usually deposits the mix in a windrow behind. It is then spread by blade graders, aerated, if necessary, and compacted.

7.12 ASPHALT PLANTS.—An asphalt mixing plant is a factory for manufacturing asphalt paving mixtures in accordance with specification requirements. Its constituent parts and methods of operation may vary with the type of mixture. Most asphalt mixes are produced in asphalt plants of two types—batch and continuous mix. The first mixes a batch of aggregate and asphalt in accurately weighed proportions and discharges the mixture before the next batch of ingredients is introduced into the pug-mill mixer. The other mixes accurately proportioned volumes of aggregate and asphalt as they pass in a continuous flow from one end of the pugmill mixer to the other where the mixture is discharged into a truck or a discharge hopper. These asphalt plants have been improved to such a state of mechanical perfection that, when properly set and adjusted, the production of uniform specification mix is almost automatic.

For instance, with the use of electric and hydraulic controls and timing devices on a batch plant, one man can start the process and watch the plant go through the various cycles of automatic weighing of aggregate, dry mixing, weighing and introducing asphalt, wet mixing, and discharging the mix into trucks. Automatic timing assures the proper sequence and prevents the starting of one operation until the previous one is complete. If the quantity of aggregate in any storage bin becomes too small to complete the batch, the mixing operation stops until the required amount of each size is in the weigh hopper. Then the mixing cycle continues. Such operations reduce the possibility of human errors.

The different units of batch and continuous mix asphalt plants are discussed in *Asphalt Plant Manual,* Manual Series No. 3 (MS-3), The Asphalt Institute.

Equipment for Spreading Asphalt Mixes

7.13 GENERAL.—Asphalt mixes are spread by the following:

    (1) Mechanical spreading and finishing machines usually called pavers

    (2) Power graders

    (3) Spreader box towed by the dumping truck

7.14 PAVERS.—Asphalt finishing machines, commonly known as pavers, in current use are similar in many respects. For all intents and purposes these machines consist of two units, one of which is known as the tractor unit and the other the screed unit. (See Figure VII-7.)

The tractor units contains the controls that regulate the flow of material to the screed. It has a hopper into which asphaltic mixtures are deposited from the trucks and from which the material is carried back to the screed unit by means of bar conveyors. The tractor unit also provides the motive power not only for itself and the screed unit, but also to push the truck that is unloading into the hopper.

The screed unit consists of leveling arms or screed arms, a screed plate, a compacting device and thickness controls. The basic connection between the screed unit and the tractor unit is through the screed arms which are pin connected at the track casing of the tractor. In theory this provides a screed with a so-called floating-action which spreads the material fed to it in the desired configuration. When the forces acting on the screed are balanced, it leaves a uniform mat. If these forces are changed, the screed will either go up or down. Thickness control is achieved by changing the tilt of the screed plate thereby disturbing the balance of forces acting on the screed mechanism. The screed mechanism reacts to these changed forces until they are balanced again during which time a change in thickness is effected.

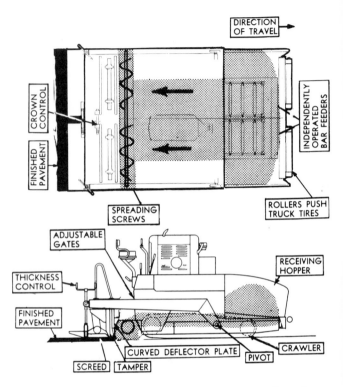

Figure VII-7—Flow of Materials Through a Typical Asphalt Paver

(Courtesy of Barber-Greene Co.)

Automatic screed controls are now available. These attachments for pavers, through "feelers" on skids or a reference line or plane, automatically adjust the screed for a smoother surface. They eliminate hand control, which so often results in overadjustment.

There are many makes of pavers in general use. These vary in the method of initial compaction: Some have a tamping bar immediately in front of the screed for initially compacting the mix before strike-off; others obtain initial compaction by vibration of the screed; while others have an oscillating strike-off bar, ahead of and pivoted with the screed which gives some initial compaction. On some pavers further compaction is provided by vibration of the screed.

All of the pavers operate on basically the same principle as to leveling and control of thickness of spreading. Pavers are discussed in more detail in *Asphalt Paving Manual,* Manual Series No. 8 (MS-8), The Asphalt Institute.

7.15 SPREADING WITH A MOTOR GRADER.— Both hot and cold asphalt mixtures are dumped from trucks through windrow eveners depositing the required amount of mixture between each station. The mix is then spread across the grade with motor graders. Long wheel base graders are used for spreading base and leveling courses as a smooth foundation for paver-laid subsequent courses. Automatic electronic devices for controlling the transverse slope of the blade and the use of a pointer attached to the blade, guided by a string line for longitudinal control make possible a very uniform surface. Motor grader spreading is frequently done simultaneously with pneumatic-tired rolling.

7.16 SPREADER BOXES.—Spreader boxes, towed by the dumping truck, are used for small jobs. These boxes usually are supported on their own wheels and have a screed or strike-off edge which is adjustable for depth of course and crown. Some are equipped with spreading screws and an oscillating screed. For more information on spreading asphalt mixes, see Asphalt Institute Manual Series No. 8, *Asphalt Paving Manual.*

7.17 SHOULDER PAVERS.—Pavers made especially for spreading asphalt mixes on shoulders and widenings up to 10 feet are available as self-propelled machines or as attachments to motor graders. They vary in details but, basically, each consists of a hopper for receiving the mix from the haul truck, an offset blade for spreading the mix on the shoulder and striking it off to the desired depth, and some means of moving the mix from the hopper to the offset blade.

Barber-Greene

Blaw-Knox

FIGURE VII-8—SOME TYPICAL TYPE

Cedarapids

Pioneer

F ASPHALT PAVING MACHINES

Compaction Equipment

7.18 GENERAL.—The equipment generally available for compaction of embankment, subgrade, subbase, base, binder and surface layers of the asphalt pavement structure is briefly described below. (See also Asphalt Institute Manual Series No. 8, *Asphalt Paving Manual*.)

7.19 TAMPING TYPE COMPACTORS.—The most common compacting equipment used in earth work is called a sheepsfoot roller. It consists of a drum from which shanks or feet protrude to provide the compactive effort. These rollers vary in size and weight and are normally towed by tractors. They are used in various combinations to achieve the desired compaction and are most effective in fine grain soils.

7.20 PNEUMATIC-TIRED ROLLERS.—Pneumatic-tired rollers are of three types:

(1) Self-propelled tandem with two to seven wheels in front, four to eight in rear; wheels generally oscillate (that is, the axle may move up and down); weighs 3 to 36 tons.

(2) The towed type may be either single row of wheels or tandem, weighs 2 to 50 tons with oscillating wheels.

(3) The chariot type has only two large wheels.

7.21 STEEL-WHEELED ROLLERS.—Steel-wheeled rollers are of the following types:

(1) Three-wheeled roller. Equipped with two drive wheels usually 55 inches to 69 inches in diameter by 18 inches to 24 inches wide, and a steering roll of smaller diameter but wider. Weights vary from 6 to 17 tons. Some have ballastable wheels to increase their weight. Some are equipped with scarifiers; others have shoe-type vibrating compactors attached to the rear which may be hoisted when not in use. Three-wheel steel-faced rollers are used mostly for breakdown rolling of asphaltic mixtures and base courses.

(2) Tandem rollers.

a. Two axle. These come in weights varying from 3 to 14 tons or more. They generally have ballastable rolls; some of the smaller sizes have auxiliary pneumatic tires for ease in moving between small jobs, and some have only one wide roller with pneumatic auxiliary and moving wheels.

b. Three-axle tandem rollers. The center axle roll is so arranged that a large part of the total weight of roller can be applied thereon as required on high spots. These rollers are made in sizes ranging in weight from 13 to 20 or more tons. These rolls are usually ballastable. Some 3-axle tandem rollers are made with a separate power unit for vibrating the center axle roll, thereby functioning as a combination vibratory compactor and tandem roller.

7.22 VIBRATORY COMPACTORS.—Vibratory compactors are generally of two types:

(1) Vibrating shoes or plates. The vibratory shoe-type has from one shoe for patches, trenches and small areas, to six or more for regular road work. These can be arranged side by side or in tandem. Shoe-type vibratory compactors are mostly used for compaction of macadam and other granular base courses. The small units are used extensively for compaction of asphalt patching mixtures used in small areas inaccessible to large rollers.

(2) Vibrating rollers. These have one or two smooth-surfaced rolls three to five feet in diameter and four to six feet wide, and are of either the tow or tandem type. The static weight is usually from a ton-and-a-half to 11 tons. As noted above, some large tandems have provision for vibrating the third axle unit. Vibratory rollers may be used for compacting most types of granular soils or asphaltic mixtures. With some materials, however, it is necessary to adjust the resonance of the dynamic force to the material.

3-WHEEL ROLLER

TANDEM STEEL WHEELED

3-AXLE TANDEM

PNEUMATIC TIRED

SHEEPSFOOT ROLLER

TRENCH ROLLER

PROOF ROLLER

VIBRATORY COMPACTOR

Figure VII-9—Types of Compactors

7.23 COMBINATION TYPES.—In addition to the 3-axle tandem with vibrating third roll referred to above, there are a number of combination steel-wheeled and pneumatic-tired rollers. There is also a three-wheel steel roller with shoe type vibrators which may be hydraulically lifted when not in use.

7.24 ASPHALT HEATER PLANERS.—A heater planer consists of a combination surface heater and planer for heating the surface of asphalt pavement and planing off the heated asphalt-aggregate mixture. Large efficient machines are available, capable of speeds of from a slow creep to about thirty-five feet per minute. Some are equipped with both serrated and smooth cutting blades. The blades are usually positioned so that the planed material is deposited in a continuous windrow behind the planer. After the application of the heater planer an asphalt concrete overlay or surface treatment may be applied or the surface, as prepared by the heater planer, may be utilized.

A repaver is a heater, grader, three-wheel roller, and spreader combined into one machine. The heating chamber heats and softens the old asphalt pavement to the consistency needed for the grader blade to move easily. The blade relevels the rough pavement and the heated steel rolls compact the softened mix. The machine will also spread and compact hot-mix asphalt from a windrow.

7.25 ASPHALT CURBING MACHINES.—Automatic curbing machines are used to construct asphalt concrete curbs. These machines lay, compact, and finish straight or curved curbs for streets, traffic islands, and parking areas. No forms are necessary. Various interchangeable mold patterns provide a wide selection of curbing shapes.

In operation, hot asphalt concrete is placed in the open hopper of the curbing machine and a motorized worm gear, or screw, at the bottom of the hopper pushes the mixture out through the mold form under pressure. This pressure provides curb compaction and causes the machine to move forward, leaving the finished curb behind.

7.26 REFERENCES.—The following Asphalt Institute publications contain details about the asphalt construction equipment described in this chapter:

(1) *Asphalt Plant Manual,* Manual Series No. 3 (MS-3)

(2) *Asphalt Paving Manual,* Manual Series No. 8 (MS-8)

(3) *Asphalt Surface Treatments,* Manual Series No. 13 (MS-13)

(4) *Asphalt Mixed-in-Place (Road-Mix) Manual,* Manual Series No. 14 (MS-14)

(5) *Specifications and Construction Methods for Asphalt Curbs and Gutters,* Specification Series No. 3 (SS-3).

Chapter VIII

CONSTRUCTION OF ASPHALT PAVEMENTS

Introduction

8.01 THE IMPORTANCE OF PROPER CON-
STRUCTION METHODS.—The key to good asphalt
construction is the intelligent selection not only of the
aggregate and binder, but also the construction method
which will economically and adequately meet the requirements for the various courses in the asphalt pavement
structure for the traffic requirements, and weather conditions. There are usually many combinations available.
The progressive engineer should make selections for each
specific application. There is a danger that he will confine
his thinking only to locally recognized types of asphalt
construction and forget to analyze completely the needs of
each of the elements involved. Control required should
be considered in selecting the pavement type, thus, high-
type asphalt concrete cannot be built if the proper controls are not available.

NOTE

**The most important single factor in produc-
ing a good job is workmanship. More problems
arise from and poorer results are realized because of poor workmanship than for any other
reason. The importance of attention to small
details as well as proper procedures in construction cannot be overemphasized.**

A.—*Preparation of Foundation for Asphalt Pavements*

Drainage and Moisture Control

8.02 GENERAL.—Accumulation of moisture in the courses of the pavement structure is probably the greatest single cause of pavement distress, a fact which is recognized and understood by all engineers. However, today's wider pavements common to multi-lane highways, are approaching the dimensions of an airfield pavement, and may introduce problems not fully recognized by some highway engineers.

8.03 DRAINAGE SYSTEMS.—Drainage systems may be classified in two categories—surface and subsurface— and each functions independently of the other. Surface drainage entails the collection and rapid removal of water from the pavement and shoulder areas. Subsurface drainage must intercept ground water and collect and remove water from the pavement structure.

8.04 SURFACE DRAINAGE.—Surface drainage is most effectively accomplished by full-width paving. On elevated grades the water should be directed to asphalt spillways by means of asphalt dikes or curbs constructed on the extreme outside edge of the shoulder. The roadways and shoulders in cut sections also should be paved full width with surface water being directed to paved ditches or drains.

8.05 SUBSURFACE DRAINAGE.—Subsurface drainage methods are generally understood by civil engineers and details of drainage structures are available in many publications. However, the unpaved raised median which is widely used in geometric design of roads offers difficult drainage problems. Regardless of the number of transverse drains employed, quantities of rain water and snow-melt will drain from a raised median into the pavement structure and subgrade, weakening the pavement. The depressed median is recommended wherever possible, but when conditions make it mandatory to construct an elevated median, transverse drains should be connected with a longitudinal drain in the median deep enough to collect all ground water before it can find its way into the pavement structure.

Subsurface seepage may, under certain conditions, develop a hydrostatic head beneath the pavement sufficient to lift the pavement completely off the base, causing cracking and, in extreme cases, complete disintegration of the pavement structure. This problem is more acute when steep grades are involved. With steep gradients the water may travel longitudinally in the base along the direction of the gradient and cause excessive hydrostatic pressures at sag vertical curves or on the low side of superelevated horizontal curves. In many cut sections there is need also for longitudinal sub-drains to prevent water from higher ground accumulating under the pavement. If not intercepted, water from a cut may flow out onto a fill and cause slumping of the fill slope and cracking of the pavement. The choice of filter material and the design of the drainage system must be given careful attention, considering both the type of material to be drained and the quantity of water expected.

If a coarse drain rock is used, contamination by the adjacent soil, particularly cohesionless silts and fine sands, may eventually cause complete clogging of the drain. Use of finer filter materials to prevent clogging may not provide the capacity necessary to accommodate the ground water flow. If heavy flows are expected in silty soils, a two-layer system, consisting of filter material to prevent contamination, and a coarse open drain rock to provide the required capacity, may be necessary.

8.06 SELECTION OF FILTER MATERIAL GRADING LIMITS.—The criterion suggested by Terzaghi and tested and adopted by the Corps of Engineers, to prevent intrusion in drain backfills, is based on the piping ratio determined by the relationship of the maximum size of the smallest 15 percent and the maximum size of the smallest 85 percent of both the soil and the filter material. The most important of these criteria are:

(1) The ratio of the 15 percent size of the filter material to the 85 percent size of the material to be drained shall not be greater than 5.

(2) The ratio of the 50 percent size of the filter material to the 50 percent size of the material to be drained shall not be greater than 25.

(3) To avoid clogging of the drain pipe the ratio of the 85 percent size of the filter material to the size of the pipe perforation must be not less than 2.

If plastic clays containing lenses or partings of sand or silt are to be drained, the size distribution of the silt or sand portion should be used rather than the clay fraction.

If the soils to be drained are not homogeneous, the filter material grading necessary to prevent clogging in one area may not be sufficiently permeable to carry the volume of water encountered in another area and a two-layer system may be required. (See Trench Design, Article 8.07.)

8.07 TRENCH DESIGN.—Drains may be placed for a wide variety of conditions and purposes. The construction of the drain will be influenced by the existing conditions and the drain should be designed for ease of construction and economy with due regard to the functions it must perform.

For shallow drains used to remove water from the base course under a pavement, a V-trench is generally the most practical. The trench may be constructed with a motor grader; the shape more nearly fits the flow pattern of the water to be removed and placement of the pipe and filter material is facilitated. For deep drains used to intercept water from a pervious layer, or to lower the water table in a uniform soil, a trench with vertical sides usually will be the most economical because of the lesser quantity of excavation. It is also more easily supported by shoring.

The following designs are suggested for consideration:

(1) Wet Cuts—If the material encountered at grade is uniformly stratified it may be possible to remove seepage water by interceptor drains at the toe of the cut

slope. A weakness of this type of construction, however, is that water very frequently will bypass the drain and rise to the surface beneath the pavement. This may be caused by variations or curvature in the stratifications or by shear zones caused by old earth movements. A much more positive means of control is obtained by placing a blanket of pervious subbase material completely across the roadway to collect any seepage water. This subbase material can then be drained by means of a relatively shallow V-trench at the low point in the cross-section.

If a heavy volume of water is expected, it may be advisable to construct a two-layer system in order to obtain greater capacity of the drain. (See Figure VIII-1.)

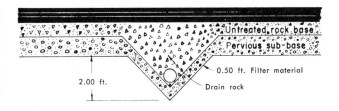

Figure VIII-1—Two-Layer System for Heavy Flow

If an appreciable gradient is involved, a cross-drain should be placed at the down-hill end of the cut to intercept any water flowing longitudinally which might otherwise saturate the fills and cause slumping of the fill slopes.

When drains are placed in cuts, the trenches constructed must not undercut the side slopes. The seepage that necessitates the installation of drains may also result in unstable slopes requiring special treatment or flattening of cut slopes. A drain trench placed at the toe of the cut slope may cause a slide during construction. Trenches at the toe of the slope may also lead to construction difficulties. Trenches with vertical sides are usually dug with a trencher and it cannot operate with one track up on the cut slope. (See Figure VIII-2.)

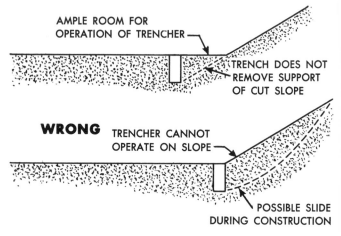

Figure VIII-2—Drainage Trench Design

(2) High Ground Water Table—Deep, vertical trenches may be placed on either side of the roadway to lower the ground water table beneath the pavement. Drains planned for this purpose should be analyzed by means of a flow net to provide all possible assurance that the drains will function as intended.

In areas of high ground water level it is better practice, and probably more economical in the final analysis to raise the grade of the highway with granular material to provide a separation between the pavement and the ground water.

8.08 CONSTRUCTION CONTROL.—The importance of rigid inspection during construction cannot be over-emphasized. This is particularly true of the grading of the filter material. An increase in the dust content of only a few percentage points may cut the permeability of the filter material to one-tenth of that which would have been obtained. The inclusion of clay lumps may completely block the flow of water and segregation of the filter material can seriously impair the functioning of the drain.

8.09 MOISTURE CONTROL.—In addition to adequate drainage, both surface and subsurface, there should be an adequate thickness of base courses that have been waterproofed and stabilized with asphalt to sustain the traffic loads at all ambient moisture conditions. It must be remembered that (1) capillarity and moisture vapor action can cause an increase of moisture throughout the pavement structure unless the materials are waterproofed with asphalt, and (2) when the moisture in non-asphaltic materials rises above the optimum moisture at which they were compacted, the materials lose strength. For these reasons an adequate thickness of asphalt base is essential.

Compaction

8.10 GENERAL.—The importance of proper compaction of each layer of embankments, subgrade, improved subgrade, and base courses is universally recognized. Compaction greatly increases the supporting power of the subgrade. Where the subgrade is not sufficiently compacted during construction, additional consolidation will occur under traffic with resulting settlement and possible failure.

8.11 COMPACTION TESTS.—Compaction tests are made in the laboratory on materials to be used in the construction to determine the maximum practical density which should be obtained. These laboratory densities should be determined on the basis of the method of test detailed in AASHO Designation T180.

8.12 COMPACTION CRITERIA.—The following criteria for compaction are recommended for construction of asphalt pavement structures:

(1) Cohesive Subgrades.—Minimum 95 percent Modified AASHO (T180, Method D) density for the top 12 inches and minimum 90 percent for all fill areas below the top 12 inches. The water content for compaction of cohesive soils should be determined by tests

and should be selected to provide the highest remolded strength consistent with expansion considerations. Generally, nonexpansive soils should be compacted one or two percent on the dry side of laboratory optimum moisture content for best results.

(2) Cohesionless Subgrades.—Minimum 100 percent of Modified AASHO (T180, Method D) density for the top 12 inches and minimum 95 percent below this for all fill areas.

(3) Bases, Subbases and Improved Subgrade.— Minimum 100 percent of Modified AASHO (T180, Method D) density.

8.13 COMPACTION EQUIPMENT.—Several kinds of compaction equipment are discussed in Chapter VII including tamping compactors, pneumatic-tired rollers, steel-wheeled rollers, vibratory compactors, and combination types.

Asphalt Paving Manual, Manual Series No. 8 (MS-8), The Asphalt Institute, contains a detailed discussion on the use of compaction equipment, with special emphasis on pneumatic-tired rollers, vibratory compactors, and proof rollers. It also touches upon the proper thickness of lifts for best compaction results, special cases involving problem soils, and compaction of cut sections.

Preparation of Old Pavements Used as Bases

8.14 PREPARATION OF OLD PAVEMENTS WHEN USED AS BASES.—This subject is covered in other parts of this *Handbook* as follows:

(1) Priming non-asphalt bases, Chapter VIII, Section F.

(2) Tack coats, Chapter VIII, Section F.

(3) Widening, Chapter IX, Section A.

(4) Reconstruction of old asphalt pavements, Chapter IX, Section A.

(5) Overlaying old rigid type pavements, Chapter IX, Section A.

For various types of asphalt bases, see other sections of this *Handbook* as follows:

(1) Hot and Cold Laid Mixes, Chapter VIII, Sections B and C.

(2) Asphalt Macadam, Chapter VIII, Section D.

(3) Asphalt Mixed-in-Place, Chapter VIII, Section E.

B.—*Manufacture, Use and Inspection of Asphalt Plant Mixes*

8.15 QUALITY AND ECONOMY OF HOT PLANT MIXES.—Because of the superior quality of accurately controlled asphalt plant mixes and the economies inherent in plant mixing, its use has greatly increased, and should be given first consideration for any course in the asphalt pavement structure for the following reasons:

(1) Aggregate can be accurately proportioned, dried, heated and mixed so that all particles can be completely coated with a uniform film of asphalt.

(2) Large highly efficient asphalt plants are generally within hauling distance of any proposed project or an asphalt plant can be moved into a nearby pit or quarry at reasonable cost in a few hours.

(3) Mixing is relatively independent of weather conditions, because the aggregate can be dried immediately after a rain and full construction resumed if the road is in condition to accept paving.

(4) Central plant mixtures can be placed with mechanical spreading finishers (or with long wheel base motor graders for leveling courses) at a minimum cost for placing, and with the assurance that a smooth surface may be obtained.

(5) The amount of asphalt can be accurately controlled and heated to provide proper viscosity of the asphalt* for thorough mixing.

---

* See Chapter IV for temperature-viscosity data.

8.16 MANUFACTURE OF ASPHALT PLANT MIXES.

—In order to produce the highest quality asphalt concrete in the most efficient manner, uniformity and balance are essential in the over-all operation of the plant. Of equal importance is the uniform quality and quantity of material being fed into the plant. The uniformity with which plant components operate also contributes to the quality of the end product.

Balance among all phases of production is necessary to maintain a continuous and uniform operation. This includes balance among the plant components, one to the other, as well as the materials that are being handled.

Before beginning operation, enough asphalt should be in the storage tank to keep the plant supplied, with due allowance for delays in delivery. Also, there should be sufficiently large stockpiles of all required sizes of aggregate to prevent delays because of low quantities. Each size should be separately stored—separated by bulkheads to prevent contamination of one size by another.

From the stockpiles, the aggregate is fed by size into separate bins. Each bin has a calibrated gate which volumetrically measures each size of aggregate as it is fed into the dryer.

After passing through the dryer, the hot aggregate is lifted by bucket elevator to vibrating screens that separate the aggregate into several predetermined sizes for temporary storage in the hot bins. Then, as aggregate is needed for proportioning into the mix, the correct amount is drawn from the hot bins by weight or by volume, depending on the type of plant—batch or continuous mix.

In the batch plant the weighed hot aggregate is dropped into the pugmill mixer, the correct amount of asphalt added, and after mixing, dropped into a truck.

In the continuous mix plant, hot aggregate is fed into one end of the pugmill mixer in a continuous measured flow while asphalt is sprayed in preset volume onto it. While being mixed, the ingredients move slowly toward the other end of the mixer box. By the time they reach the discharge point the mixture is complete.

The flow of materials through a typical batch plant is

shown in Figure VIII-3; and through a typical continuous mix plant in Figure VIII-4.

The manufacture of asphalt plant mixes is discussed in detail in *Asphalt Plant Manual*, Manual Series No. 3 (MS-3), The Asphalt Institute.

8.17 SAMPLING AND TESTING.—Sampling and testing are two of the most important functions in asphalt mixing plant control. Data from tests on the aggregate, the asphalt, and the finished mix are the tools with which the quality of the product is controlled. For this reason, great care must be used to follow correct sampling and testing procedures. These important phases in the manufacture of asphalt plant mixes are described in *Asphalt Plant Manual,* Manual Series No. 3 (MS-3), The Asphalt Institute.

8.18 POSSIBLE CAUSES OF IMPERFECTIONS IN PLANT MIXED PAVING MIXTURES.—Table VIII-1 shows the most common causes of imperfections in plant mixed paving mixtures.

C.—Hauling, Spreading and Compacting Asphalt Plant Mixes

8.19 HAULING THE MIX.—The mix must reach its point of use in a condition essentially as discharged from the mixer.

The trucks should be free from body leaks or deep indentations that might cause the mix to stick, and free from material that might be detrimental to the mix.

A mild lime water, soap, or detergent solution is recommended for coating the truck bodies. Any of these agents may be detrimental to the mix if used to excess. In all cases, truck bodies must be raised so that excess material is drained before placing mixture in the truck. Petroleum products should not be used.

The bodies of the transporting vehicles should be covered and insulated, if need be, to maintain the heat loss within the specification requirements.

Types of Deficiencies That May Be Encountered in Producing Plant-Mix Paving Mixtures.

Deficiency columns (left to right):

- D1 — Asphalt Content Does Not Check Job Mix Formula
- D2 — Aggregate Gradation Does Not Check Job Mix Formula
- D3 — Excessive Fines in Mix
- D4 — Uniform Temperatures Difficult to Maintain
- D5 — Truck Weights Do Not Check Batch Weights
- D6 — Free Asphalt on Mix in Truck
- D7 — Free Dust on Mix in Truck
- D8 — Large Aggregates Uncoated
- D9 — Mixture in Truck Not Uniform
- D10 — Mixture in Truck Fat on One Side
- D11 — Mixture Flattens in Truck
- D12 — Mixture Burned
- D13 — Mixture Too Brown or Gray
- D14 — Mixture Too Fat
- D15 — Mixture Smokes in Truck
- D16 — Mixture Steams in Truck
- D17 — Mixture Appears Dull in Truck

Possible Cause	D1	D2	D3	D4	D5	D6	D7	D8	D9	D10	D11	D12	D13	D14	D15	D16	D17
Faulty Sampling	A	A															
Irregular Plant Operation				A					A	A	A	A	A	A	A	A	A
Occasional Dust Shakedown in Bins		A	A						A								A
Asphalt and Aggregate Feed Not Synchronized	C	C	C			C		C	C		C		C	C			
Faulty Dump Gate	A						B				B						
Improperly Set or Worn Paddles	A	A				A		A	A	A							
Mixing Time Not Proper	B		B					B	B	B							
Undersize or Oversize Batch	B	B	B			B	B		B		B	B		B	B		
Asphalt Meter Out of Adjustment	C					C	C		C				C	C			
Asphalt Scales Out of Adjustment	B					B		B	B				B	B			
Faulty Distribution of Asphalt to Aggregates	A					A		A	A	A	A					A	
Too Much Asphalt	A					A			A					A		A	
Insufficient Asphalt	A					A							A				A
Improper Weighing Sequence					B				B	B							
Insufficient Aggregates in Hot Bins	A	A							A							A	
Feed of Mineral Filler Not Uniform	A	A							A							A	
Improper Weighing	B	B	B		B	B			A				B				
Aggregate Scales Out of Adjustment	B	B	B		B	B			B							B	
Carryover in Bins Due to Overloading Screens	A	A							A								
Segregation of Aggregates in Bins	A	A							A								
Leaky Bins	A	A		B					A								
Bin Overflows Not Functioning	A	A							A								
Faulty Screen Operation	A	A							A				A				
Worn Out Screens	A																
Aggregate Temperature Too High				A								A			A		A
Temp. Indicator Out of Adjustment				A					A			A	A		A	A	A
Improper Dryer Operation				A					A			A	A		A	A	A
Dryer Set Too Steep				A					A						A		A
Over-Rated Dryer Capacity				A					A						A		A
Aggregate Feed Gates Not Properly Set	A	A	A										A				
Inadequate Bunker Separation	A	A															
Aggregates Too Wet				A					A						A		A

A—Applies to Batch and Continuous Type Plants.   B—Applies to Batch Plants only.   C—Applies to Continuous Plants only.

8.20 PREPARATION OF SURFACE FOR SPREADING MIX.

—Plant mixtures may be laid over any kind of stable base. When the mix is placed over untreated surfaces, the base should be primed with all it will absorb. Prime applications usually range from 0.20 to 0.50 gallons per square yard. When the mix is placed over a paved surface, a tack coat should be applied. This serves as a bond between the old and the new and prevents slipping of the material during compaction. Tack coat applications range from 0.05 to 0.15 gallons per square yard. SS-1, SS-1h, SS-K, or SS-Kh emulsion diluted with equal parts water provides a thin uniform tack coat. (See "Tack Coats" in Section F of this chapter.)

CAUTION

(1) The prime should be completely cured before paving; however, leaving the asphalt prime uncovered long enough to permit dusting may cause poor bond between base and pavements and a tack coat may be necessary.

(2) Irregular thickness of prime will lead to poor bond in spots and over-asphalting of pavement in others. (This is mainly a function of irregularity of surface texture rather than of asphalt application, and is avoided by preventing segregation of base material.)

Spreading Asphalt Plant Mix

8.21 GENERAL.—Asphalt mixtures usually are spread by a paver and motor graders are sometimes used for spreading leveling courses. Cold mixtures should be spread and rolled in several layers, each not exceeding 1½ times the maximum size aggregate (if over ½ inch). Aeration may be needed, however, before spreading and rolling. For maximum sizes of ½ inch and under, each layer may be up to one inch in thickness.

8.22 SPREADING WITH PAVERS.—Pavers spread and partially compact the mix to a uniform surface. All consist essentially of a hopper, conveyor, distributing screws, and screed. There are two principal types of modern pavers in use—those which partially compact the mix, (1) by tamping bars, and (2) by vibrating screeds. Manufacturers can supply detailed instructions for adjustment and operation of their equipment. Good paver operation involves the following:

(1) The paving operation should be maintained as continuously as possible. When the paver stops for any considerable time, the mix cools below the optimum viscosity of the asphalt for proper spreading and compaction, resulting in roughness in the finished surface and poor densification of the finished mix. Therefore the speed of paver should be adjusted to the plant capacity and the hauling carefully regulated for continuity of operation.

(2) Sufficient material should be maintained in the hopper to supply the spreading screws with enough mix to cover at least ⅔ of the depth of the screws out to their ends. The amount of material carried around the screws should fluctuate as little as is practical. Control gates in the hopper should be set so the screws and feeders will operate 85 percent or more of the time.

(3) The speed of the paver should be adjusted to the type and thickness of mix being placed. (See also (1) above.)

(4) The screed should be heated when starting, or as otherwise necessary.

(5) A hot joint is always better than a cold one. Joint heaters will provide a hot joint when the volume does not justify two pavers.

(6) The essentials in making good joints are as follows:

a. No joint should be over the joint in the underlying course. The joints in courses should be offset or staggered about six inches.

b. Keep the joints straight. It is impossible to get a good joint if the paver is allowed to zig zag and wander back and forth across the desired line.

c. Maintain as nearly vertical a face on the first course as possible.

d. Keep the joint clean and free of loose particles of material.

e. Keep the overlap uniform. The desirable amount of overlap depends on the type of mix and the thickness of the course; generally 2 inches of overlap is required to provide material for proper compaction into a good, tight and dense joint.

f. When laying adjacent to a previously compacted surface, allow sufficient thickness for compaction. The amount of extra height of the course above the older surface will vary with the type of mix, the thickness of the course, and the amount of compaction effected by the paving machine. A rule of thumb is 1.25 times the desired compacted thickness of mix as measured behind the paver.

g. Roll the joint as soon as possible so as to put a large part of the roller weight on a narrow width (usually three to six inches) of the roller wheel. To do this, the roller is operated on the finished lane with only three to six inches of one wheel projecting on the new lane.

h. Begin rolling at the joint. When the joint and a width of a foot or so from the joint is thoroughly compacted, go to the other side of the lay and roll the balance of the strip into it.

i. If joint faces are left long enough to dry out or become dusty they should be treated with an application of tack coat.

8.23 SPREADING WITH MOTOR GRADERS.—

For spreading with a motor grader the mixed material is placed on the roadbed in a properly proportioned windrow by a windrow-sizer, or other approved measuring device, so that the proper amount of mixture is available. The material should be spread to the required thickness, line and grade, with a uniform surface texture while at a workable temperature. Automatic controls which hold the blade in a set position regardless of vertical movements of the grader wheels are extensively used to supplement the skill of the operator. These are an aid in assuring proper transverse section. Longitudinal uniformity is aided by a pointer on the blade and a string or wire line set to proper grade. Care should be exercised as to the length of the windrowed mix ahead of the spreading operations, taking into account the workability of the mix, weather conditions, and time required for this type of operation. Pneumatic-tired rolling usually accompanies or follows closely the spreading by grader.

8.24 DETAILS ON SPREADING ASPHALT PLANT MIXES.—For a detailed discussion on spreading asphalt plant mixes refer to *Asphalt Paving Manual*, Manual Series No. 8 (MS-8), The Asphalt Institute.

Figure VIII-5—Spreading Sand Asphalt Base With a Paver

(Courtesy of South Carolina Highway Department)

Compacting the Mix

8.25 ADDITIONAL INFORMATION ON COM-PACTING THE MIX.—The following articles describe briefly the procedures for compacting asphalt mixes. *Asphalt Paving Manual*, Manual Series No. 8 (MS-8), discusses this subject in more detail.

8.26 NUMBER OF ROLLERS REQUIRED.—At least two rollers should be required at all times. As many additional rollers should be used as necessary to provide specified pavement density. For types of rollers see Chapter VII.

8.27 ROLLING PROCEDURE.—During rolling, the roller wheels should be kept moist with only enough water to avoid picking up the material. Rollers should move at a slow but uniform speed with the drive roll or wheels nearest the paver. The speed should not exceed 3 mph for steel wheeled rollers or 5 mph for pneumatic tired rollers. Rollers should be in good condition, capable of being reversed without backlash. The line of rolling should not be suddenly changed nor the direction of rolling suddenly reversed, thereby displacing the mix. Any pronounced change in direction of the roller should be made on stable material. If rolling causes displace-ment of the material, the affected areas should be loosened at once with lutes or rakes and restored to the original grade with loose material before being re-rolled. Heavy equipment, including rollers, should not be permitted to stand on the finished surface before it has thoroughly cooled or set.

Correct rolling patterns for single lane paving and for echelon paving are discussed in *Asphalt Paving Manual*, Manual Series No. 8 (MS-8), The Asphalt Institute.

8.28 TRANSVERSE JOINTS.—In both intermediate and surface courses transverse joints should be carefully constructed and thoroughly compacted to provide a smooth riding surface over these joints in the pavement. Joints should be straight-edged or string-lined to assure smoothness and true alignment. Transverse joints should be constructed and compacted in the same manner as described for longitudinal joints. See below.

8.29 LONGITUDINAL JOINTS.—Longitudinal joints should be rolled directly behind the paving operation. The first lane placed should be true to line and grade and have a vertical face at the lane edge. The material being placed in the abutting lane should then be tightly crowded against the vertical face of the previously placed lane as follows:

(1) Push the overlap material back three to six inches on the new lane adjacent to the joint.

(2) Move the roller on to the previously compacted lane, letting one wheel project only three to six inches on to the new lane. Make two or more passes so as to thoroughly compact this narrow strip adjacent to the joint with its extra material (secured by overlapping the new layer over the old lane) down to and even with the old lane.

If a single paver is being used, a joint heater attachment may help obtain a sound bond between the adjoining edges.

8.30 EDGES.—The edges of the pavement should be rolled concurrently with the longitudinal joint. When rolling pavement edge, the roll shall extend two to four inches beyond the edge of the pavement.

8.31 BREAKDOWN ROLLING.—Breakdown rolling should immediately follow the rolling of the longitudinal joint and edges. Rollers should be operated as close to the paver as necessary to obtain adequate density without causing undue displacement. The breakdown roller should be operated with the drive roll or wheels nearest the finishing machine. Exceptions may be made when working on steep slopes or super-elevated curves. When both three-wheel rollers and tandem rollers are used, the three-wheel rollers should work directly behind the paver followed by the tandem rollers.

8.32 THE SECOND ROLLING.—Pneumatic-tired rollers are considered best for the second rolling, which should follow the breakdown rolling as closely as possible and while the paving mix is still at a temperature that will result in maximum density. Pneumatic-tired rolling should be continuous after the initial rolling until all the mix placed has been thoroughly compacted. Abrupt turning of rollers on the paving mix which causes undue displacement should not be permitted.

Figure VIII-6—Intermediate (Second) Rolling of Asphalt Concrete Wearing Coat

8.33 THE FINISH ROLLING.—Finish rolling should be accomplished with two-axle tandems or three-axle tandems while the material is still workable enough for removal of roller marks. However, some engineers prefer the use of pneumatic-tired rollers to obtain the surface finish which they desire.

It may be desirable to take advantage of the kneading action of a rubber-tired roller on the pavement surface, after all other rolling is completed. Normally the kneading action derived from traffic knits the surface particles together to provide a traffic seal. In the event that little or no traffic is to use a completed pavement for a considerable period of time, or if the pavement is completed in cool weather, this traffic seal may be achieved with the rubber-tired roller.

8.34 KNEADING ROLLING.—The rubber-tire rolling described above is most effective immediately after construction. However, fifteen or twenty coverages with the roller when the pavement has been warmed somewhat by the sun will do much to provide the surface texture desired.

8.35 SURFACE REQUIREMENTS.—To obtain a smooth finished surface, care must be used in the construction of every course in the asphalt pavement structure. Irregularities which may appear during or immediately after breakdown rolling should be remedied by loosening the mix and removing or adding material as may be required. The three-axle tandem roller with vibrating center roll may be effective in flattening down high areas if used before the mix is too cold.

8.36 CORRECTING SURFACE IRREGULARITIES.—Should any irregularities or defects remain in any course after compaction, they should be removed promptly and replaced with new material to provide a uniform textured surface conforming to line and grade.

8.37 ROAD INSPECTION.—The duties of the asphalt road inspector are covered in detail in Asphalt Institute Manual Series No. 8, *Asphalt Paving Manual.*

8.38 POSSIBLE CAUSES OF IMPERFECTIONS IN FINISHED PAVEMENTS.—Table VIII-2 shows the most common causes of imperfections in finished pavements.

TABLE VIII-2—POSSIBLE CAUSES OF IMPERFECTIONS IN FINISHED PAVEMENTS

Types of Pavement Imperfections That May Be Encountered In Laying Plant Mix Paving Mixtures.

Possible Cause	Bleeding	Brown, Dead Appearance	Rich or Fat Spots	Poor Surface Texture	Rough Uneven Surface	Honeycomb or Raveling	Uneven Joints	Roller Marks	Pushing or Waves	Cracking (Many Fine Cracks)	Cracking (Large Long Cracks)	Rocks Broken by Roller	Tearing of Surface During Laying	Surface Slipping on Base
Traffic Put On Mix While Too Hot									X					
Mix Laid in Too Thick Course									X					
Operating Finishing Machine Too Fast				X	X								X	
Faulty Allowance for Compaction						X								
Excessive Segregation in Laying			X	X	X	X							X	
Labor Careless or Unskilled			X	X	X	X	X							
Excessive Hand Raking			X	X	X	X			X					
Poor Handwork Behind Spreader			X	X	X	X								
Excessive Prime Coat or Tack Coat	X	X												X
Excessive Moisture in Subsoil										X	X			X
Unstable Base Course				X		X			X	X	X		X	X
Roller Vibration				X					X					
Overweight Rollers				X					X	X	X	X	X	X
Roller Standing on Hot Pavement				X					X					
Rolling Mixture When Too Cold			X	X	X	X								X
Rolling Mixture When Too Hot			X	X				X	X	X	X		X	
Over-Rolling				X						X	X	X		X
Rolling at Wrong Time			X	X	X	X		X	X	X	X		X	X
Inadequate Rolling			X	X	X	X								
Spreader in Poor Condition			X	X	X	X			X			X	X	
Poor Spreader Operation			X	X	X	X			X			X	X	
Mixture Too Cold			X	X	X	X						X	X	X
Mixture Too Hot or Burned	X												X	
Excess Moisture in Mixture	X								X					X
Unsatisfactory Batches in Load	X		X	X	X	X			X					
Improperly Proportioned Mixture	X		X	X	X	X			X	X	X		X	X
Excess Asphalt	X	X							X	X				X
Insufficient Asphalt		X				X			X		X		X	
Excess Fines in Mixture				X				X	X	X				X
Mixture Too Coarse			X	X	X	X						X	X	
Improperly Cured Prime or Tack Coat				X					X					X
Insufficient or Non-Uniform Tack Coat				X					X					X

D.—*Asphalt Macadam*

8.39 GENERAL.—Asphalt macadam is made of coarse and intermediate size aggregate and asphalt. It may be central plant mixed or the asphalt and aggregate may be combined by

(1) Mixing-in-place or roadmixing.

(2) Spraying asphalt to penetrate into the coarse aggregate and covering with the intermediate size aggregate.

The latter is called asphalt penetration macadam.

8.40 ASPHALT PENETRATION MACADAM.— Asphalt penetration macadam can be used as a surface course for medium to heavy trafficked roads but has been largely replaced by asphalt concrete as a surface for heavy and very heavy traffic. It is used as a base course for all types of traffic for the highest type highways. Its high stability, derived from the mechanical interlock of the relatively large aggregate as well as from the thick coat of asphalt, makes it a desirable type of construction where crushed aggregate of the proper size is economically available.

Asphalt macadam can be constructed with a minimum of equipment. The only equipment necessary is hauling equipment, stone spreader, asphalt distributor and compaction equipment.

Some of the limitations in the use of asphalt penetration macadam arise from peculiarities of this type of construction. In obtaining the two or more separate sizes usually required in asphalt penetration macadam construction it may be necessary to waste some of the crushed product. The separate sizes must be placed and penetrated in separate layers. No course should be appreciably thicker than its maximum size aggregate. It is frequently difficult to obtain proper smoothness in each layer on account of the large size of aggregate.

If asphalt penetration macadam is used on a material containing plastic fines, there is danger of base infiltration. This can be prevented, however, by a blanket course of fine material such as crusher screenings or sand, three to

Figure VIII-7—The Beautiful Interstate 95 in Maine Has an
Asphalt Penetration Macadam Base

four inches thick. As compared to hot plant mixing there is little control of moisture in the aggregate. As compared to plant mixing or good mix-in-place methods, penetration does not coat all sides of the aggregate as thoroughly or uniformly.

A brief outline of construction procedures for asphalt penetration macadam is given in the following two articles. For specifications and more details on equipment and construction procedures refer to *Asphalt Surface Treatments and Asphalt Penetration Macadam*, Manual Series No. 13 (MS-13), The Asphalt Institute.

8.41 PENETRATION MACADAM USING AS-PHALT CEMENT.—The principal steps in penetration macadam construction using asphalt cement are as follows:

(1) Prepare the underlying course. This may consist of priming a non-asphalt base, sealing a mixed-in-place base course, or placing an insulation course of crushed stone screenings, or sharp sand, usually three or four inches thick, to prevent intrusion of plastic foundation soil.

(2) Spread the first layer of coarse aggregate of the size and in amount required by the specification.

(3) Key the first course, usually by rolling with steel-wheeled roller. Care should be used not to over-roll so as to round the coarse aggregate.

(4) Make first application of asphalt, at proper temperature, of the type and in the amount required by the specifications.

(5) Cover immediately with the second application of aggregate and compact thoroughly with steel-wheeled and vibratory rollers.

(6) Where the penetration macadam is to serve as a surface course, additional applications of asphalt and cover aggregate are used.

(7) When used as a base course, a tack coat should be applied before the asphalt concrete is laid.

**Figure VIII-8—Asphalt Macadam Base Being Placed on
the New Jersey Turnpike**

8.42 PENETRATION MACADAM USING EMUL-
SIFIED ASPHALT OR LIGHT CUTBACKS.—The
procedure for penetration macadam construction using
emulsified asphalt or light cutbacks is different from that
using asphalt cement. Because of the lower viscosity of
these asphalts, more uniformly graded aggregate is used
and the asphalt is applied in two nearly equal increments
as follows:

(1) Prepare underlying course, spread and key first
layer of aggregate.

(2) Spread the first layer of aggregate of size and
in the amount required by the specifications.

(3) Key the first course with steel-wheeled and
vibratory rollers.

(4) Make first application of asphalt in the amount
required by the specifications.

(5) Spread second layer of aggregate in the required amount and compact.

(6) Make second application of asphalt in the required amount.

(7) If the course must be used for a time by traffic,
a light application, 10-20 pounds per square yard of

No. 9 aggregate, AASHO Specification M 43, (No. 4 to No. 16) should be spread on the second application of asphalt and compacted with a pneumatic-tired roller. Before the surface course is applied this should be swept clean and a tack coat applied.

(8) When used as a base course under asphalt concrete, a lower amount of asphalt than for surface is generally adequate, and no further aggregate cover or seal is needed.

(9) When course is to be a part of a surface course, a higher amount of asphalt should be used, followed by a surface treatment.

(10) When used as a base for asphalt concrete, no further applications are required if the asphalt concrete is laid immediately.

E.—Asphalt Mixed-in-Place (Road-Mix) Construction

8.43 GENERAL.—Mixed-in-place (also called road-mix) construction may be used for surface, base or subbase courses. As a surface course it is normally suitable for medium and light traffic. For base or subbase, mixed-in-place is suitable for all types of traffic. A seal coat may or not be required.

The principal advantage of mixing-in-place is that it utilizes aggregate already on the roadbed, or which is available from nearby sources. When using such materials, aggregate and asphalt can be mixed in place at low cost, with a minimum of equipment. Before selecting mixed-in-place construction, however, consideration should be given to central plant mixing, as better control is obtained, often at no increase in cost. Some features of mixed-in-place construction are as follows:

(1) Fair control of the moisture and volatile content through aeration with road-mixing equipment.

(2) Uniform coating of the asphalt on all aggregate surfaces.

(3) Where a road mix is made on the soil subgrade, and unless thoroughly skilled operators are available, trouble is sometimes encountered in controlling the depth of blading. The tendency is to pick

up additional soil and thus dilute the mix; or conversely, to drop out some of the mix material and produce too thin a layer which is over-asphalted. Where an old pavement or surface not in use is available, it is often utilized as a mixing platform, the mix being windrowed on it and later moved to the place of use. This is most often used in maintenance, and sometimes the mixing platform is also used as storage area.

(4) Mixed-in-place, or road mix, is economical when properly controlled because of the high production rates possible compared with the cost of equipment and its operation. It has special advantages for outlying areas, long stretches of farm and desert or ranch roads, and other locations where a problem exists in getting the necessary improved mileage. In urban and heavy traffic areas, plant-mix operations should be used.

(5) Mixed-in-place construction should be done only when weather conditions are favorably hot and dry.

Aggregate

8.44 GENERAL.—A wide variety of aggregates and soil-aggregate combinations can be processed satisfactorily by mixed-in-place methods. For surface course construction, higher quality aggregates are normally required than for base and subbase construction. Aggregate suitable for use in asphalt macadam may also be used for road-mix construction.

8.45 CRUSHED AGGREGATE.—Commercially crushed stone, slag, gravel and sand are widely available for mixing-in-place. There are, also, many localities where it will be economical to crush stone from road cuts or nearby quarry sites. Crusher run material with from 0 to 5 percent passing a No. 200 sieve, to a maximum size up to two inches or $\frac{2}{3}$ of the course thickness, whichever is smaller, provide excellent materials for mixed-in-place bases. Modern equipment for mixing-in-place has tended to decrease the cost so that it is competitive with asphalt penetration macadam. Generally the entire output of the crusher, below the specified maximum size, may be used in the asphalt pavement structure for maximum economy.

8.46 LOCALLY AVAILABLE MATERIALS.—In many areas, sand and gravel are more economically available than crushed aggregate. Suitable materials* range all the way from granular soils with as much as 25 percent passing a No. 200 sieve, liquid limit up to 30 and P.I. up to 6, through the range of clean sands and gravels. Higher limits can be used for some aggregates where experience shows them suitable. On many projects, by careful selection, suitable materials for road-mix courses may be obtained from common excavation material or borrow. On other projects, suitable materials may be available within or adjacent to the right-of-way either as they are in the pits, or by blending different strata or areas of the pits, or by blending with other materials at the pit or on the road. Well-graded aggregates are always desirable for any course of the asphalt pavement structure, but many poorly graded and gap-graded aggregates have proven adequate for base course road mixes.

Aggregate which is economically available should not be rejected without thorough tests. Determination of the suitability of road-mix materials can be made by the various tests now utilized by state highway departments, or other road building agencies.**

Asphalt

8.47 TYPES AND GRADES.—The types and grades of asphalt for use in road mix construction are determined by the characteristics of the aggregate, type of road mixing equipment to be used, and climatic conditions. Table I-1 is a guide for selection of types and grades.

8.48 EMULSIONS.—Emulsions are often preferred for use with damp aggregate. Very dry aggregate with considerable fines should be dampened with water before emulsions are applied.

See American Road Builders' Association Technical Bulletin No. 200 (1953).

**See AASHO specifications.*

8.49 AMOUNT OF ASPHALT.—The amount of asphalt for mixed-in-place can be determined by the methods outlined in ASTM Methods of Test D915, D1560, and D1561 and the California Division of Highways, "Materials Manual, Testing and Control Procedures," Vol. 1.

Mixed-in-Place (Road-Mix) Construction

8.50 TYPES OF EQUIPMENT.—The types of road mixing equipment are covered in Chapter VII.

8.51 PREPARATION OF SUBGRADE.—Prior to road-mixing operations, the base on which the mixed material is to be placed must be thoroughly shaped and compacted, then a prime coat must be applied and allowed to cure. Where the prime coat does not completely penetrate into the base, the excess asphalt should be blotted with a suitable granular material.

8.52 TRAVEL-PLANT MIXING.—An advantage of travel-plant mixing is that closer control of the mixing operations can be achieved. The proportioning of the asphalt with the aggregate, as well as the uniformity with which the two can be incorporated, are of the greatest importance. In order to achieve a uniform product it is necessary that several precautions be taken:

1. A windrow of prepared material, uniform in cross-section, must first be established.

2. The uniformity of the gradation of the material in the windrow must be carefully checked.

3. The proper amount of asphalt necessary for incorporation with the aggregate must be determined.

4. The road-mixing machine must be in satisfactory operating condition.

In performing this type of work, the mixing machine moves through the windrow adding asphalt as it goes. If the windrow is so large that all of the asphalt cannot be incorporated in one mixing pass, the windrow should be split and the asphalt added to each windrow in one mixing pass. Usually, however, further mixing of the windrowed material after the addition of the asphalt is necessary.

This further mixing in most cases will have to be done with motor grader to make sure that all of the windrowed material is incorporated into the mix, to provide further mixing of the aggregate and the asphalt, and to aerate the mixture in order to remove moisture and volatiles. The number of passes necessary with the motor grader for this purpose will vary under different job conditions. However, in general a minimum of five or six passes will be necessary. After the mixing has been completed, the windrow should be removed to one side of the roadway in preparation for spreading.

Another type of travel plant mixes the asphalt and aggregate which is deposited directly from the truck into the hopper of the travel plant, and spreads the mix in one pass of the machine. Extreme care must be taken to be sure that sufficient volatiles have evaporated from the spread mix prior to compaction. Breakdown rolling should be done with pneumatic-tired roller and final rolling with a steel-wheeled roller.

8.53 BLADE MIXING.—In road-mix construction utilizing a motor grader for mixing, uniformity of quantity and the gradation of the aggregate to be mixed is of great importance. The material placed in the windrow should be placed either through a spreader box or by running through a windrow sizer prior to the addition of asphalt. The asphalt demand of the aggregate in the windrow must be determined and the amount needed per lineal foot of windrow calculated.

The asphalt binder may be applied by successive applications from a distributor truck on the flattened windrow. It is necessary to apply the total requirement of asphalt binder prior to completing the mixing operations. Best results are obtained by applying the asphalt in multiple applications and folding the asphalt into the windrow immediately behind the distributor truck.

It must be kept in mind that there is a possibility of variation of the grading of the aggregate in the windrow and therefore a fluctuation in the asphalt demand. As the mixing progresses close attention should be paid to the uniformity of the appearance of the mix in the windrow. The mixing of the material in the windrow should consist of as many manipulations with the motor grader as is necessary to thoroughly disperse the asphalt in the aggregate and coat the aggregate particles.

During mixing some attention should be paid to the vertical angle of the mold board of the grader. The setting of the mold board should be adjusted so that a complete rolling action of the material is obtained when the windrow is manipulated.

During the mixing operation care must be exercised that extra material is not taken from the mixing table and incorporated into the windrow. At the same time none of the windrow should be lost over the edge of the mixing table. In some instances, if great difficulty is experienced in breaking up "oil balls" the condition can be corrected by throwing the mixture into a compacted windrow and allowing it to cure for a few days.

After mixing has been completed the windrow should be removed to one side of the roadbed in preparation for spreading.

8.54 ROTARY MIXING.—Rotary type of mixing combines the asphalt and aggregate under a hood with whirling tines or blades as the machine moves over the surface. Most are now equipped with a spray system which applies the asphalt while mixing. When using the rotary type of mixer the following steps usually are followed:

(1) The aggregate is spread to uniform grade and cross section with motor graders.

(2) The aggregate is thoroughly mixed by one or more passes of the mixer. If the aggregate is too wet, the hood may be raised and the aggregate aerated to dry it to proper moisture content.

(3) Asphalt is added in increments of about one-half gallon per square yard until the total required amount of asphalt is applied and mixed in. A total of 0.4 to 0.6 gallons per square yard per inch of compacted thickness of the course is usually required. If

the mixer is not equipped with spray bars the asphalt may be applied with an asphalt distributor and folded in with a motor grader.

(4) It may be necessary to make one or more passes of the mixer between applications of asphalt to thoroughly mix it in.

(5) After all the asphalt is mixed in, the mix is aerated to proper volatile content (or moisture content if emulsions are used).

(6) The surface is maintained true to grade and cross section by a motor grader during the mixing operations.

8.55 MOISTURE AND VOLATILE CONTENT.— Graded granular aggregate mixtures usually are not highly critical in regard to moisture and volatile content. However, fine grain aggregate mixtures should be aerated to a total moisture and volatile content considerably below the Proctor optimum moisture for maximum compaction. Experience with the particular mixture being used and trial rolling are methods of determining the proper moisture and volatile content when test data are not available. The mixture should be rolled as soon as it will bear the weight of the roller without shoving.

8.56 SPREADING AND COMPACTING.—After aeration of the mixture has been completed the material may be spread loose on the roadbed or it may be in one or more windrows at the sides of the road. If a prime coat has not previously been placed, it may be advisable to use one or a tack coat prior to spreading and compacting the mixed material. Normally, the spreading is done by moving the material from the windrow by motor grader. Care should be taken to assure placement of material in thin lifts. This material should be compacted by the use of pneumatic tired rollers following each spread. This operation should be repeated as many times as necessary to spread and compact all of the mixed material and to bring the road to proper crown and grade. Lifts should not exceed four inches. After the course has been thoroughly compacted and cured, other courses may be placed on it.

F.—*Surface Treatments and Seal Coats*

8.57 DEFINITION.—Asphalt surface treatment is a broad term embracing several types of asphalt and asphalt-aggregate applications, usually less than one inch thick, to any kind of road surface. The types of surface treatment range from single, light applications of liquid asphalt to multiple surface courses made up of alternate applications of asphalt and aggregate. Sealing and adding life to road surfaces are common to all, but each type has one or more special uses.

This section discusses surface treatments and seal coats briefly. *Asphalt Surface Treatments and Asphalt Penetration Macadam*, Manual Series No. 13 (MS-13), The Asphalt Institute, covers thoroughly their design and construction.

8.58 SURFACE TREATMENTS MUST HAVE ADEQUATE BASE.—A surface treatment is not a pavement in itself, rather it affords only a waterproof cover over its base and provides resistance to abrasion of traffic. Being usually less than an inch in thickness, it is not intended in itself to increase the strength of the base. The engineer is frequently confronted with the problem as to when an unpaved road should be changed to an all-weather type. The temptation is to surface treat whether or not an adequate foundation exists. This has created many miles of surface-treated highways with insufficient base which are a source of constant trouble and expense. If the base is inadequate, a dust palliative should be used as a maintenance step in the progressive improvement of the base until it will support the anticipated traffic. (See Chapter IX for stage construction.)

8.59 FROST AREAS.—In frost areas the base must be of non-frost susceptible material. Otherwise, the surface treatment will not survive severe freezing and thawing cycles. For criteria in determining non-frost susceptible material for base courses refer to *Thickness Design-Asphalt Pavement Structures for Highways and Streets*, Manual Series No. 1 (MS-1), The Asphalt Institute.

8.60 UNPAVED ROADS.—For unpaved roads the desirable clay content for sufficiently binding the unpaved surface course may be too high to be permissible under a paved surface. Therefore, when surface treatment is placed on an old clay-gravel or sand-clay unpaved road, care should be used to determine that the plasticity index of the old road material is sufficiently low that it will not become soft from moisture trapped under the new surface treatment. Generally, a material having a plasticity index more than six should be carefully investigated in this regard.

8.61 DUST LAYING.—Dust laying, also called dust palliative, is a simple application of liquid asphaltic material to a road surface. The following types of liquid asphalt are used:

(1) Medium-curing liquid asphalt—MC-30 and MC-70.

(2) Slow-curing liquid asphalt—SC-70.

(3) Slow-setting emulsified asphalt—SS-1.

These are usually applied at the rate of 0.1 to 0.5 gallons per square yard. When the emulsion is used, it should be diluted with up to five or more parts of water by volume.

The use of liquid asphalt only as a dust palliative is frequently called road oiling. A dust palliative treatment may be preliminary to progressive improvement of low-type roads.

Single and Multiple Surface Treatments

8.62 DEFINITION.—A single surface treatment consists of an application of asphalt followed by an application of aggregate. If the process is repeated, the resulting surfaces are referred to as double, triple, etc., surface treatments depending on the number of applications.

8.63 USAGE.—These surface treatments may be applied on a primed non-asphalt base, asphalt base course or any type of existing pavement. This type of surface treatment with a good prime provides the lowest cost waterproof covering for an untreated aggregate base course and with good aggregate will provide an economical wearing surface to meet the needs of medium and low volumes of traffic.

This type of surface treatment is very useful as a wearing surface on base courses in the stage construction of highways pending placement of asphalt concrete surface courses. See Chapter IX for more on stage construction.

8.64 LIMITS.—The use of single and multiple surface treatments is subject to the following limitations:

(1) Weather conditions must be favorable to secure a good job.

(2) The surface on which the asphalt is sprayed must be hard, clean and dry for the surface treatment to adhere properly.

(3) The amount and viscosity of the asphalt must be carefully balanced with the size and amount of cover to assure proper retention of the aggregate.

(4) Heavy high speed traffic tends to dislodge the aggregate from the asphalt and "whip it off" the road.

Because of these limitations, the use of plant-mix surfaces should be considered, when the above conditions may be encountered.

8.65 AMOUNT OF ASPHALT AND AGGREGATE.—Table VIII-3 shows the quantities of aggregate and the type and quantities of asphalt suitable for use in surface treatments and seal coats. The table shows the type and amount of asphalt for the proper imbedment of the size aggregate shown.

8.66 USE OF ASPHALT FOG SEAL ON SURFACE TREATMENTS.—An asphalt fog seal coat (Refer to Article 8.70) may be used as a finish on any of the above surface treatments, applied at 0.1 to 0.2 gallons per square yard to: (1) Aid in retention of aggregate, (2) Prevent dust on the aggregate from becoming a nuisance.

TABLE VIII-3—QUANTITIES OF ASPHALT AND AGGREGATE FOR SINGLE SURFACE TREATMENTS AND SEAL COATS*

Line No.	Size of Aggregate	Size	Lbs. of Aggregate Per Sq. Yd. [1, 2]	Gallons of Asphalt Per Sq. Yd. [1, 3]	Hot Weather (80°F+)		Cool Weather (Up to 80°F)	
					Hard Aggregate	Absorbent Aggregate	Hard Aggregate	Absorbent Aggregate
1	¾ to ⅜	6	40–50	.40–.50	120–150 RC3000, RS2. RS-2K, RS-3K	RC3000, RS2. RS-2K. RS-3K	RC800, RS2. RS-2K. RS-3K	RC800, RS2. RS-2K. RS-3K
2	½ to No. 4	7	25–30	.25–.30	200–300[4] RC250.800. RS1. RS2. RS-2K, RS-3K	RC250.800, RS1, RS2. RS-2K. RS-3K	RC250.800, RS1, RS2. RS-2K. RS-3K	RC250.800. RS1, RS2. RS-2K. RS-3K
3	⅜ to No. 8	8	15–20	.15–.20	RC250.800. RS1, RS2. RS-2K, RS-3K	RC250.800. RS1, RS2. RS-2K. RS-3K	RC250.800. RS1, RS2. RS-2K. RS-3K	RC250.800. RS1, RS2. RS-2K. RS-3K
4	¼ to No. 8	9	10–15	.10–.15	RC250.800. RS1. RS2. RS-2K. RS-3K	RC250.800, RS1, RS2. RS-2K. RS-3K	RC250.800. RS1, RS2. RS-2K, RS-3K	RC.250.800. RS1, RS2. RS-2K, RS-3K

5	Sand	10-15	.10-.15	RC250,800. RS1, RS2. RS-2K, RS-3K. SS-1, SS-K	RC250,800. RS1, RS2. RS-2K, RS-3K. SS-1, SS-K	RC250,800. RS1, RS2. RS-2K, RS-3K. SS-1, SS-K	RC250,800. RS1. RS-2K, RS-3K. SS-1, SS-K	RC250,800. RS1. RS-2K, RS-3K. SS-1, SS-K

* These quantities and types of materials may be varied according to local conditions and experience.

1 The lower application rates of asphalt shown in the table should be used for aggregate having gradings on the fine side of the limits specified. The higher application rates should be used for aggregate having gradings on the coarse side of the limits specified.

2 The weight of aggregate shown in the table is based on aggregate with a specific gravity of 2.65. In case the specific gravity of the aggregate used is less than 2.55 or more than 2.75 the amount shown in the table above should be multiplied by the ratio which the bulk specific gravity of the aggregate used bears to 2.65.

3 Under certain conditions, the grades of MC liquid asphalts may be used satisfactorily.

4 In some areas difficulty in retaining aggregate has been experienced with 200–300 penetration asphalt cements.

NOTE

Single Surface Treatments. The maximum size aggregate should not be over $1/2$ inch. Use line 2. For lighter surface treatments, use line 3 or 4; however, lines 3 and 4 are more for light seal coats. For sand seals use line 5.

Double Surface Treatments. The maximum size aggregate can be up to $3/4$ inch. First course, use line 1; second course, use line 3 or 4. For lighter double surface treatments use for first course, line 2; for second course, line 3 or 4.

Triple Surface Treatments. The maximum size aggregate is usually $3/4$ inch. The following is recommended: first course, line 1; second course, line 2; third course, line 3 or 4. For most situations, the best probably is lines 1, 2 and 4 for the three courses.

8.67 CONSTRUCTION OF SURFACE TREATMENTS.—

(1) **Weather.** Weather conditions are an important factor for success in the construction of sprayed asphalt with cover aggregate surface treatments and seal coats. For best results in aggregate retention, it is desirable that the pavement temperature be relatively high during the application of the seal coat. A certain amount of curing, or set, is required even with the heaviest liquid asphaltic materials. This curing takes place best when the air temperature is well above 50°F, and the relative humidity is low. A survey of surface treatments rated excellent shows more than 85 percent were placed in the hot summer months. Every effort should be made to plan the work for fast operation in best summer weather. After completion of surface treatment, traffic should be controlled until curing has occurred.

(2) **The Asphalt Distributor.** It is essential that the distributor be capable of spraying the asphalt uniformly over the surface to be treated. For best results in surface treatments the following points especially should be observed:

a. Maintain uniform pressure and temperature on all spray nozzles. The fan of the spray from each nozzle must be uniform and set at the proper angle (according to manufacturer's instructions) with the spraybar so that the spray fans do not interfere with each other.

b. The spray bar must be maintained at the proper height (according to manufacturer's instructions) above the road surface to provide complete and uniform overlap of the spray fans.

c. The distributor road speed must be uniform.

d. Before the start of work the spread of the distributor spray bar should be checked. Valve action should be instantaneous, both in opening and cut-off. The spraying operation should be inspected frequently to be sure that the nozzles are the proper height from the road surface and working fully. An otherwise good job may be spoiled because one or more spray nozzles may be clogged. For more on the asphalt distributor see Chapter VII and *Asphalt Surface Treatments and Asphalt Penetration Macadam,* Manual Series No. 13 (MS-13), The Asphalt Institute.

(3) Spreading Aggregate.

a. Before application of asphalt an adequate aggregate spreader should be available and properly adjusted for the aggregate actually to be used. The spray bar width of the asphalt distributor should be equal to the width of the aggregate being spread

Figure VIII-9—Applying Surface Treatment Aggregate with a Self-Propelled Spreader

in one pass. Normally, this is the width of one traffic lane. An adequate supply of aggregate should be on hand to cover the asphalt spread without interruption in the shortest practical time after the asphalt hits the surface. In addition, the aggregate spreader should be filled, in place, and ready to spread aggregate before commencing the asphalt spray. A common fault is to operate the distributor too far ahead of the aggregate spreader.

b. Aggregate spreaders vary from a simple controllable gate box attached to the dump truck, to very efficient self-propelled units which apply the larger size aggregate on the bottom and the finer on top, which is desirable. See also Chapter VII.

(4) **Rolling.** Both pneumatic-tired and steel-wheeled rollers can be used for surface treatments. However, The Asphalt Institute recommends self-propelled smooth-tread pneumatic-tired rollers for this type of construction. The resilient tires on these rollers force the aggregate firmly into the asphalt binder without crushing the particles. Steel-wheeled rollers will bridge over the smaller size particles and small depressions in the surface and fail to press the aggregate in these places into the asphalt. These rollers also may crush the softer particles so that degradation takes place even before traffic uses the new surface. If steel-wheeled rollers are used they should supplement pneumatic-tired rollers.

When double or triple surface treatments are used, each course should be rolled before the next one is placed.

(5) **Traffic Control.** It is extremely important that traffic should be controlled to prevent loss of aggregate. One method of controlling traffic is to form a single line of traffic behind a pilot car with red flag between stops at each end of the work area.

Seal Coats

8.68 DEFINITION.—A seal coat is a thin surface treatment used to improve the texture of and waterproof an asphalt surface. Depending on the purpose, seal coats may or may not be covered with aggregate. The main types of seal coats are aggregate seals, fog seals, emulsion slurry seals, and sand seals.

8.69 USAGE.—A seal coat may be used when it is desired to accomplish one or more of the following:

(1) Enliven a dry or weathered surface.

(2) Seal and fill cracks to prevent moisture and air from entering the pavement structure.

(3) Correct slight pavement deformation or raveling.

(4) Provide a skid-resistant surface by using non-polishing aggregate or covering an old over-asphalted surface.

(5) Provide additional asphalt binder to the exposed surface to facilitate traffic sealing.

(6) Improve visibility by color contrast.

(7) Provide lane demarcation—a seal coat with large aggregate is useful as a noise producing surface by causing tire rumble in danger areas as in the lanes approaching an intersection or on shoulders.

CAUTION

A seal coat is not intended in itself to increase the strength of an existing pavement. Where additional strength is required, an asphalt concrete overlay, or other appropriate type of strengthening course, should be used.

Fog Seal

8.70 DEFINITION.—A fog seal is a light application of slow-setting asphalt emulsion diluted with water. It is used to renew old asphalt surfaces and seal small cracks and surface voids. The emulsion is diluted with an equal amount of water and sprayed at the rate of 0.1 to 0.2 gallon (of diluted material) per square yard, depending on the texture and dryness of the old pavement. Cover aggregate is not required, and under normal conditions the break is rapid, permitting traffic within an hour or two.

8.71 USAGE.—Fog seals are used to rejuvenate an old asphalt pavement and seal small cracks and surface voids. They are especially useful for pavements carrying a low volume of traffic.

A fog seal may also be used:

(1) To seal surface voids in new asphalt plant-mix.

(2) On sprayed asphalt with cover aggregate surface treatments to prevent dust immediately after construction in congested areas, increase aggregate retention, and provide uniform dark color.

Emulsion Slurry Seals

8.72 DEFINITION.—Emulsion slurry is a mixture of slow-setting asphalt emulsion, fine aggregate, mineral filler, and water.

8.73 USAGE.—Emulsion slurry is used to fill cracks and scaled areas of old pavements to restore a uniform surface texture and to seal the surface to prevent moisture and air intrusion into the pavement. If an old asphalt pavement has no large cracks or scaled areas and needs rejuvenation only, a fog seal would be indicated. Emulsion slurry may be followed with another type of surface treatment or an asphalt concrete overlay.

Figure VIII-10—Single Unit Slurry Seal Machine

Sand Seal

8.74 DEFINITION.—A sand seal is an application of asphaltic material covered with fine aggregate.

8.75 USAGE.—A sand seal may be used to improve the skid resistance of slippery pavements and to seal against air and water intrusion.

Primes

8.76 DEFINITION.—Priming consists of an application of low viscosity liquid asphalt to an absorbent surface.

8.77 USAGE.—A prime is used to prepare an untreated base for an asphalt surface. The prime penetrates into the base and plugs the voids, hardens the top and helps bind it to the overlying asphalt course. A prime coat also is valuable in reducing maintenance of a compacted aggregate base before the asphalt pavement is placed.

Priming is accomplished by the following:

Spraying from 0.20 to 0.50 gallons per square yard of low viscosity liquid asphalt such as MC-30, MC-70 or MC-250, RC-70, RC-250, SC-70 or SC-250 on the prepared surface of the base and allowing the asphalt to penetrate as far as possible.

Tack Coats

8.78 DEFINITION.—A tack coat is a very light application of liquid asphalt, usually asphalt emulsion diluted with water. It is used to insure a bond between the surface being paved and the overlying course.

8.79 USAGE.—Because many tack coats have been entirely too heavy, thereby leaving a surplus of asphalt which flushes into the overlying course, there has been a tendency to avoid their use. A thin tack coat such as described above does no harm to the pavement. On the other hand, it will properly bond the courses.

8.80 APPLICATION.—The asphalt emulsion is diluted with equal parts of water to assure a light, even coverage. From 0.05 to 0.15 gallon per square yard of

SS-1, SS-1h, SS-K or SS-Kh emulsion is sufficient quantity for a tack coat.

Work should be planned so that no more tack coat than is necessary for the day's operation is placed on the surface. All traffic not essential to the work should be kept off the tack coat.

In places where the distributor bars cannot reach, it will be necessary to apply the tack coat with a hand spray attached to the distributor by a hose. When hand spray methods are used, care should be taken to give the surface a very light application of the asphalt.

Mastic Seal Coats

8.81 DEFINITION.—Mastic seal coats may be either cold or hot. The mastic is a dense, impervious, voidless mixture of asphalt, mineral aggregate, and mineral dust. The surface to be covered is first cleaned and usually primed with an asphalt primer, compatible with the asphalt mastic.

8.82 COLD ASPHALT MASTICS.—Cold asphalt mastic seals may be prepared in small drum mixers. One composition which has been used satisfactorily is as follows:

```
1 part portland cement........  94 lbs. (1 cu. ft.)
3½ parts concrete sand........ 350 lbs. (3½ cu. ft.)
1½ part emulsified asphalt
   SS-1h or SS-Kh*
   (11.25 gals.)..............  94 lbs. (1½ cu. ft.)
1 part water (approx. 7½ gals.)..  62 lbs. (1 cu. ft.)
   Total Wet Weight......... 600 lbs.
   Total Dry Weight.........
      (Compacted) .......... 500 lbs. (3.33 cu. ft.)
```

With the old surface primed with emulsified asphalt, this mix is screeded into place to a ¾-in. max. thickness. Edges may be feathered, when necessary. After initial set of the cement (4-6 hours), the surface must be hand-troweled. Then it must be protected against rapid dehy-

---

There are special proprietary emulsified asphalts designed especially for the manufacture of mastics containing portland cement.

dration for 48 hours so cement can properly hydrate for a hard, durable finish.

8.83 HOT ASPHALT MASTICS.—Hot asphalt mastic seals are usually prepared from low penetration grades of asphalt, fine aggregate and mineral filler.

Selection of the type of aggregate and filler is important where the mastic must resist acids. Asphalt itself is usually not affected by most acids but the effect of acids on the aggregate and filler should be determined by laboratory tests for each type of acid to be encountered. In general, limestone aggregates are most vulnerable.

8.84 ROLLING HOT MASTIC.—The mastic should be lightly rolled with light tandem steel-wheeled or pneumatic-tired roller.

8.85 USAGE.—Asphalt mastic seal coats are generally used to smooth out surface irregularities and, when hot, to provide acid resistance to the underlying asphaltic courses.

Asphalt mastic mixtures are also used as protective coatings for pipe lines, refer to Asphalt Institute Construction Series No. 96, *Asphalt Protective Coatings for Pipe Lines,* which gives specifications for primer, asphalt binder, gradations of aggregate and mineral filler, characteristics of mastic mixtures, as well as methods for testing the materials entering into the mixture and tests on the mastic mixture.

There are numerous proprietary cold and hot asphalt mastic preparations on the market.

Plant Mixed Surface Treatment

8.86 DEFINITION.—A plant-mixed surface treatment consists of a layer, less than one inch thick, of aggregate that is coated with asphalt in a plant. Plant-mixed surface treatments are used extensively for providing skid-resistant surfaces. Hot mix types usually are preferred. Hot plant-mixed surface treatment may have all of the superior qualities of accurately controlled plant-mix. Another advantage is the fact that plant-mix surface treatments can be completed speedily and immediately turned over to traffic.

For more on plant mixes refer to *Specifications and Construction Methods for Asphalt Concrete and Other Plant-Mix Types,* Specification Series No. 1 (SS-1), The Asphalt Institute.

CAUTION

Surface treatments are not substitutes for overlays. **When strengthening is required surface treatments should not be substituted for strengthening overlay courses.**

Treatments for Skid Resistance

8.87 USAGE.—Surface treatments are extensively used to provide or restore a skid-resistant surface. Two types are useful for different traffic as follows:

(1) Single and multiple surface treatments may be used for light traffic, and as stage construction for medium and heavy traffic.

(2) Plant-mix treatments may be used for heavy traffic.

8.88 AGGREGATES.—The aggregates used in these treatments must have high resistance to polishing. Currently, there is no standard test for measuring polishing. However, experience has shown that some of the following aggregates have been successfully used for this purpose:

(1) Sharp silica sand or selected crushed sandstone
(2) Crushed blast furnace slag
(3) Selected crushed trap rock and granite
(4) Selected crushed gravels

8.89 NEW CONSTRUCTION.—For new construction, in areas where the prevailing aggregate has polishing characteristics and non-polishing aggregate is expensive, a thin surface course, ½ to 1 inch thick, using non-polishing aggregate is placed as the surface course in the initial construction. By the use of plant-mix treatments made with non-polishing aggregates in areas where the locally available aggregate has high-polishing characteristics, engineers may provide safe driving surfaces and also achieve maximum economy by the use of locally available aggregates for all other courses of the pavement structure.

8.90 EXISTING PAVEMENTS.—On existing pavements which have become slippery from polishing of aggregate or from an excess of asphalt on the surface the treatment should be from ¾ to 1 inch thick except where grade restrictions are tight, as on bridges and city streets.

On bridges and city streets where expansion joints, curbs, manholes, drainage grates, etc., require a minimum change in grade, fine silica sand or blast furnace slag sand mixes are advantageous.

The old pavement surface should be thoroughly cleaned and a light tack applied. The mix is then spread with a paver using from as low as 25 pounds per square yard to 100 pounds per square yard. Generally, the rate of spread is from 40 to 50 pounds per square yard. The mix is feathered to fit sliding plate expansion joints, drainage grates, etc., and rolled. It has been found that pneumatic-tired rollers give the best results, particularly with the thinner layers.

8.91 REFERENCES.—The following Asphalt Institute publications contain detailed information on the construction of asphalt pavements:

(1) *Specifications and Construction Methods for Asphalt Concrete and Other Plant Mix Types,* Specification Series No. 1 (SS-1)

(2) *Thickness Design—Asphalt Pavement Structures for Highways and Streets,* Manual Series No. 1 (MS-1)

(3) *Mix Design Methods for Asphalt Concrete and Other Hot-Mix Types,* Manual Series No. 2 (MS-2)

(4) *Asphalt Plant Manual,* Manual Series No. 3 (MS-3)

(5) *Asphalt Paving Manual,* Manual Series No. 8 (MS-8)

(6) *Asphalt Pavements for Airports,* Manual Series No. 11 (MS-11)

(7) *Asphalt Surface Treatments and Asphalt Penetration Macadam,* Manual Series No. 13 (MS-13)

(8) *Asphalt Mixed-in-Place (Road-Mix) Manual,* Manual Series No. 14 (MS-14)

(9) *Asphalt Protective Coatings for Pipe Lines,* Construction Series No. 96 (CS-96).

Chapter IX

STAGE CONSTRUCTION, RECONSTRUCTION, AND MAINTENANCE

A.—*Stage Construction, Reconstruction*

9.01 TYPES OF STAGE CONSTRUCTION.—Stage construction may be of two classes:

(1) Progressive improvement of low-type roads.

(2) Construction of high-type roads in two or more increments.

9.02 PROGRESSIVE IMPROVEMENT OF LOW-TYPE ROADS.—Asphalt lends itself particularly well to stage construction for two reasons:

(1) It is the simplest and lowest cost procedure for changing untreated surfaces to all-weather ones, and

(2) Each additional treatment or new layer of asphalt mixture can be bonded completely with that previously placed so that it becomes an integral part of the composite structure, thereby increasing strength with relatively small added thickness. The additional thickness needed can be calculated quite exactly and placed only as traffic requires. The usual steps in stage construction are: (a) From untreated aggregate surface to either surface treatment or mixed-in-place, (b) From surface treatment or mixed-in-place to plant-mixed surface. The method thus provides all-weather surface at the earliest possible date without overbuilding. In this way, low-type roads are developed into heavy-duty highways.

When an untreated aggregate surface is deficient in thickness, and funds are insufficient to place all needed new material in one year, maintenance funds can be applied to a gradual strengthening process. The method is applicable particularly to the thousands of miles of low-class roads where heaviest traffic occurs in summer. The first year the old surface is bladed, an inch or two of new aggregate added, and an asphalt treatment of ¼ to

½ gallon per square yard applied. Light blading under traffic will produce a smooth, dustless surface which usually will last through the first winter.

The following year a second application of aggregate and asphalt is then applied. The third year the definitely weak areas can then be located and strengthened with pre-mixed patch material or aggregate base material. The fourth year should find a surface which can be used as a base for a heavier wearing course or maintained by lighter treatment at intervals of several years. The procedure is applicable to sandy soils, sandy gravels, screenings, shell, and many other local aggregates. Either emulsified asphalts or lighter MC liquid grades or road oils are used. In initial treatments it may seem at first that the asphalt is completely lost; actually it is only dispersed in thin films and subsequent applications add to each preceding one until it becomes all effective.

9.03 CONSTRUCTION OF HIGH-TYPE ROADS IN TWO OR MORE INCREMENTS.—Reasons for stage construction are:

(1) Settlement in certain areas will inevitably occur with all types of pavement no matter how carefully initial construction is accomplished. After embankments have reached equilibrium in accordance with local moisture and climatic conditions, a smooth resurfacing course should be applied to obtain the smoothest riding surface.

(2) Traffic is increasing almost everywhere. This increase cannot always be predetermined when the project is designed.

(3) More miles of new highway pavement are initially secured from the available construction funds and additional strength can be provided later as needed with a resurfacing course which becomes an integral part of the original pavement structure.

9.04 IMPORTANCE OF STAGE CONSTRUCTION.—The importance of stage construction in such a major highway program as the Interstate Highway System is recognized by the U. S. Bureau of Public Roads under provisions of the 1956 Highway Act.

Stage construction of high-type highways usually is divided as follows:

(1) Drainage, grading, and improved subgrade

(2) Subbase and base courses with a surface treatment or a thin surface course to carry traffic for a few years

(3) Completion of the surface courses in accordance with original plan.

Where asphalt base courses are placed, they often serve to carry traffic for a considerable time before the final surfacing. A seal coat may be desirable if the asphalt base course is of open-surface texture.

9.05 WIDENING.—Modern two-lane pavement should be 24 to 26 feet in width. Many thousands of miles on the primary routes, paved in the 1920's and 1930's are now inadequate, both in width and thickness. Existing roads of lesser width should first be widened before resurfacing. Skillful handling of such widening can greatly improve on the original alignment by placing most or all of the widening at one side or the other around curves. Moreover, sharp curves widened on the inner side to 30 feet and superelevated will often correct a dangerous situation.

Very efficient equipment for rapid cutting of trenches and filling with foundation material is now available, and work can proceed with minimum interference to traffic. Old pavements, both rigid and flexible, may be widened by essentially the same procedures. Both types require trenching to adequate width and construction of an asphalt base of sufficient depth to carry the expected traffic. The asphalt base should be placed in layers and compacted to the required density. Steel wheeled vibratory rollers are good for this type of work.

9.06 SHOULDER IMPROVEMENT.—An asphalt paved shoulder is an excellent safety feature. It also provides high lateral support which enhances the strength of the pavement structure. Where materials are economically available, base and subbase layers may be extended across the shoulder to the ditch slope. However, with the wide roadway sections now in common use, full-width construction with structural layers of the pavement may be quite costly. Accordingly, alternate shoulder designs should be considered and one chosen which will give adequate service at minimum cost.

At one time it was believed that shoulders should be of material different in texture from the pavement proper, to prevent use as an additional traffic lane. With asphalt concrete surfacing now so extensively used, experience has shown that it is best to carry the same surface material completely across the shoulder. A solid white or yellow painted band, along the desired edge of the pavement proper, affords sufficient demarcation of the shoulder.

Figure IX-1—Asphalt Concrete Base Applied With Special Paver Attachment in Widening of Road

Furthermore, after a few months, weathering under different traffic intensity, effects a color difference which is completely effective in assuring proper traffic use. If rumble is desired, a surface treatment can be placed on the shoulder area. If further contrast is desired, it may be easily obtained by a surface treatment on the shoulder portion using colored aggregate.

9.07 REPAIRING OLD BITUMINOUS PAVE-MENTS.—Structural distress in old bituminous pavements usually is the result of inadequate design of the pavement structure for today's traffic, inadequate compaction during construction, or both. Improper mix design also may cause several types of distress. Excess asphalt, particularly in mixes containing high percentages of fines, may cause corrugation or shoving of the surface. Insufficient asphalt may cause surface cracking or ravelling.

Fatigue cracking may be caused by excessive deflection of the pavement or by brittleness of the mix. Excessive deflection, in turn, may be caused by an inadequate pavement structure or by a springy, resilient foundation. Brittleness may result from the improper design of the aggregate portions of the mix, or from hardening of the asphalt because of overheating, or from a high void content in the mix.

The remedy for these failures depends upon the extent of distress. If extensive, it is probable that reconstruction is necessary. *Reconstruction of an old asphalt pavement should not be undertaken, however, until a complete and thorough investigation has definitely established the cause of the failures and the most feasible and economical measures have been determined.*

Asphalt pavements may fail because of inadequate support, often caused by bad drainage. Such areas may show "alligator cracking" and should be investigated to see whether they should be removed and replaced with suitable base and adequate drainage.

Reconstruction can be done as follows:

(1) If the existing pavement is uniform it can be brought to required strength by an asphalt concrete overlay of designed thickness;

(2) If the old pavement is clearly inadequate and badly broken up, the following is suggested:

a. Scarify the old pavement to a depth of six to eight inches if that thick, and break it down to original aggregate with heavy rotary pulverizer, grid roller, traveling hammer mill, or similar equipment.

b. Blade and reshape the old material to proper grade and cross section.

c. Add new aggregate to bring old and new to the required thickness determined from the investigation.

d. Add asphalt to bring total content of old and new asphalt to amount indicated for the aggregate by the proper design method. It is well to start with a cutback rather high in volatile content to soften up the old asphalt. The asphalt should be added in increments of about a half gallon per square yard, and mixed in after each application. When all the required asphalt has been added and mixed in, and the mix aerated to proper moisture and volatile content, the surface should again be bladed to proper grade and section.

e. Thoroughly compact the mixture with suitable compaction equipment.

f. Add new construction courses as required to complete an adequate pavement for traffic and load conditions.

9.08 PAVEMENT DISTRESS.—Asphalt pavements may become distressed because of many reasons. Before reconstruction or modernization, the causes of distress should be determined and their corrections be included in the reconstruction program.

9.09 OVERLAYING RIGID-TYPE PAVEMENT.— While there is no essential difference in the widening and shoulder construction of bituminous and rigid-type pavements there is some difference required in pretreatment of rigid-type pavements to assure stability after resurfacing is completed. Cracks, one-half inch or more in width, should be filled with a dense, fine-graded asphalt mixture. Pumping at the joints on rigid-type pavement will frequently cause failure by removing soil from beneath the slab. Often the pavement has cracked and broken at the joints. If broken into pieces only a foot or two in area they should be replaced with a full depth patch.

The most economical patch material is the asphalt intermediate course mix, placed and compacted in lifts of not more than three inches. Usually, however, the pavement can be stabilized by undersealing with an asphalt cement having a *softening point* between 160°F and 200°F, a standard process fully covered by specifications.* If most of the slab is broken to the point where it cannot be undersealed it should be further broken into pieces less than 12 inches in diameter, rolled with a heavy pneumatic-tired roller, and covered with an asphalt leveling course. If it is not practical to break the slab into smaller pieces it should be seated with a heavy proof roller and then covered with an asphalt leveling course. Rigid-type pavements have transverse premolded expansion and longitudinal joints. These must be cleaned out for a depth of two inches; otherwise they may bleed through the resurfacing or be forced up and cause a bump.

9.10 ADEQUATE THICKNESS IMPORTANT.— It is essential when resurfacing rigid-type pavements to have adequate total thickness of the added asphalt layers to provide the required strength and to minimize reflection of the cracks in the rigid-type pavement. A resurfacing consists of one or more leveling courses to establish proper gradient and cross-section over the old and widened areas. An intermediate and surface course of asphalt concrete is then placed with paver. The total thickness of asphalt overlay on rigid-type base courses to minimize crack reflection should be not less than three

---

* See *Asphalt Institute "Specifications for Undersealing Portland Cement Concrete Pavement," CS-92 and SS-2 (6th edition).*

inches. Additional thickness may be required to provide adequate strength of the composite pavement structure. Refer to *Thickness Design—Asphalt Pavement Structures for Highways and Streets,* Manual Series No. 1 (MS-1), for the design procedure.

B.—*Maintenance*

9.11 GENERAL.—Maintenance is the art of keeping a pavement at its maximum utility with a minimum expenditure and inconvenience to traffic. With proper maintenance and stage construction to meet traffic growth demands, the only reason for reconstruction is required changes in location or elevation.

There are numerous types of distress that may be encountered in streets or highways. The reason for the distress should be determined and action taken to correct the condition that caused the trouble.

Water is probably the greatest cause of distress in a pavement structure. Therefore, the control of surface and sub-surface water is one of the most important parts of maintenance.

9.12 TYPES OF PAVEMENT DISTRESS.—Some of the surface evidences of various types of pavement distress are:

(1) Weathering
(2) Ravelling
(3) Long cracks
(4) Alligator cracks
(5) Chuck holes
(6) Bleeding and instability
(7) Depressions
(8) Edge breaking

Frequently there will be more than one of these surface characteristics which will be in evidence at the same time. Sometimes one type of distress may progress to a more serious type of distress, or may progress to failure when not cared for properly.

9.13 CORRECTION OF PAVEMENT DISTRESS.
—The maintenance man has a variety of materials and corrective actions which may be used for the types of distress listed above. Some of these, which may be used singularly or in combinations, are:

(1) **Surface Treatments**

a. *Fog Seal.* Water diluted emulsion—usually applied at approximately 0.10 gallon per square yard of diluted material.

b. *Sand Seal.* Spray application of either emulsion or liquid asphalt with sand cover.

c. *Chip Seal.* Spray application of emulsion, paving grade or liquid asphalt, with clean aggregate cover.

d. *Slurry Seal.* A mixture of sand, emulsion, and water squeegeed in place.

e. *Multiple Surface Treatment.*

(2) **Patch Mixes**

a. *Hot Plant Mix.* Graded aggregate mixed in a central or portable plant usually with a light grade of paving asphalt for immediate use.

b. *Cold Plant Mix.* Local aggregate mixed in a central plant with a liquid asphalt for immediate use or stockpiling.

c. *Cold Pre-Mix.* Normally thought of as a local aggregate, road-mixed on a mixing table utilizing medium or slow-curing liquid asphalts and stockpiled for future use.

From the list it can be seen that there are many types of distress that vary considerably in relative seriousness. Regardless of the degree of distress, however, it is axiomatic that pavement maintenance should be timely for maximum effectiveness. The sooner the repair of a distressed area in a pavement is undertaken, the easier and more economical will be the required work and the more beneficial it will be for the entire surface. This is especially true if the pavement surface is broken or cracked because deterioration is accelerated greatly once this has occurred and it becomes possible for water to enter the pavement foundation.

While there are many types of distress, there is also a rather wide choice of treatments available with which to perform corrective work. Frequently a combination of two treatments can be utilized to provide the best results.

9.14 MAINTENANCE TREATMENTS.—The most common treatment for the general evidence of distress will normally be as follows:

9.15 WEATHERED SURFACE.—A weathered surface that is dry but has little or no ravelling will generally require only a fog seal treatment.

(1) Clean the surface.

(2) Apply a fog seal of approximately 0.10 gallon per square yard of water diluted emulsion.

(3) A slurry seal may be required if it is necessary to fill slightly pitted areas in the surface.

9.16 RAVELLED SURFACE.—A ravelled surface shows the loss of surface material by traffic abrasion. It may also result from the placement of a dry mix. One of the surface treatments will probably repair the surface.

(1) Clean the surface.

(2) Apply a seal coat. If the ravelling has not progressed too far, a fog seal may supply sufficient asphalt to hold surface particles in place to prevent further ravelling. If ravelling is pronounced or well advanced, it may be necessary to apply a sand seal, a chip seal, or a slurry seal.

9.17 LONG CRACKS.—Long cracks may be caused by contraction or settlement. If they are less than ⅛ inch wide, it may be wise to leave them alone unless water is able to enter the base and cause further damage. If the cracks are wider than ⅛ inch, they should be filled.

(1) Clean foreign and loose material from the crack with a jet of compressed air (if loose sand is in the crack, it may be possible to leave it there and treat it).

(2) If there are spalled areas along the crack, the loosened edge of material should be removed.

(3) Fill the cracks by one of these methods. In cleaned cracks, special crack-filling asphalt can be

poured; or, a slurry seal application can be made by holding the squeegee tight against the pavement so that the slurry runs into the crack; or fill the crack by brooming a lean sand-asphalt mixture into the crack until it is full. In the latter method, an RC-70 liquid asphalt should be poured on the filled cracks with sufficient quantity to seal the top of the sand mix and tie to the edge of the crack.

9.18 ALLIGATOR CRACKS.—Alligator cracks are usually caused by a base failure or the existence of a resilient subgrade. There are three commonly used maintenance procedures, only one of which can be considered as a permanent correction. The other two maintenance procedures should be considered for use as a matter of expediency where permanent repairs cannot be immediately made.

(1) **Deep Patch** (Permanent Repair).

a. Remove the surfacing and base material in the alligatored area to the depth at which the base failure has occurred. In some instances, this will mean that some of the subgrade under the base will also have to be removed. It will frequently be noted at this stage of the repair that water is contributing to the failure. If such is the case, provision should be made to get rid of the water.

b. In removing the base and surfacing, the excavation should be made at least one foot outside of the perimeter of the cracked area. This is in order that the patch will be tied into solid material all around the perimeter. If this is not done, alligator cracking will appear again, later on, around the perimeter of the patch, usually in an area about six inches to a foot wide all the way around.

c. In excavating material from the area to be patched, the cut faces should be straight and vertical. The hole should be shaped so that a square shoulder in the direction of traffic is provided against which the patch can be placed.

d. Backfill the excavated area with a good granular base material, compacted in layers, if necessary. If a graded base material is not readily available, the backfill should be made with the most suitable local material available. In some cases, where the area to be patched is not too deep, the entire backfill can be done with the mix material that will be used for the surfacing.

e. Prime the surface of the granular base that has been placed.

f. Replace the surfacing with an asphalt mixture. It is preferable that this be the hot-mix material, but if none is available, cold mix can be used satisfactorily.

g. Regardless of the material used, each layer should be thoroughly compacted.

(2) **Skin Patch** (Temporary Repair)

a. Broom clean the surface of the alligatored area.

b. Apply a tack coat.

c. Place a skin patch with a mixed asphaltic material—again it is preferable that this be hot mix, but if none is available, cold mix can be used. In making this type of patch, care should be taken to make the feathered edges carefully, removing the coarse aggregate particles before final compaction.

d. Compact the skin patch. This can adequately be done by wheel-rolling by the truck that carries the mix. If the area to be patched is large, compaction should be with a roller. (A pneumatic-tired roller is quite effective.)

(3) **Seal Coat with Cover Aggregate** (Temporary Repair)

a. Broom clean the surface to be patched.

b. Apply a spray application of asphalt in the amount necessary. Usually 0.15 to 0.25 gallons per square yard is adequate for the seal coat; however, if an excessive amount of the asphalt is lost in the alligatored cracks, slightly more asphalt should be applied.

c. Apply the cover aggregate.

d. Roll the seal coat with rubber-tired equipment.

e. A second seal application can be made if it is necessary to build up the patch area to the level of the adjacent pavement.

9.19 CHUCK HOLES.—Chuck holes are breaks in the surface with the hole extending into or through the base. There are two general methods of repair:

(1) Mix Method

a. Clean the chuck hole thoroughly by brooming.

b. Shape the hole, if necessary, in order to provide a square shoulder in the direction of traffic against which the patch can be placed. The sides of the hole should be nearly vertical.

c. Prime the chuck hole with emulsion or a light cutback, whichever is most readily available.

d. Fill the hole with a mixed material. If the hole is deep, the mix should be placed in layers and compacted. Upon completion, the compacted patch in the pot hole should be approximately $1/8$ inch to $1/4$ inch above the level of the adjacent pavement.

e. The compaction can be obtained by tamping or, where possible, by wheel-rolling the mix with the wheel of the truck from which the mix is taken.

(2) Penetration Method

a. Clean the hole thoroughly by brooming.

b. Shape the hole, if necessary, to provide a square shoulder in the direction of traffic against which the patch can be placed.

c. Prime the hole.

d. Build up a rock and asphalt patch in successive applications. In this method, the rocks should be placed in the hole first and keyed in place by compacting and then applying the asphalt. A word of caution in this regard is to use the minimum amount of asphalt so that subsequent bleeding does not occur.

e. After the patch has been built up to the level of the adjacent pavement, screenings should be rolled into the top with no further application of asphalt.

9.20 BLEEDING AND INSTABILITY.—Bleeding and instability usually occur in pavements with an excess of asphalt in the mix, or because of the use of too much asphaltic material in a seal coat operation. This type of distress presents a slick surface because of the excessive amount of asphalt on the pavement. It may also cause surface corrugations due to instability. The excess asphalt must be removed.

(1) **Cutting the Surface**

a. Remove the excess asphalt and corrugations by cutting with a cold-chisel type of planer (motor grader blade or special machine). This can be done only in cases where the surface is easily cut.

b. A disc type of planer and blade (mounted on motor grader) has been successfully used. With this type of machine, the bulk of the cutting is done with the discs while the blade immediately behind trims the resultant surface.

c. Remove the excess asphalt with a heater planer or repaver. These machines heat the pavement surface prior to cutting it with a blade. They are more commonly used on city streets than on the open highway. They are probably the most expensive method of cutting.

(2) After cutting, the surface can be left as planed. This, however, often leaves a pavement with a rough-surfaced texture which may not be desirable.

(3) Applying a new surface

a. A hot asphalt concrete resurfacing is preferable.

b. A chip seal can be applied.

c. A slurry seal can be applied.

9.21 DEPRESSIONS.—Depressions usually occur because of subgrade settlement. They may be long swales, or may have sheared sides because of sudden earth movements. In some cases there may be an abrupt difference in elevation of various parts of the pavement. Generally, the smooth riding quality of the surface must be regained.

(1) Mix Method

a. The surface of the depressed area should be broomed clean.

b. Apply a light tack coat.

c. Place mixed material in the depression (preferably hot mix). In depressed areas that are rather long, the best method is to dump the material from trucks and spread it with a motor grader. In depressions of smaller area, the hot-mix material can be placed by hand and then rolled.

d. In some instances, it is wise to place a sand seal over the mix in the depressed area and extend it to approximately one foot outside of the patch. This is to prevent the possibility of water getting under the patch, where it has no chance to escape, and causing subsequent trouble.

Figure IX-2—Undersealing Portland Cement Concrete with Hot Asphalt

9.22 EDGE BREAKING.—Edge breaking is usually caused by lack of lateral support by earth shoulders. It may also be caused by excessive moisture or drying along the pavement edge. Maintenance for this kind of distress should actually be the preventive type to preclude edge breaking. This type of distress is minimized by the use of paved shoulders. Where the shoulders are not paved, frequent attention will normally eliminate edge repairs. Maintenance depends upon the degree of damage and deterioration. A sand or chip seal may be sufficient in some instances. Crack filling and skin patching may be necessary, or total replacement may be called for. Whatever the repairs, the shoulder should be improved so as to provide lateral support to the pavement edge.

9.23 UNDERSEALING PORTLAND CEMENT CONCRETE PAVEMENTS WITH ASPHALT.—The undersealing of portland cement concrete pavements to prevent water from seeping through the joints and cracks of the pavement or accumulating under the slabs from the subgrade should be performed at the first signs of distress. Water accumulating under a portland cement concrete pavement, either from the surface or the subgrade, will reduce the bearing capacity of the subgrade beneath the slab, thus allowing excessive deflection and the resultant cracking and breaking up of the pavement. This is particularly prevalent at the edges and corners of slabs where repeated loadings tend to produce additional compaction of the subgrade, and leave cavities in which surface water can accumulate and soften the subgrade. Effective undersealing of the joints and edges before this condition becomes exaggerated is highly desirable as a preventive maintenance measure.

Detection of subgrade deficiencies or cavities in their early stages may be difficult at times, requiring the experienced eye of a trained maintenance engineer, plus a certain amount of field investigation. Immediately following a heavy rain, or as soon thereafter as the surface of the pavement has become dry, is an ideal time to observe any tendencies toward slab movement, indicated by water seeping or being pumped back up through the joints or out from underneath the pavement at the edges of the slab. As such a condition becomes progressively worse, discolored water and then mud will be pumped to the surface of the slab. Other symptoms include the hollow rumbling of a vehicle as it passes over a cavity or the settlement of a slab adjacent to the joints which, even in its early stages, may produce a rough riding pavement and ultimately the breaking up of the slab, starting with corner and edge cracks.

Undersealing of portland cement concrete pavement is normally done in conjunction with resurfacing the concrete with an asphalt concrete. Since all slabs and concrete surfaces should be stabilized as completely as possible, it is always advisable to resurface with asphalt soon after the undersealing has been done.

9.24 EQUIPMENT REQUIREMENTS.—For a minimum single crew organization, the following equipment is necessary:

(1) One insulated pressure distributor, not less than 500 gallons tank capacity, equipped with:
    a. Mercury actuated thermometer.
    b. Pump pressure gauge.
    c. Motor driven positive-pressure rotary pump.
    d. Full circulating delivery lines.
    e. One or more asphalt delivery valves. *Note: Some contractors may wish to operate two nozzles from one distributor.*

(2) One retort or booster heater of sufficient capacity to service the project. *Note: This equipment is not needed if asphalt is delivered on project at the desired temperature.*

(3) One insulated service tank truck equipped with heaters to service distributor on the job. *Note: This equipment is needed only on long hauls from the supply point to the project.*

(4) One compressed air drilling device of sufficient capacity to operate two air drills, equipped with extra air hose for blowing out holes.

(5) One or two asphalt applicators, such as the "Asphalt Nozzle" or a similar device equipped with a satisfactory shut-off or by-pass valve which will adequately control the flow of hot asphalt under the concrete pavement. Applicators should be equipped with metallic flexible hose for connecting asphalt applicator to distributor.

(6) Other equipment should include:

    a. Proper safety clothing for applicator operators.

    b. Wooden plugs for plugging holes.

    c. Flags and barricades for traffic control.

    d. Other miscellaneous small tools and service trucks.

The number and size of the various pieces of equipment required will depend upon the volume of work and the allowable days of operation, and the contractor should be required to so equip and organize his work as to comply with the terms of the contract.

9.25 SAFETY REQUIREMENTS.—All ordinary safety rules and regulations should be observed in the operation of pressure distributors and, in addition, extra precautions should be taken in the handling of the extraordinarily hot asphalt hose and nozzle. The workmen must have suitable masks and asbestos gloves. They should also wear sufficiently heavy clothing, closely fitting the ankles, wrists, and neck to protect themselves from hot asphalt. No greater pressure should be used in pumping the asphalt than is necessary to accomplish the desired results. The engineer should prescribe and enforce such safety requirements as are essential in connection with ground or air traffic.

9.26 SPACING OF HOLES.—In general, for minor cavities or where there is no settlement of the slab, holes should be drilled 12 to 18 inches from the transverse crack or joint. Where settlement has occurred, the holes should be drilled 24 to 36 inches back from the crack or joint. One hole 36 inches from the transverse crack in the center of the traffic lane may satisfactorily raise as well as seal a more serious condition. If necessary to obtain complete under-slab coverage, in addition to the joint holes described above, holes should be placed longitudinally from 12 to 25 feet, depending on the condition of the pavement, and alternated across the centerline approximately three feet from the centerline.

If drilling costs are low, it may be advisable to drill holes on a set pattern, one hole to approximately each ten square yards of pavement. When this pattern is used, probably not more than two-thirds of the holes need be pumped; the balance of the holes can serve for inspection holes and can be plugged when asphalt appears.

For airport runway slabs, the holes should be drilled on alternate sides of the joints and spaced approximately 12 feet on centers. Difficulty has not been encountered with slabs breaking while following this method of under-sealing. Other patterns may be developed due to the particular circumstances surrounding a project, but care should be exercised to avoid breaking the concrete slabs.

9.27 ASPHALT TEMPERATURE CONTROL.—Within the specified range, the engineer should adjust the temperature of the asphalt in accordance with the type of holes being filled and the grade of asphalt being used. In general, small or particularly wet cavities require a higher temperature than do the larger ones.

9.28 PRECAUTIONS WHEN PUMPING ASPHALT.—Care should be exercised to prevent raising the slabs higher than desired. To avoid clogging of drainage structures when working near manholes, drains or culverts, a close check should be made so asphalt will not be pumped out through or around these utilities.

9.29 TYPE AND QUANTITY OF ASPHALT.—The amount of asphalt required, using this method, will vary depending upon the condition of the pavement and the subgrade when the work begins.*

Where only minor cavities exist and the slab movement has not resulted in serious pumping, as little as one-half

---

* For type of asphalt, see Chapter IV.

gallon per square yard, or 15 to 20 gallons per joint, will underseal the pavement. From these minimum quantities, up to 40 to 50 gallons per joint, or possibly one and one-half gallons per square yard, may be required when a more serious condition exists. Exceptionally bad pumping joints or sunken slabs may require as much as 100 to 150 gallons per joint to completely raise and seal the pavement or slab.

9.30 JOINTS AND CRACKS.—Undersealing programs should not be confused with regular (top of slab) joint and crack sealing operations. If joints and cracks require sealing, this operation should be performed in advance of and separately from an undersealing program.

9.31 REFERENCES.—Additional information concerning stage construction, reconstruction, and maintenance of pavement structures is contained in the following Asphalt Institute technical publications:

(1) *Thickness Design—Asphalt Pavement Structures for Highways and Streets*, Manual Series No. 1 (MS-1)

(2) *Asphalt Paving Manual*, Manual Series No. 8 (MS-8)

(3) *Asphalt Pavements for Airports*, Manual Series No. 11 (MS-11)

(4) *Asphalt Surface Treatments and Asphalt Penetration Macadam*, Manual Series No. 13 (MS-13)

(5) *Asphalt Mixed-in-Place (Road-Mix) Manual,* Manual Series No. 14 (MS-14)

(6) *Undersealing Portland Cement Concrete Pavements with Asphalt,* Construction Series No. 92 (CS-92).

Chapter X

ROADWAY APPURTENANCES

10.01 GENERAL.—Important asphalt appurtenances in modern street and highway construction include:

- (A) Paved or treated shoulders
- (B) Dikes
- (C) Paved ditches and spillways
- (D) Paved slopes
- (E) Paved revetments
- (F) Curbs and gutters
- (G) Sidewalks

Asphalt is employed also in certain erosion controls, such as tie-down for mulch covers, and wind erosion control in desert areas. (See Chapter XV.)

A.—Paved or Treated Shoulders

10.02 SHOULDERS.—Research and experience have given evidence that an asphalt-paved shoulder not only is an excellent safety feature, but also provides high lateral support which enhances the strength of the pavement proper. This eliminates infiltration of water at the pavement edge.

Geometric design of shoulders depends upon volume and intensity of traffic. On heavy-duty highways, it is essential that shoulders be of ample width to accommodate the largest vehicles, and strong enough to support their loads without deformation or ravelling.

With asphalt concrete surfacing now so extensively used, experience has shown that it is best to carry the same surface material completely across the shoulder; then a solid white or yellow stripe should be painted along the edge of the pavement proper, to demarcate the shoulder. (See Figure X-2.) If contrast is desired, it may be obtained by a surface treatment on the shoulder portion using colored aggregate.

A secondary highway may require only well consolidated granular materials in its shoulders. Only at intervals it is required to have enough room to drive completely off the pavement. Whether such shoulders require an asphalt treatment or not depends largely upon the rate of erosion and the maintenance needed for restoration.

Figure X-1—Full-width Shoulder Paving

B.—Dikes

10.03 DIKES.—On modern dual-lane turnpikes and interstate highways, asphalt dikes (curbs) often are constructed at the outer edge of the paved shoulders, on elevated grades to prevent erosion of the slopes. Shoulder dikes are constructed with slip forms such as, or similar

Figure X-2—Full-length Shoulder Striping Is a Safety Feature Enthusiastically Accepted by the Motorist

to, those used in asphalt curbs, and a similar aggregate-asphalt mixture is used. Asphalt-paved spillways then carry the accumulated run-off down the embankment.

C.—*Paved Ditches and Spillways*

10.04 DITCHES AND SPILLWAYS.—Ditches, as differentiated from gutters, occur parallel to the rural highway at the foot of the outer embankment, or between dual lane pavements having a depressed median strip. They may be so wide and so gentle in slope that grass sod will be sufficient. In rolling terrain, however, there will be many locations where pavement is required to prevent costly erosion. In cut sections also, it often is desirable to construct ditches over the top of the slopes and around the ends to prevent slope erosion and even heavy slides. Spillways down the embankment have been noted previously. In all cases such ditches should be sufficiently wide and so shaped that the heaviest rainfall is carried away smoothly.

In some instances, very large outfall ditches may be necessary to carry run-off completely away from the right-of-way. The type of paving will depend upon gradient and type of soil. In areas of very erosive soils careful design is of great importance. In general, hot mixtures are best for the purpose, although penetration macadam has been used successfully. High asphalt content is necessary to insure durability and waterproofness. High stability is not a factor as much as durability and capacity to become adjusted to minor settlements without cracking.

D.—*Paved Slopes*

10.05 SLOPE PAVING.—Slope paving is of two general classes:

(1) Pavement is applied to the face of a cut slope, for some distance above the ditch, to prevent under-cutting and consequent slides. This paving is an extension of the outer side of the ditch itself, although it may be of different thickness. The essential item, in

addition to dense composition and high asphalt content, is firm anchorage to prevent intrusion of water.

(2) Embankment slopes are paved to prevent erosion. One type of embankment paving is that used under the ends of open-type bridges. Another form of embankment paving is levee slope paving. For embankment paving an open-type hot mix with a high asphalt content permits escape of embankment moisture.

E.—Paved Revetments

10.06 REVETMENTS.—Revetments are paved embankment slopes adjacent to moving water. In most instances such pavements are used to prevent scouring and undermining. With torrential streams, or adjacent to lakes or oceans, where wave action is a factor, substantial anchorage of the revetments may be required. Normally, dense-graded asphalt mixes with relatively high asphalt content are required.

Careful workmanship is required to insure continuity of the mat with sufficient anchorage top and bottom to prevent undercutting. Where wave action is a factor, the slope should be so laid as to avoid needless impact. Constant repetition of small waves causes most of the erosion.

Where there is continuous or long-time exposure to wave action, special tests should be made on the aggregates to determine if this action will strip the asphalt from them.

F.—Asphalt Curbs

10.07 GENERAL.—Asphalt curbs have become increasingly popular as accessories to new road and street paving in this period of accelerated construction activity.

These curbs have these distinct advantages over other types:

(1) They are more economical to construct.
(2) They are easier to construct.
(3) They can be built much faster.
(4) They are not affected by ice- and snow-melting chemicals.

Most new construction of asphalt-concrete curbs is being performed with automatic curbing machines. These machines lay, compact and finish straight or curved curbs for streets, traffic islands and parking areas.

No forms are necessary. Various interchangeable mold patterns provide a wide selection of curbing shapes.

10.08 OPERATION OF THE CURBING MACHINE.—Hot-mix asphalt concrete with the proper grade and quantity of asphalt cement is placed in the open hopper of the curbing machine. A motorized worm gear, or screw, pushes the mixture out through the mold form under pressure. This pressure provides curb compaction and causes the machine to move forward.

Only two or three men are needed to perform the operation. One man guides the machine along a chalk line, placed over the foundation, while the other two keep the hopper filled with asphalt hot mix.

Detailed information for building asphalt curbs is contained in *Specifications and Construction Methods for Asphalt Curbs and Gutters, Specification Series No. 3* (SS-3), The Asphalt Institute.

Figure X-3—Asphalt Curbs are Economical and Easy to Place with Curbing Machines

G.—Sidewalks

10.09 GENERAL.—The use of asphalt provides an inexpensive method of constructing durable sidewalks and walkway areas. There are several treatments that can be used, however, the most common for the surfacing of the sidewalk area is asphalt concrete. It can be readily placed on a foundation requiring the minimum amount of preparation. While not absolutely necessary, the appearance of the completed sidewalk will be considerably improved by the use of wooden side forms, when hand placing methods are used, to delineate edges neatly. If desired, the sidewalk surface can be made green or red by application of special pigmented asphalt mastics.

10.10 WIDTHS.—The minimum width should generally be three feet which permits two persons to walk abreast. The width of four or five feet is desirable and should be provided on locations having much foot traffic. Uniformity in width is desirable but not necessary, narrowing being permissible where construction otherwise would be costly.

10.11 DRAINAGE.—Walks should be sloped ¼ to ⅜ inch per foot across the pavement and about twice this much or more on the adjacent sod area to assure proper run-off.

10.12 SIDEWALK SURFACING.—Sidewalks may be surfaced with the following: asphalt concrete, asphalt macadam, asphalt cold mix, asphalt mixed-in-place, and asphalt surface treatments.

Selection of the surface type in respect to service life and cost are approximately the same as for highways. Asphalt concrete is frequently the first choice because of long life, smoothness and the ease of construction with the small pavers now available.

10.13 THICKNESS.—Thickness of asphalt sidewalks are shown in Figure X-4. Local condition of soil, moisture, frost, and available materials may modify these thicknesses.

ASPHALT CONCRETE

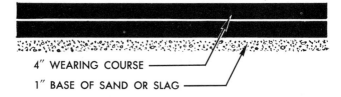

4″ WEARING COURSE ————————

1″ BASE OF SAND OR SLAG ————

COLD LAID MIX

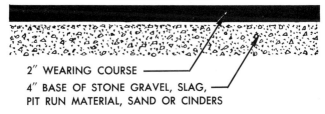

2″ WEARING COURSE ————————

4″ BASE OF STONE GRAVEL, SLAG, ——
PIT RUN MATERIAL, SAND OR CINDERS

ASPHALT BLOCK

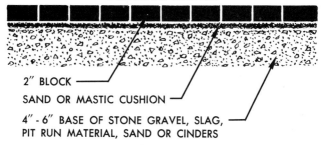

2″ BLOCK ————————

SAND OR MASTIC CUSHION ——

4″ - 6″ BASE OF STONE GRAVEL, SLAG, ——
PIT RUN MATERIAL, SAND OR CINDERS

Figure X-4—Thickness Design for Sidewalk Construction

10.14 BASE COURSE MATERIALS.—Crushed stone, slag, gravel, pit-run material, sand or cinders are usually suitable for sidewalk bases. At driveways and road crossings the base courses shown in Figure X-4 should be increased so as to be adequate for the traffic anticipated.

10.15 COMPOSITION OF MIXES FOR SIDE-WALKS.—Asphalt concrete mixtures for sidewalks are usually of the dense or fine-graded types. Asphalt Institute Specification Series No. 1, *Specifications and Construction Methods for Asphalt Concrete and Other Plant-Mix Types*, covers complete specifications for materials used in asphalt concrete and other mix compositions which might be used. Asphalt Institute Manual Series No. 2, *Mix Design Methods for Asphalt Concrete and Other Hot-Mix Types*, covers the design of asphalt mixes. Sidewalk paving for the lighter type of traffic should contain from one to two percent more asphalt in the mixture than is usually used in roadway pavements.

10.16 COMPACTION OF SIDEWALK MATE-RIALS.—For sidewalk construction with asphalt mixtures it is essential that the mix be thoroughly compacted. Normally, conventional highway compaction equipment is recommended.

10.17 MAINTENANCE OF SIDEWALKS.—A fog seal every five or ten years is usually the only maintenance needed on asphalt concrete sidewalks.

10.18 REFERENCES.—Other Asphalt Institute technical publications containing information on the roadway appurtenances discussed in this chapter are:

(1) *Specifications and Construction Methods for Asphalt Curbs and Gutters*, Specification Series No. 3 (SS-3)

(2) *Thickness Design—Asphalt Pavement Structures for Highways and Streets*, Manual Series No. 1 (MS-1)

(3) *Asphalt Paving Manual*, Manual Series No. 8 (MS-8)

(4) *Asphalt in Hydraulic Structures*, Manual Series No. 12 (MS-12).

Chapter XI

ASPHALT SURFACES ON BRIDGES

11.01 GENERAL.—Asphalt surfaces are desirable for bridges for the following reasons:

(1) Because of exposure from above and below, bridge floors freeze quicker and therefore accumulate more ice than earthborne surfaces. This requires more salts for ice removal. An asphalt surface is unaffected by salts used in ice removal.

(2) An asphalt surface carefully and properly constructed may waterproof the bridge floor, preventing water and salts from entering and damaging the structural members of the bridge.

(3) An asphalt surface can be constructed so as to be highly skid resistant providing the safest bridge floor.

There are over 78,000 bridges in the United States, not including a substantial mileage of viaducts. Sooner or later each one will require maintenance if not complete reconstruction. It is, therefore, best procedure to construct new bridge floors so that an asphalt surface may be placed and renewed as required. For new bridges this is being increasingly done, but for existing bridges it is often necessary to change the existing floor to meet present day traffic needs.

The development of sags resulting in rough riding of concrete bridge floors supported on concrete girders is quite frequent in all but prestressed types. For rectifying the riding qualities, an asphalt surface is the only practical method.

A.—Surfacing New Bridges

11.02 TYPES OF FLOOR SYSTEMS.—New bridges surfaced with asphalt usually have one of two types of floors: portland cement concrete or steel.

11.03 PORTLAND CEMENT CONCRETE FLOOR SLABS.

—On this type the expansion dams, curbs, drainage gratings, and other appurtances are designed and set at the proper height so that dense-graded asphalt concrete binder and surface courses from two to three inches total thickness can be used. The construction steps after the portland cement concrete slab is placed are as follows:

(1) Clean the slab surface of all foreign matter, laitance, and loose or scaled concrete with power wire brooms and compressed air, down to clean, firm concrete.

(2) Cover the entire surface with a tack coat of 0.05 to 0.20 gallon per square yard of SS-1h or SS-Kh emulsion diluted half and half with water. Vertical surfaces also should be painted to above the thickness of the subsequent asphalt courses. Scrub in the tack coat.

(3) Lay from ¾ inch to a maximum of 1½ inches of asphalt concrete leveling course (Asphalt Institute mix Type IVa) and compact to proper density.

(4) Cover the entire leveling course with a tack coat of 0.05 to 0.10 gallon per square yard of SS-1h or SS-Kh emulsion diluted half and half with water.

(5) Lay the intermediate course (Asphalt Institute mix Type IVa) to a thickness within ½ inch to ¾ inch of the finished pavement grade.

(6) Lay the final or wearing course to a depth of ½ inch to ¾ inch. Sheet asphalt (Asphalt Institute mix Types VII or VIII) should be placed where chemicals are expected to be used to de-ice the pavement. Where de-icing chemicals will not be used, Type IVa mix can be used for the wearing course. In areas where chemicals are used for ice control, aggregates that will not react with the de-icing chemicals should be selected.

(7) Roll all courses with pneumatic-tired equipment capable of producing at least 80 pounds per square inch contact pressure. Inaccessible areas should be compacted with small vibratory compactors or hand tampers.

(8) Cover the wearing course, for a distance of from 12 inches to 18 inches out from the curbing, with hot asphalt cement (85-100 penetration grade) by mopping or spraying. (This should be a yearly operation since traffic will rarely use this small portion of the floor.)

Figure XI-1—Asphalt-Paved Deck on New Woodrow Wilson Bridge, Capital Beltway, Washington, D.C.

11.04 STEEL FLOOR SYSTEMS.—New asphalt surfaced bridges with steel floor systems are now mostly made with corrugated or channel shapes with depressions of one inch to two inches. The construction steps after the steel floor is welded in place are usually as follows:

(1) Clean the steel flooring of all foreign matter.

(2) Paint the steel thoroughly with heavy asphalt paint.

(3) Place a dense graded asphalt concrete leveling course (Asphalt Institute mix Type IVa) to a com-

pacted depth of ½ inch above the top of the corrugations.

(4) Roll transversely (parallel to the corrugations). This has been found to be more effective in compacting the mix well into the corrugations or shapes.

(5) Cover the entire leveling course with a tack coat of 0.05 to 0.10 gallon per square yard of SS-1h or SS-Kh emulsion diluted half and half with water.

(6) Lay ½ inch to ¾ inch of asphalt concrete (Asphalt Institute mix Type IVa). Where chemicals are expected to be used to de-ice the pavement, sheet asphalt (Asphalt Institute mix Types VII or VIII) should be placed as the wearing course, and aggregates that will not react with the de-icing chemicals should be selected.

(7) Roll the surface course with pneumatic-tired and tandem rollers, with as much transverse and diagonal rolling as possible. The contact pressures of the pneumatic-tired rollers should be not less than 80 psi.

(8) Mop or spray the surface of the asphalt concrete a distance of 12 inches to 18 inches out from the curbing with hot asphalt cement, (85-100 penetration grade). Since this part of the pavement surface does not get much traffic this should be a yearly operation.

B.—Resurfacing Old Bridges

11.05 TYPES OF FLOOR SYSTEMS.—Old bridges are of the following types as to floor systems: portland cement concrete slabs which generally serve both as structural members and roadway surfaces; steel and wood.

11.06 PORTLAND CEMENT CONCRETE FLOOR SLABS.—Bridges with portland cement concrete slabs often have scaled down to the reinforcement. They are frequently cracked so that water and salt are penetrating deep into the slab and damaging the main reinforcing bars. The best procedure for resurfacing such bridges is as follows:

(1) Thoroughly clean all loose, scaled and foreign matter down to clean, sound concrete, using air hammers (if necessary), power wire brooms, and compressed air. Flush with high pressure fresh water to remove all salt deposits.

(2) Cut all cracks to a clean rectangular trench, usually not less than ½ inch wide by 1½ inches deep.

(3) Fill these trenches to ½ inch below their tops with a high softening point asphalt mastic or joint filling compound which will adhere to the sides and stretch without cracking throughout any possible movement or temperature changes.

(4) Paint the surface of the concrete for three to four inches on both sides of the trench with asphalt emulsion, Type SS-1h, SS-Kh, or liquid asphalt RC-3000, and cover with 30-pound asphalt impregnated felt four inches wider than the trench.

(5) Provide mechanical water-stops, drainage, and expansion dams at all moving expansion joints.

(6) Cover the entire surface with a tack coat of 0.05 to 0.20 gallon per square yard of SS-1h or SS-Kh emulsion diluted half and half with water. Vertical surfaces should also be painted to above the thickness of the subsequent asphalt courses. Scrub in the tack coat.

(7) Lay from ¾ inch to a maximum of 1½ inches of asphalt concrete leveling course (Asphalt Institute mix Type IVa) and compact to proper density.*

(8) Cover the entire leveling course with a tack coat of 0.05 to 0.10 gallon per square yard of SS-1h or SS-Kh emulsion diluted half and half with water.

(9) Lay the intermediate course (Asphalt Institute mix Type IVa) to a thickness within ½ inch to ¾ inch of the finished pavement grade.

(10) Lay the final or wearing course to a depth of ½ inch to ¾ inch. Sheet asphalt (Asphalt Institute

---

* The dead load strength of the bridge, the height of the expansion dams, drainage gratings, and other appurtenances will control the final thickness of the asphalt concrete surfacing.

mix Types VII or VIII) should be placed where chemicals are expected to be used to de-ice the pavement. Where de-icing chemicals will not be used, Type IVa mixes can be used for the wearing course. In areas where chemicals are used for ice control, aggregates that will not react with the de-icing chemicals should be selected.

(11) Roll all courses with pneumatic-tired equipment capable of producing at least 80 pounds per square inch contact pressure. Areas that are not accessible to this equipment should be compacted with small vibratory compactors or hand tamped.

(12) Cover the wearing course, for a distance of from 12 inches to 18 inches out from the curbing, with hot asphalt cement (85-100 penetration grade) by mopping or spraying. (This should be a yearly operation since traffic will rarely use this small portion of the floor.)

Figure XI-2—Resurfacing Scaled Portland Cement Concrete Bridge Decks with Asphalt Concrete

11.07 STEEL FLOOR SYSTEMS.—Old bridges with steel floors vary from flat, thin steel plates rigidly fastened over the stringers to several types of open grids.

11.08 FLAT PLATE STEEL DECKS.—Steel bridges often have been constructed with a flat thin steel plate rigidly fastened over the stringers. This is called battleship deck. It is very difficult to hold surfacing of any type pavement over this deck without firm anchorage because temperature stresses are such that sooner or later separation and breaking will occur. Anchorage is best provided by welding a steel grid to the steel plates in such manner as will permit expansion and contraction without separation. This grid then should be filled with a sheet asphalt mixture (Asphalt Institute mix Types VII or VIII) to a depth of approximately ½ inch above the top of the cross members, after which the surface should be thoroughly rolled with pneumatic-tired rollers. The usual depth of the grid is about 1½ inches.

11.09 OPEN GRID-TYPE STEEL FLOORS.—Another type of steel deck used is the open-grid type, bolted or welded directly to the supporting stringers. Such decks are light in weight but are a hazard because of frost in northern climates and a disconcerting tire-grip, in the transition from flat adjacent pavements. Corrective reconstruction calls for (1) a welded cover plate of steel, 14 gauge, usually 1 foot x 3 foot size, with holes to take care of condensation, and coated with bituminous paint, (2) a combination of ⅜-inch steel spacer bars two foot centers and 3 x 6-inch 10/10 steel fabric welded thereto. Hot-mix asphalt concrete (Asphalt Institute mix Type IVa) is then placed in two courses. Where de-icing chemicals are used, sheet asphalt (Asphalt Institute mix Types VII or VIII) should be used for the wearing course.

11.10 WOOD DECKS.—There are still in use a great many old steel bridges having wooden plank or wood block decks, and they are both difficult and costly to maintain. They are often loose which not only makes for a very noisy condition but also sets up vibration in the whole bridge structure with resultant accelerating deterioration. Most of these old bridges originally had wooden stringers, to which were nailed 3-inch wooden planks in transverse fashion. As these stringers rotted, new ones were often added without removal of the old, so that a bad matter became worse, and occasionally a truck would break through the floor between the cross beams. However, in spite of changing traffic conditions and the fact that the wooden deck was originally designed for a uniform loading, the total load on cross beams and trusses was but little less than occasioned by modern traffic from concentrated loads. By reconstructing the stringers so as to distribute this concentrated loading to the deck beams, many such old bridges can be made safe and useful for a long time to come, particularly on county and township roads.

11.11 METHODS OF RECONSTRUCTING WOOD DECKS.—The development of portable electric welding outfits makes it possible to install steel stringers easily in place of the wooden ones and, where necessary, to build up old steel floor beams to a full section where corrosion has occurred, so that a proper bearing may be obtained. Also all truss members can be restored whenever necessary by cutting out and welding on new plates. All connections should be tightened, particularly with eye-bar construction and turnbuckle bracing, until the whole structure is in good condition. One of two methods may then be followed, depending on funds available:

(1) The preferred method is: after proper reconstruction of floor members a special type corrugated steel plate, placed transversely, is fastened to the stringers by welding. See Article 11.04 for construction steps after the steel floor is welded into place. Careful design of this character will produce a new floor at a weight of less than 50 pounds per square foot.

(2) Where funds are limited and lumber is readily available, a good floor can be built for light traffic as follows: To the outside steel stringers (which should be channels with the flanges turned out) should be

bolted wooden timbers, chamfered at the edges to fit against the web, but projecting outside the flanges for a couple of inches. Two to three inch planks then should be placed transversely and spiked to these timbers, followed by another layer of plank placed longitudinally and spiked to the first layer. A timber hub guard with proper drainage vents should then be placed at each edge.

Wherever possible treated timber only should be used, as the extra life is well worth the cost. Untreated timber may be preserved to a certain extent through coating with liquid asphalt at the bridge site by dipping in a trough. A surface treatment is then applied. A thick surface should be avoided as movement of the floor will break it loose. Rather a thin, pliable, but strongly adhering coating is desirable, covered with fine aggregate, preferably sand. The first application should be a cutback asphalt or emulsion, often as much as 0.5 gallon per square yard, to penetrate the top layer of plank and penetrate under it and over the lower layer. After curing under traffic, a second application of cut-back asphalt or emulsion (approximately 0.15 gallon per square yard) should be applied and covered with sharp coarse sand. The final mat should not exceed $\frac{1}{4}$ inch in thickness.

(3) In place of two layers of planks, 2 inch x 4 inch or 2 inch x 6 inch, planks are sometimes placed with larger dimension vertical. They are preshaped so that after placement, a proper camber is provided. Each succeeding piece is nailed to the previously laid timber, with staggered joints, until the entire floor is covered. Unplaned timber is usually employed, so that the finished surface is slightly uneven, and serves as good anchorage for the surface treatment. Somewhat thicker asphalt-sand or asphalt concrete mats are feasible with this type of timber base.

Wooden decks constructed by either of the described methods are sometimes called laminated decks, the first being a horizontal lamination, the second a vertical lamination. The first type can be used for some time without treatment, but the second must be seal-coated at once after building; otherwise water will be retained in the vertical joints and cause swelling. While these decks are a little thicker than the old single plank, they are much stronger, silent and will give a service life of approximately ten years with occasional treatment.

11.12 ASPHALT PLANK SURFACE.—Asphalt planks are used for surfacing wooden bridge decks. The planks are preformed mixtures of asphalt cement, asbestos fibre and mineral filler. They are usually made in three- and six-foot lengths and six- and eight-inch widths. The best asphalt planks contain mineral grits, so that a sand-paper texture is maintained throughout their life. They are placed longitudinally and may be nailed to a wooden deck or cemented with hot asphalt cement to a concrete or steel deck. It is important that very strict specifications be employed for asphalt planks to be used under heavy-duty conditions. One present-day use is on floors of the draw spans of lift bridges. Usually these floors are steel plates having ribs, both longitudinal and transverse, between which the asphalt plank (1¼ inches thick) is placed, thoroughly cemented to the plates with an asphalt mastic.

11.13 SUB-STRUCTURE TREATMENT.—In localities where bridge structures are subjected to the use of chemicals for ice control, absorption due to condensation, or surface drain spillage, the underdeck or sub-structure of exposed sections should be treated as follows:

(1) *Concrete Sub-structure:* Exposed areas should be treated with three applications of dilute SS-1, or SS-1h, SS-K or SS-Kh, emulsion. The emulsion can be applied by spraying.

(2) *Steel Sub-structure:* Exposed areas should be painted or sprayed with a coat of MC-250 cutback asphalt or asphalt base aluminum paint. The paint may be used in place of MC-250 cutback for appearance, if desired.

11.14 REFERENCES.—The following Asphalt Institute publications contain information on the asphalts, mixes, and surface treatments referred to in this chapter:

(1) *Specifications and Construction Methods for Asphalt Concrete and Other Plant-Mix Types*, Specification Series No. 1 (SS-1)

(2) *Specifications for Asphalt Cements and Liquid Asphalts*, Specification Series No. 2 (SS-2)

(3) *Asphalt Surface Treatments and Asphalt Penetration Macadam,* Manual Series No. 13 (MS-13).

Chapter XII

RAILROAD USAGE (INCLUDING CROSSING)

A.—Asphalt in Track Construction

12.01 GENERAL.—Asphalt mixtures have been extensively used at grade crossings, surfacing between and adjacent to tracks in city streets, and for resurfacing over tracks no longer in use or where rails have been removed. In recent years, experimental work has indicated that asphalt treatment of railroad roadbeds will substantially reduce maintenance-of-way costs. There are also indications that asphalt treatment of timber bridges will prolong the life of such structures and result in reduced maintenance costs.

12.02 GRADE CROSSINGS.—Rail movements and vibrations from trains impose severe conditions on pavements at grade crossings. The more resilient types of asphalt pavements are therefore to be preferred for such areas. Where traffic volumes are relatively low, the ballast stone may be brought to within about one inch of the top of rails and a double surface treatment applied. For heavier traffic volumes, asphalt macadam should be placed beneath, between and over the ties to within about one inch of the surface. A fine-graded asphalt mix with a slight excess of asphalt may then be used for the surface course.

12.03 TRACKS IN CITY STREETS.—Street car and railroad track structures are subjected to heavier loadings than the adjacent street. The supporting courses beneath such tracks should therefore be adequate to support these heavier loads without undue deflections. Where portland cement concrete is used for the adjacent street areas, a joint should be constructed beyond the ends of the ties. Ties should be laid on five to eight inches of asphalt macadam, placed over a properly prepared subbase. Asphalt macadam should then be tamped between and over the ties to within about one inch of the finished surface. The entire area should then be surfaced with a fine-graded asphalt mix.

12.04 RESURFACING ABANDONED TRACKS.— Where street car or railroad tracks in city streets have been abandoned, the first decision is as to whether the tracks should be removed or covered over. Factors to be considered in making this decision are as follows:

(1) Condition of the cross ties. If the ties are not very old and are treated timber, heart cypress, or locust, it is probable that they will last a long time and that it would be safe to leave them in. However, if they are old untreated or nondurable wood, they should be removed and the track area paved with a properly designed asphalt pavement structure.

(2) The second factor to be considered is as to whether the rails should be removed. Two factors are here involved—

a. Grade of the rails

b. Salvage value of the rail steel as compared to removing the rails and patching pavement torn out in pulling the rails.

If the tracks are allowed to remain, the asphalt surface over the tracks should be not less than 1½ inches thick. Before any surfacing is applied, however, the rails and flanges should be cleaned thoroughly and a light coat of liquid asphalt brushed on them. The troughs formed by the rails and the flanges should then be filled with a fine-graded asphalt mix and compacted. After this preliminary work, the street resurfacing can proceed in the normal fashion.

B.—Asphalt Treatment of Railroad Roadbeds

12.05 GENERAL.—The use of asphalt for the treatment of railroad roadbeds has been under study for several years. Experimental work begun in 1943 and continued for the next ten years indicated that substantial benefits are derived from this type of treatment. Special equipment has therefore been developed for the application of asphalt and cover stone to railroad roadbed ballast. The use of this treatment with modern equipment will undoubtedly increase in the future.

12.06 SPECIAL EQUIPMENT.—The experimental equipment consists of two units. Asphalt distributor equipment is mounted on a railroad flat car. Hot asphalt cement is supplied from insulated tank cars, ahead of and to the rear of the distributor car, by means of flexible, insulated hose connections. A spray bar is mounted beneath the distributor car and swinging spray bars are mounted on each side of the car in such a manner that they can be retracted while the car is in transit. The distributor car is also equipped with a suitable pump, steam generator for maintaining heated supply lines, tachometer for governing rate of asphalt equipment and other necessary appurtenances.

The aggregate-spreading car is a conventional, bottom-dump gondola car of 50-ton capacity, on which has been mounted beneath the bottom openings specially designed equipment for spreading the aggregate at a uniform and controlled rate.

12.07 CONSTRUCTION PROCEDURES.—Because of the limited experience in this type of work to date, precise construction procedures have not yet been definitely established. The rate of asphalt application should be varied in accordance with the requirements of the ballast to which it is being applied. Generally speaking, the rate varies from about two gallons per square yard for very open and porous ballast to about one gallon per square yard for the more densely-graded ballast. The penetration grade of asphalt was varied on early projects within the range of about 85-200 to determine the most suitable grade for such treatments. Later, it is likely that liquid asphalts will also be tried. The distributor equipment has been designed to handle adequately any of these types and grades of asphalt.

The maximum size of chip or slag cover should be selected after an inspection of the ballast to be treated but, in no case should the maximum size of the cover aggregate exceed ¾ inch. The average rate of cover application should be about 25 pounds per square yard for stone and 20 pounds per square yard for slag.

12.08 ECONOMIC BENEFITS.—Based on findings in the early experimental work, and subsequent studies, it is possible to make an approximate analysis of the economic benefits which may reasonably be expected in the maintenance of railroad roadways with the use of asphalt treatment. This analysis indicates that it will be reasonable to expect that such treatment may result in savings of up to 50 percent.

C.—*Asphalt Treatment of Timber Railroad Bridges*

12.09 GENERAL.—As indicated in the preceding discussion, asphalt treatment of cross ties served to extend materially their service life. Similarly, asphalt treatment can be expected to prolong materially the service life of bridge timbers, replacing expensive procedures now in use.

Equipment described in the preceding paragraphs may also be used for economically treating bridge timbers. Further experimental work will be required to establish proper methods for such treatments and to establish the proper type, grade, and quantity of asphalt.

Chapter XIII

PAVED PARKING AREAS AND DRIVEWAYS

13.01 INTRODUCTION.—In practically every center of human activity there exists an imperative need for economical, efficient parking facilities. The need for vehicle parking space has grown with each increase in the vehicle population.

In some large cities where space is at a premium, vertically-constructed parking structures are replacing the open-air lots. (See Section B of this Chapter for roof deck parking.) In the sprawling suburban developments, vast areas of asphalt pavements are providing space for shoppers and business people, and for commuters who transfer to public transportation into the city.

A.—Asphalt-Paved Parking Areas

13.02 ASPHALT SURFACE TYPES FOR PARKING AREA PAVING.—There are four types of asphalt surfacing widely used for passenger car parking areas.

(1) *Asphalt Concrete.* Asphalt concrete can be laid easily and quickly at the parking site. This is particularly advantageous in congested urban areas, where a minimum of construction time is of special benefit. Asphalt concrete is a mixture of asphalt cement and graded aggregate (crushed stone, gravel, slag, sand, mineral dust, etc.). The mixture is made at controlled hot temperatures in a hot-mix asphalt plant and hauled by truck to the construction site where it is spread over a firm foundation and compacted while still hot.

(2) *Asphalt Macadam Penetration.* Asphalt macadam penetration consists of using a coarse, open-graded aggregate produced by crushing and screening stone, slag, or gravel. This is spread in the required

thickness and compacted. Asphalt is applied by spraying in controlled quantities. This is then covered with a smaller sized aggregate and again rolled.

(3) *Cold-laid Asphalt.* Cold-laid asphalt may be similar to asphalt concrete except that in place of using a hot mixture of asphalt cement and aggregate, various combinations of liquid asphalt and cold aggregate are used, rendering the mixture pliable, permitting shipment long distances and allowing placement and compaction after long periods of time.

(4) *Asphalt Surface Treatment.* Asphalt surface treatments serve well in light-duty parking areas but should be used only as a temporary expedient under heavy-duty conditions. It consists of application of an asphaltic material to a prepared base with a cover of mineral aggregate, producing a thickness of not more than one inch.

Asphalt concrete is recommended for parking of heavy trucks and trailers, with penetration macadam as the second choice. For lighter duty service cold-laid asphalt or surface treatment may be used if the foundation is satisfactory and the funds available are limited.

In some localities asphalt blocks are available which are suitable for heavy-duty service when placed on a firm foundation—they are especially adaptable to paving steep ramps and roof parking areas.

Tables XIII-1 and XIII-2 show thickness for the various courses of pavements for parking areas.

13.03 EARTH WORK.—For new construction the area to be paved should be graded to the required cross-section and brought to a firm, unyielding surface by rolling with an approved power roller. Areas inaccessible to a power roller should be thoroughly compacted by other acceptable methods.

13.04 DRAINAGE.—In the construction of all asphalt paved parking areas the design and consruction should incorporate provision for both surface drainage and subsurface drainage as necessary. There should be a minimum slope of two percent.

Figure XIII-1—An Asphalt-Paved Parking Lot

13.05 INSULATION COURSE.—When non-asphalt base or subbase is used on plastic clay soils an insulation course should be provided as shown in Tables XIII-1 and XIII-2 and should consist of free-draining material placed on the prepared subgrade and compacted by a power roller weighing not less than five tons. Places inaccessible to power rolling should be thoroughly consolidated by vibratory compaction or by hand tamping.

B.—Roof Deck Parking Areas

13.06 INTRODUCTION.—The urgent need for space for parking facilities in congested areas has stimulated the development of roof deck parking.

There is not universal agreement as to the best method of waterproofing and paving roofs for use as parking areas. However, there is agreement that:

Table XIII-1—PAVEMENT THICKNESS FOR PARKING AREAS FOR PASSENGER CARS

THICKNESS REQUIREMENTS IN INCHES

	FULL DEPTH ASPHALT CONCRETE		ASPHALT CONCRETE SURFACE		PLANT-MIX SURFACE USING LIQUID ASPHALT		ASPHALT SURFACE TREATMENT	
	Asphalt Concrete Surface	Asphalt Concrete Base [1]	Asphalt Concrete Surface	Crushed Rock Base [2]	Asphalt Plant-Mix Surface	Crushed Rock Base [2]	Asphalt Surface Treatment	Crushed Rock Base [2]
Gravelly or sandy soils, well drained	1	2–3	3	2	4.5*	2	1**	6–8
Average clay loam soils, not plastic	1	3–4	3	2–4	4.5*	2–4	1**	8–10
Soft clay soils, plastic when wet	1	4–5	3	4–6***	4.5*	4–6***	1**	10–12***

[1] Prime required on subgrade.
[2] Prime required on base.
* Must be spread and compacted in layers not exceeding 1½ inches in depth and the volatiles (petroleum solvents or water) allowed to evaporate before the next layer is placed. Also, a seal coat may be required as a final surfacing.
** Economical but relatively limited service life. Usually less than 1 inch thick.
*** Two inches of coarse sand or stone screenings recommended between subgrade and base as an insulation course.

Table XIII-2—PAVEMENT THICKNESS FOR PARKING AREAS FOR HEAVY TRUCKS

	THICKNESS REQUIREMENTS IN INCHES							
	FULL DEPTH ASPHALT CONCRETE		ASPHALT CONCRETE SURFACE		SURFACE TREATMENT ON PENTRATION MACADAM		PLANT-MIX SURFACE USING LIQUID ASPHALT	
	Asphalt Concrete Surface	Asphalt Concrete Base [1]	Asphalt Concrete Surface	Crushed Rock Base [2]	Asphalt Surface Treatment	Asphalt Penetration Macadam Base [1]	Asphalt Plant-Mix Surface	Crushed Rock Base [2]
Gravelly or sandy soils, well drained	1.5	3–5	4.5	0–4	1*	7–10	7**	2–4
Average clay loam soils, not plastic	1.5	5–6	4.5	4–6	1*	10–11.5	7**	4–6
Soft clay soils, plastic when wet	1.5	6–8	4.5	6–10***	1*	11.5–14.5	7**	6–10***

[1] Prime required on subgrade.
[2] Prime required on base.
* Usually less than 1 inch thick.
** Must be spread and compacted in layers not exceeding 1½ inches in depth and the volatiles (petroleum solvents or water) allowed to evaporate before the next layer is placed. Also, seal coat may be required as a final surfacing.
*** Two inches of coarse sand or stone screenings recommended between subgrade and base as an insulation course.

(1) Careful attention should be given to grade control to insure good run-off and prevent puddling or collection of water;

(2) Specially designed roof drains should be spaced so that water has only a short distance to travel;

(3) Flashing details are important to prevent leakage where the roof deck meets the parapet wall;

(4) Construction and expansion joints and cracks in the roof deck should be sealed, chiseling them out if necessary, and filling with an elastic and highly adhesive joint filler usually composed of asphalt and rubber; and

(5) The deck surface should be mopped with asphalt and covered with some sort of membrane or building paper.

There are two types of roof deck paving discussed in this section—slab and pavement with a built-in movement plane and slab and pavement bonded together. For additional information refer to "Paving Roof Decks and Industrial Floors," by Lansing Tuttle, Information Series No. 130 (IS-130), The Asphalt Institute.

13.07 FREE-MOVEMENT-PLANE CONSTRUCTION.—This type of construction provides a distinct free movement plane between the structural roof slab and the subsequent pavement. The construction steps are:

(1) A positive bond breaker, such as lime, fine sand, or portland cement, is provided between the concrete deck to be covered and the built-up roofing to allow for freedom of movement between the concrete deck and the pavement.

(2) A conventional built-up roof utilizing four or five plies of lightweight roofing felts is placed without final flood coat and aggregate cover.

(3) A very light tack coat, using a hard grade of asphalt (diluted SS-1h or SS-Kh), is applied to the top felt layer.

(4) A minimum of two inches of hot asphalt concrete is placed in two courses as the wearing surface, using very dense-graded asphalt concrete with a maximum size aggregate of approximately ⅜ inch.

13.08 BONDING ROOF DECK AND PAVEMENT.

—To bond the pavement to the roof deck after sealing the cracks and joints, a conventional four to five ply built-up roof is applied using asphalt roofing felt, glass fiber membranes, or cotton fabric, each layer, except the surface of the top layer, thoroughly mopped with asphalt. This is then covered with one to three inches of a dense asphalt concrete as above.

Another method is to use an asphalt membrane which contains mineral filler and asbestos or other fibers for body and strength. The asphalt cement is a low penetration grade in the 40-50 range. Great pains are taken to insure a uniform thickness, and no further operation is allowed on the membrane until it has fully cured in place.

The cured membrane is overlaid with two lifts of asphalt concrete which is a fine impervious mix with high asphalt content and maximum aggregate size of $3/8$ or $1/4$ inch. The total thickness of mix would not exceed three inches. The effort is to get an impervious mixture which will weather well with the lack of kneading traffic and have a stability of plus 500 pounds Marshall.

Small rollers or sidewalk rollers usually are used because of the restricted working area and the maximum allowable live loads for the building. This probably means a roller not exceeding three to four tons. Small hand operated electric or gasoline vibratory compactors are used to work around areas inaccessible to rollers.

CAUTION

Asphalt concrete paving mixtures should be placed over asphalt membranes only. Differences in temperature susceptibility when asphalt concrete is placed over a membrane of a different material may result in melting of the membrane, gas blisters, and flushing of the membrane to the surface. Also, lack of consolidation and slipping of the surfacing can occur.

13.09 ASPHALT PANELS.—Some of the reinforced molded asphalt panels, similar to those used for reservoir linings or possibly thinner, occasionally are used as the waterproofing member.

13.10 POROUS LAYER BENEATH ASPHALT SURFACE.—A porous layer is used sometimes on top of the built-up layers of asphalt and membranes before the asphalt concrete wearing surface is placed. This might consist of a very open-graded intermediate course, followed by the asphalt concrete courses as in the above. With this type of construction, care must be exercised in providing catch basins, down drains, or other methods for water removal. The previous layer functions as a stratum through which percolated or condensed water may flow to drains. It also serves as a bond breaker to allow for freedom of movement between the portland cement concrete roof and the asphalt concrete surface. The customary roof flashings are necessary.

13.11 SURFACE DRESSING.—Some specifications provide for a surface dressing in the nature of an emulsified asphalt slurry on top of the surface course of asphalt concrete as follows:

Surface Dressing Materials: Where a surface dressing is to be used, the materials and proportions recommended are as follows:

Portland Cement . . . . 94 lbs. (1 cu. ft.)
Silica Sand (60 mesh) . . . . .170 lbs. (2 cu. ft.)
Emulsified Asphalt SS-1h or
   SS-Kh* (10 gal.) . . . . 83 lbs. (1.33 cu. ft.)
Water (1.5 gal.) . . . . 62 lbs. (1 cu. ft.)

Total wet weight. . . . . .409 lbs.
Total dry weight, compacted. . .314 lbs. (2.50 cu. ft.)

Cement: Use standard portland cement only.

Silica Sand: A commercial product obtainable from building supply dealers.

Emulsified Asphalt: Grade SS-1h or SS-Kh conforming to currently published Asphalt Institute specifications for the grade used.

Water: Any domestic water supply.

---

* There are special proprietary emulsified asphalts designed especially for the manufacture of mastics containing portland cement.

NOTE: This mixture should be prepared in a small drum mixer. The mixture should be spread with a squeegee so as to cover completely the asphalt concrete.

Some specifications may require a fog seal of emulsified asphalt SS-1, SS-1h, SS-K or SS-Kh diluted, if necessary, with up to three or four parts of water and applied on the surface course of asphalt concrete after compaction is completed.

13.12 PAVING OF RAMPS TO ROOF-DECK PARKING AREAS.—Because of the good run-off due to the slope of ramps, it is not necessary to place the layers of built-up roofing on ramps. Usual practice is to finish the portland cement concrete slab with a rough, corrugated surface. Binder and surface courses are then laid as described above for the roof-deck parking area. A gradual transition should be provided between the ramp and the practically level roof-deck parking area. Care must also be used in this area to prevent slippage of the asphalt concrete courses.

C.—Asphalt-Paved Driveways

13.13 INTRODUCTION.—Asphalt-paved driveways are commonly used in most residential areas. These driveways are easy and economical to construct. When properly built, they have a long service life and require little maintenance.

They have a particular advantage in that they resist ice and snow formation and are unaffected by the corrosive action of ice melting salts. In addition, these asphalt paved driveways make excellent play areas for children.

13.14 SELECTION OF DESIGN CROSS-SECTION. —In selecting an asphalt-paved driveway the home owner should take into consideration requirements that the pavement will have to fulfill. In addition, the conditions of the native soil, drainage and availability of materials must be taken into account.

Table XIII-3—PAVEMENT THICKNESS FOR DRIVEWAYS FOR PASSENGER CARS

THICKNESS REQUIREMENTS IN INCHES

	FULL DEPTH ASPHALT CONCRETE		ASPHALT CONCRETE SURFACE		PLANT-MIX SURFACE USING LIQUID ASPHALT		ASPHALT SURFACE TREATMENT	
	Asphalt Concrete Surface	Asphalt Concrete Base[1]	Asphalt Concrete Surface	Crushed Rock Base[2]	Asphalt Plant-Mix Surface	Crushed Rock Base[2]	Asphalt Surface Treatment	Crushed Rock Base[2]
Gravelly or sandy soils, well drained	1	2–3	3	2	4.5*	2	1**	6–8
Average clay loam soils, not plastic	1	3–4	3	2–4	4.5*	2–4	1**	8–10
Soft clay soils, plastic when wet	1	4–5	3	4–6***	4.5*	4–6***	1**	10–12***

[1] Prime required on subgrade.
[2] Prime required on base.
* Must be spread and compacted in layers not exceeding 1½ inches in depth and the volatiles (petroleum solvents or water) allowed to evaporate before the next layer is placed. Also, a seal coat may be required as a final surfacing.
** Economical but relatively limited service life. Usually less than 1 inch thick.
*** Two inches of coarse sand or stone screenings recommended between subgrade and base as an insulation course.

After these factors have been determined the structural section should be designed in conformance with the recommendations in Table XIII-3.

13.15 TYPICAL DRIVEWAY CROSS-SECTION. —The width of the asphalt pavement should be at least eight feet. In those cases where the driveway is used for a combination driveway and entrance, however, a width of ten feet is recommended. Figure XIII-3 shows a typical driveway cross-section. The use of drain tile on either side of the base course is optional, depending on the amount of rainfall and the slope of the driveway. The use of the drain tile is highly recommended, however, for all locations where water would tend to collect at the edge of the driveway pavement.

13.16 SUBGRADE PREPARATION.—The foundation or subgrade for the driveway should receive careful preparation depending largely upon the type of soil that exists within the confines of the driveway. Generally, sand or granular soils provide a better foundation than those of clay or silt.

Sometimes in new construction, debris, consisting of small waste pieces of wood, metal containers, or other materials, are buried around the building. These materials upon rotting will leave a void in the filled-in area. This is poor practice and may ultimately result in settlement of the driveway. Care should be exercised to see that debris material is not included in any of the filled-in areas where the driveway will be placed. If such material is found, it should be removed and the area refilled with suitable soil.

It is also good practice to sterilize the subgrade soil before placing the overlying layers. Commercial sterilants containing chemical compounds such as sodium chlorate, borate, or arsenate will prevent the germination of weed seeds in the pavement structure.

After such fundamental requirements have been met, the next step is to lay out the driveway, establishing the lines and grades that best suit the surrounding terrain and the convenience of the user.

Figure XIII-2—An Asphalt-Paved Driveway

The soil should be compacted thoroughly prior to constructing the pavement.

13.17 DRAINAGE.—In establishing a drainage system it is necessary to see that the water is drained away from the residence or building, using an underground system of pipe if necessary. In a free-draining sand or gravel-type soil it is usually not necessary to construct an elaborate drainage system. In silt and clay it will be necessary to use every precaution to see that water is not ponded alongside of the building or the area adjacent to the driveway foundation. Roof drainage from downspouts should be piped far enough away from the driveway to make certain that water does not seep under the pavement. The driveway should be sloped for fast removal of surface water. The recommended minimum grade is two percent.

13.18 BASE CONSTRUCTION.—All types of asphalt pavement require some sort of base between the wearing course and the subgrade. The purpose of this base is to spread the load that is transmitted through the surface course onto the subgrade. Local materials are often acceptable for the base.

If the subgrade is of good quality, such as sand or gravel with low clay content, or if a granular subbase at least five inches thick is placed over poor subgrade, one inch of asphalt concrete base can be used for each two inches of granular base and three inches of subbase called for in the design. If these substitutions are made the total thickness of asphalt courses should be not less than three inches.

The base course must be placed true to lines, grades, and cross-sections, and brought to a firm, unyielding surface by rolling with the heaviest type of compacting equipment that is available and is practical to use in the

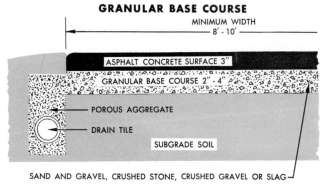

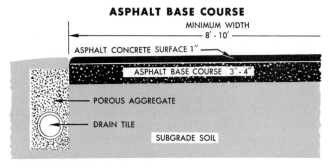

Figure XIII-3—Typical Driveway Cross-Section

area where the driveway is being constructed. In the absence of special requirements, it is safe practice to use the local highway department, city or town specifications. It should be remembered at this stage that the serviceability and good performance of the driveway is dependent upon the establishment of a good base course.

13.19 ASPHALT WEARING COURSE.—There are a number of types of asphalt surfacing for driveways that are in general use. Here only three of the many types are suggested. Modifications which will fit local conditions, however, may be made in any of the types. They are: (1) Asphalt Concrete (Hot Mix), (2) Asphalt Cold Mix, and (3) Surface Treatment.

(1) **Asphalt Concrete (Hot Mix).** This is the most durable type of pavement, the one that will give the greatest service with the least maintenance cost.

Asphalt concrete consists of well-graded aggregates and asphalt mixed in a central plant. It is mixed hot and laid while hot (225°-325°F). This pavement, when rolled, is virtually waterproof, easy to clean, and presents a smooth, even-textured surface. The thickness to be used should be as designated in Table XIII-3.

(2) **Asphalt Cold Mix.** Cold mix is a combination of asphaltic materials and aggregates prepared in a central mixing plant. The aggregate is mixed without heating with either a liquid or emulsified asphalt. The mix may be laid while cold and, for that reason, has found considerable favor where work is apt to progress slowly.

The texture of cold mix is of a slightly open nature. Cold mix is quite similar in appearance to the pavement usually found in parks and recreational areas. This pavement, even after a considerable amount of traffic, is inclined to remain somewhat porous. While it may be laid as thin as one inch, the thickness should be as suggested in Table XIII-3.

(3) **Surface Treatment.** This consists of a thin wearing course, usually less than an inch in thickness, composed of two or more applications of liquid asphalt covered with mineral aggregates. Surface treatment is

an economical type of pavement that serves quite well for a limited period of time. It may be used as one step in stage construction.

A surface treatment provides a water-tight wearing surface adequate for light traffic. When first constructed, some loose aggregate will remain on the surface, but after several weeks the loose pieces may be swept off the pavement.

D.—Asphalt-Paved Service Station Lots

13.20 INTRODUCTION.—Asphalt-paved service station lots are attractive and economical. They will last for many years with a minimum of maintenance if they are designed properly and constructed according to recommended practice.

Design is preceded by an investigation of drainage and subgrade conditions and includes the best use of local materials. Good construction procedure involves working only in favorable weather, proper preparation of materials, adequate compaction, and correct installation of drainage facilities and utilities.

13.21 BACKFILL.—The backfill over buried storage tanks and pipelines can be a source of heavy maintenance if it is not properly placed. Granular material should be used as backfill in excavations for tanks and in ditches for pipelines and utilities. If the surrounding subgrade soil is impervious, drainage should be provided to keep water from accumulating in the granular backfill. To prevent future differential settlement, the backfill must be tightly compacted in thin layers by vibratory compactors.

13.22 DRAINAGE.—Underdrainage should be installed unless the subgrade soil is of a character (gravelly or sandy) that drains well. With a proper cross-section, quick runoff of surface water can be assured, either to the outer limits of the paved area, to a shallow gutter through the center, or to drop inlets spaced so that standing water will not be left on the surface at any time. The outer edges of the area should be designed in such a manner as to keep water from seeping under the surface.

The slope to all gutters or drop inlets should be not less than one inch in ten feet. For parking areas, where water can be drained in two directions from a centerline, the slope should be as much as ¼ inch to the foot.

13.23 SUBGRADE PREPARATION.—All unstable materials encountered, such as saturated subgrade soils, logs or tree stumps, should be removed before embankment or fill soils are placed. When construction is carried out on filled areas which have been built up over a long period of time, soundings should be made to determine the type and stability of the subgrade soil. This information should be used to insure that the materials are well compacted within the top four to six feet and thereby avoid any undue settlement caused by further deterioration of unstable materials. Heterogeneous fills should be scarified to a depth of at least one foot, thoroughly mixed, and recompacted.

Embankments should be placed in layers not exceeding eight inches loose depth. Each lift should be compacted with equipment best suited for the material being placed; sheepsfoot rollers for fine grained soils, pneumatic-tired rollers or vibratory compactors (rollers or shoe-type) for granular material. Suggested compaction criteria are specified in Article 8.12.

The subgrade should be finished to a firm and smooth surface, conforming to the final grades within a tolerance of ± ½ inch. Pockets or humps that would show up in the final surface should not be permitted.

13.24 PAVEMENT THICKNESS.—Tables XIII-1 and XIII-2 can be used as guides for minimum designs for service station lots. Table XIII-2 should be used if several heavy trucks daily are expected to use the pavement. If the subgrade is in extremely poor condition, tests should be made and the pavement designed according to the procedures outlined in *Thickness Design—Asphalt Pavement Structures for Highways and Streets*, Manual Series No. 1 (MS-1), The Asphalt Institute.

13.25 BASE CONSTRUCTION.—See Article 13.18.

13.26 ASPHALT WEARING COURSE.—Although there are several types of asphalt surfacing that can be used for service station paving, The Asphalt Institute recommends dense-graded asphalt concrete with the grades of asphalt cement suggested in Table I-2. Applicable specifications are contained in the Institute's publication, *Specifications and Construction Methods for Asphalt Concrete and Other Plant-Mix Types*, Specification Series No. 1 (SS-1), The Asphalt Institute.

13.27 REFERENCES.—Publications of The Asphalt Institute containing information relevant to paved parking areas and driveways are:

(1) *Specifications and Construction Methods for Asphalt Concrete and Other Plant-Mix Types*, Specification Series No. 1 (SS-1)

(2) *Thickness Design—Asphalt Pavement Structures for Highways and Streets*, Manual Series No. 1 (MS-1)

(3) *Asphalt Paving Manual*, Manual Series No. 8 (MS-8)

(4) *Asphalt Surface Treatments and Asphalt Penetration Macadam*, Manual Series No. 13 (MS-13)

(5) *Paving Roof Decks and Industrial Floors* by Lansing Tuttle, Information Series No. 130 (IS-130)

Chapter XIV

ASPHALT IN HYDRAULICS

A.—Introduction

14.01 GENERAL.—The use of asphalt in hydraulic construction dates from earliest recorded history and, through inherent merit, its use is becoming constantly more widespread. The versatility of asphalt naturally has led to many variations in its employment in hydraulic structures. Some of these uses that will be covered later in the chapter are: linings for canals, reservoirs, ditches, storm drains, and waste treatment systems; revetments for stream erosion control; beach and lake erosion control structures; and dam facings.

In using asphalt for hydraulic structures no unnecessary chances should be taken. Informed engineering and laboratory service should always be utilized. There are aggregates available in practically all areas which have proven satisfactory for this type of construction. In the event that the use of unproven materials appears necessary in the interest of economy, engineering and laboratory studies should be made to guide their use before and during construction.

14.02 SUBGRADE.—It is obvious that asphaltic material for hydraulic linings does not have the same relationship to the foundation, or subgrade, as similar work for use under traffic. Nevertheless, there are parallels in design, construction and serviceability factors. Consolidation of the subgrade under the lining is important; first, because a firm foundation is essential to act as a base for placing and compacting operations; and second, because side slopes must be stable of themselves. Rarely will a base course of selected, imported material be necessary. However, established engineering principles governing soil control and consolidation should be exercised to the greatest practicable degree on banks, slopes and bottoms. In addition to consolidation, it is recommended that the junction between side slope and bottom be rounded. Experience has shown that a radius of curvature of not less than one-half the bottom width and preferably three feet or more, will facilitate the placing and the compaction of the asphalt lining, and will also render the junction less liable to be cracked when compacted. The top edges should be extended a minimum of six inches over the berm and subsequently covered with earth; or in lieu thereof, the edge should be slightly thickened. Side slopes should never be steeper than 1½:1, with 2:1 or more gentle slopes being preferable (see typical slope cross-section, Figure XIV-1).

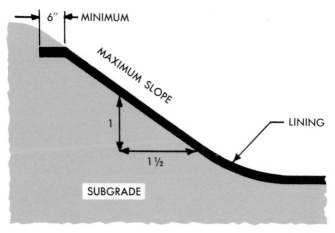

Figure XIV-1—Typical Section, Canal or Reservoir Lining

14.03 WEED CONTROL.—Weeds and other plants are a potential hazard to linings when certain favorable growth conditions exist. These conditions are: (1) Subgrade contaminated with weed seeds or roots of perennial plants; (2) subgrade moisture conditions favorable to seed germination or root growth; and (3) a subgrade temperature which favors growth for appreciable periods. Absence of any one of these conditions will prevent vegetation trouble but the simultaneous occurrence of all three means the eruptions of growth through the average lining. When such conditions are anticipated, the use of a soil sterilant is advisable. Where vegetation is present, the subgrade should be carefully grubbed before treatment. This will be required more frequently in lining existing structures than in new construction.

The soil sterilant desired is not a simple weed-killer but a compound which attacks roots and seeds and remains effective for an extended period. There are many commercial products which will accomplish this. Most of them are either chemical compounds or petroleum derivatives.

Chemical compounds which have proven effective in use are: sodium chlorate (must be handled carefully because organic matter treated with it becomes very combustible); combinations of sodium chlorate and calcium chloride; borates; arsenates; substituted urea compounds; and combinations of urea derivates with chlorates and borates. It is possible that there are still other compounds with equal records of use and effectiveness.

These chemical compounds are marketed under a variety of names. Each product carries the manufacturer's recommendation for rate and method of application. Most of them are soluble or wettable powders, and are designed for spray application. Some can be applied in dry form, and one or two *must* be applied that way. For dry application, sprinkling or precipitation is relied on to carry the sterilant to the root zone. Rates of application vary from a low of about 50 pounds to the acre to a high of about 1,800 pounds to the acre.

The service history of petroleum derivatives is limited as compared to the chemicals, but certain petroleum distillates are naturally toxic to plants. Also others less toxic, such as diesel fuel, have been fortified with soluble sterilants. One such mixture is diesel fuel containing 1½ percent of pentachlorophenol. These sterilants are sprayed on the subgrade at the rate of two thirds to one gallon per square yard in increments of about two-tenths gallons. After spraying they should be allowed to penetrate and weather for several days before the lining is placed.

14.04 DESIGN.—The objectives to accomplish in hydraulic structures are several fold. Among these are: (1) prevention of loss of water; (2) protection of banks from erosion; (3) lessening of hydraulic friction; and (4) the reduction of required maintenance. To do these things satisfactorily, the lining should be tough and durable, have mechanical stability, have a smooth surface, possess sufficient flexibility to adapt itself to minor repair, and must be impermeable. Asphalt linings and structures when properly designed and installed will fulfill all of these requirements. Various types of linings and mixes have been used in hydraulic structures and a careful evaluation and design should be made for each type of installation. In the construction of the hydraulic structure, detailed procedures should be formulated and followed in order to obtain a serviceable installation.

14.05 TYPES.—Several types of asphalt linings are used in the construction of reservoirs, canals and storm channels. Some of these are: asphalt concrete, buried membranes, prefabricated materials and asphalt macadam. All of these types have merit in their respective fields and are worthy of investigation. The design criteria for these linings will vary depending on each particular use.

B.—Asphalt Concrete Linings

14.06 MIX DESIGN.—Hot-mixed, hot-laid asphalt concrete through many years of successful performance has established itself in the field of hydraulic control as a proven method of construction. It will fulfill all of the requirements given in the article on design.

The type of asphalt concrete mix which most adequately serves all of the above various functional demands, is a well-graded, dense, rich mix. Such a mix, containing less than 5 percent voids in the compacted state, may be considered impermeable. The mix should be made from a well-graded, sound aggregate not exceeding ¾ inch maximum size, graded to fine rather than coarse, and contain the maximum amount of asphalt commensurate with high stability. Two recommended gradings are listed in Table XIV-1.

Table XIV-1—SUGGESTED MIX COMPOSITIONS FOR DENSE-GRADED ASPHALT CONCRETE LININGS

SIEVE SIZE	FOR MIN. THICKNESS OF 1½" Percent Passing	FOR MIN. THICKNESS OF 1" Percent Passing
¾ in.	100	
½ in.	95–100	
⅜ in.	—	100
No. 4	60–80	90–97
No. 8	45–60	70–85
No. 30	28–39	42–52
No. 100	16–25	20–28
No. 200	8–15	10–16
Asphalt Cement Percent by Weight of Total Mix	6.5–8.5	7.5–9.5

The paving grade asphalt should have a penetration of not less than 60 nor more than 100, with the 60-70 penetration grade being preferred. Mixes made with the harder asphalts have greater resistance to weed growth, mud curling, stripping, and transverse creep; are less damaged by animals' hoofs, and the truck traffic connected with construction and maintenance; are less susceptible to temperature change; and are tough and lasting under extremes of weather.

14.07 CONSTRUCTION.—Construction of asphalt concrete linings is discussed in the Asphalt Institute publication, *Asphalt in Hydraulic Structures*, Manual Series No. 12 (MS-12).

14.08 USE.—Asphalt concrete linings are used in all types of structures that contain or carry water. Canals, laterals, storm and other drainage ditches and channels, and highway ditches may all be paved or lined with this versatile material. It is used to line water supply reservoirs (large and small), industrial waste reservoirs, sewage lagoons, and farm ponds.

In reservoir construction asphalt concrete plays a dual role. It serves either as an impermeable water-tight lining or as a porous lining. Where used as an exposed porous lining an underlying blanket of earth or some other type of seal provides imperviousness. Use of porous asphalt concrete lining relieves uplift pressures and prevents upheaval of the lining on drawdown of the water level by allowing water in the bank to seep harmlessly back into the reservoir. The principal function of porous asphalt concrete is to prevent erosion and provide a working surface for cleaning and maintenance problems. It is sometimes used as a buried porous layer to serve as a drainage course to control seepage losses. A type of porous mix is illustrated in Table XIV-2. Note that, compared to the mix in Table XIV-1, it has very little mineral filler, reduced asphalt cement content and a much larger proportion of coarse aggregate.

Figure XIV-2—An Asphalt Concrete-Lined Canal

Figure XIV-3—Placing Asphalt Concrete Lining by Improvised Methods—Lemont Water Company Reservoir, Pennsylvania

Table XIV-2—SUGGESTED MIX GRADATIONS FOR PERMEABLE ASPHALT CONCRETE

SIEVE SIZE	PERCENT PASSING
1 in.	100
¾ in.	95–100
½ in.	85–95
⅜ in.	—
No. 4	44–56
No. 8	30–40
No. 16	—
No. 30	13–22
No. 100	3–8
No. 200	1–4
Asphalt Cement Percent by Weight of Total Mix	5–6

C.—Buried Asphalt Membrane Linings (Hot-Sprayed Type)

14.09 GENERAL.—Buried asphalt membranes, as the name implies, are asphalt seals which are covered with earth, sand, gravel, cobbles, or other erosion-resistant and protective material.

These linings are placed primarily for the purpose of controlling seepage and leakage from canals and reservoirs, particularly where they are constructed in permeable sandy or gravelly soils, or where faulted and fractured shales or similar materials are encountered. When cover materials of sand, gravel, cobbles, and the like are used to depths of six inches to two feet, an erosion-resistant as well as leak-proof lining is obtained frequently at a fraction of the cost of more conventionally constructed linings. The asphalt membrane, protected from air and actinic solar radiation, may be expected to endure for many years. Primary considerations in constructing buried membrane linings are the obtaining of a sufficiently thick asphalt membrane, and the construction of a sufficient depth of cover with materials and with slopes which will prevent sloughing of the cover under operating conditions.

Figure XIV-4—Spray-bar Offset from Distributor Truck Places Hot Asphalt as a Membrane to Line a Large Canal

14.10 MATERIALS.—Asphaltic materials used for buried membranes must be tough enough to withstand mutilation during the earth cover replacements yet sufficiently ductile to resist cracking during possible earth movement. Excessive sag prior to placement of the earth cover is undesirable. A continuous unbroken film is the objective. Table IV-8 describes an asphalt cement with a high softening point and a special ductility requirement at 77°F which was developed to meet these requirements. A cross-section of a typical buried membrane asphalt canal lining is shown in Figure XIV-5.

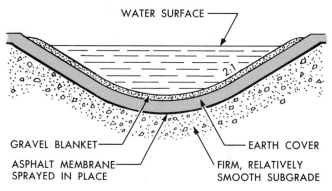

WATER SURFACE

2:1

GRAVEL BLANKET

EARTH COVER

ASPHALT MEMBRANE SPRAYED IN PLACE

FIRM, RELATIVELY SMOOTH SUBGRADE

Figure XIV-5—Available Earth Makes a Satisfactory Cover for a Sprayed-on Membrane. (Gravel is sometimes needed to prevent wash.)

14.11 CONSTRUCTION PROCEDURES.—Procedures for constructing asphalt membrane lining are detailed in *Asphalt in Hydraulic Structures*, Manual Series No. 12 (MS-12), The Asphalt Institute.

D.—Prefabricated Asphalt Linings

14.12 GENERAL.—Prefabricated asphalt lining materials are manufactured in two general types. One type, the prefabricated asphalt panel (board or sheet) is made in standard widths of 3 or 4 feet. Lengths may be varied on order; a common length is 14 or 15 feet, a convenient size to handle, but panels may be as long as 30 feet.

Thickness varies from ⅛ through ½ inch. The ½-inch panel is the one in widest use. Typically a panel is a sandwich. The core may be a very dense mixture of asphalt and filler. The outside layers are some tough asphalt-impregnated material, such as an asbestos felt, or one of the synthetic fibers or plastics. Or the center may be the reinforcing material with heavy coatings of filled asphalt on each side of it. The panel is molded together under heat and pressure.

The other type of prepared material is lighter and more flexible. It is fabricated in rolls 3 feet wide by 36 feet long (the standard size of rolls of roofing material). Make-up of the material varies. One fabricator's product is a rot-resistant jute thoroughly saturated and coated with an asphalt of special characteristics. Other fabricators use different materials as reinforcing, such as poly-vinyl-chloride sheets, asbestos felt or glass fiber.

Construction of linings from prefabricated materials does not require heavy paving machinery. Hence they are used where mix plant and paving machinery are not

Figure XIV-6—Industrial Reservoir of Prefabricated Asphalt Panels

available or where space limitations prevent their use. They are also recommended for use when a lining must conform to very strict specifications as to thickness, density and impermeability. Such qualities can be assured since the materials are manufactured under factory conditions where precise controls are possible.

These prefabricated materials may be used to construct hydraulic lining under varied conditions. The prefabricated asphalt panels may be used as a complete lining, or they may be used as the surface layer of a multilayer lining, or they may be used to reline a cracked and deteriorated concrete lining. Although the joint pattern roughens the surface considerably, it is smooth enough for easy cleaning and can be used in canals where the increased hydraulic friction is not a problem.

The prefabricated rolls are designed for use where less strength and toughness are sufficient and where more flexibility is required. This type may also be used to construct a buried membrane type of lining. Substituting for the hot-sprayed membrane, it is readily applied in many cases where the asphalt distributor cannot be used on account of space or the soft condition of a subgrade, or where this equipment is not available.

E.—Asphalt Macadam

14.13 GENERAL.—The use of a permeable yet erosion-resistant lining for canals, drainage ditches and reservoirs is frequently desirable. The permeability of such a lining permits the escape of water from behind the lining, preventing any build-up of hydrostatic pressure and permitting drainage of adjacent areas. A properly constructed asphalt macadam provides such a lining. It affords a tough, stable, erosion-resistant surface which is permeable because of the open gradation of aggregate used. For the above purpose it is placed directly on the prepared subgrade. Asphalt macadam may also be used as the erosion-resistant element of a multi-layer lining structure.

Figure XIV-7—Placing Reservoir Lining of Prefabricated
Asphalt Rolls

F.—Asphalt Revetments

14.14 GENERAL.—Various types of asphalt mixes and methods have been used to control erosion along streams, flood channels, river banks, and lake shores. Erosion in these instances presents many varied problems and each type of erosion may have to be treated in a different manner. In many cases bank paving may be accomplished in much the same manner as in constructing an asphalt concrete reservoir lining. Other types which have been used successfully may require special considerations in the design and placing of the asphalt mix. The differences in design may require consideration of one or more of the following additional factors: increased thickness, permeable mix, wire reinforcement, grade of asphalt cement, and use of local aggregates.

Figure XIV-8—Upper Bank Revetment, Mississippi River

14.15 THICKNESS.—Thicknesses greater than three inches may be required in mass levee construction where severe wave action can be expected; also in flood channels where large boulders may be carried into the protected channel during flood stage. Such increases in thickness are a matter of judgment with due recourse to previous experience with installations of a similar nature and no general design criteria are applicable.

14.16 PERMEABLE CONSTRUCTION.—Many installations of asphalt concrete for erosion control on flood channels or upper banks subject to intermittent flow wherein hydraulic back pressure can be expected may require a permeable type of mix. This is especially true over dense or semi-dense soils with a high plasticity index.

Another approach to permeable blankets that has been used, is the practice of little or no compaction of a more densely graded mix. By not rolling the surface after placement the void content remains relatively high and even a dense mix remains somewhat permeable. As a rule this practice is not recommended because of danger of instability of the asphalt concrete blanket and increased susceptibility to damage from flotsam. It is, however, mentioned as a possible approach to the problem of desired permeability, especially when dense-graded local aggregates are economically available. In general, the better practice is to design a permeable mix and thoroughly compact it in the usual manner.

Current practice of the Corps of Engineers, U. S. Army, for upper bank paving (revetment) of the lower Mississippi River is to use an uncompacted hot mix of sand and asphalt. The aggregate is bank-run sand, excavated (not pumped), which must have not less than one percent, nor more than eight percent, passing the 100 mesh sieve. For this mix about six percent of an 85-100 penetration asphalt cement is used. The mix is prepared in a floating asphalt plant utilizing a continuous type pugmill mixer. It is placed at temperatures ranging from 225°F to 275°F, with a spreader box to a thickness of five inches, and left uncompacted.

The strip of bank from the subaqueous mattress at the water's edge to the top of the bank is thus paved. The pavement is designed to be porous so as to permit water from the bank to seep through. This avoids damaging back pressure. It is left uncompacted to allow for some adjustment to bank contours in the event of loss of material from underneath. Upper bank revetments of this, or similar types, have been in place for many years and have successfully withstood wave wash, floods, and other attacks. A study recently completed on the life expectancy of this type places it at twenty years or better.

Still another approach to hydraulic back pressures, which has been used successfully, is the practice of placing a blanket of free-draining granular material beneath the asphalt concrete surfacing. If this is done and impermeability is desired a dense type of mix can be used. The choice of treatment is a matter of local economics and functional requirements.

14.17 WIRE REINFORCEMENT.—There have been three general methods used in protecting asphalt concrete at the toe of a slope from undercutting and subsequent damage. One method is to extend the toe to an elevation four to six feet below the normal stream bed level. This, of course, is only feasible when the channel is dry during the construction season. If this method is used, the value of reinforcement is doubtful. A second method is to dump heavy riprap along the toe and by a concentration of the riprap at this critical point, prevent scour and undercutting. The third method is the use of wire reinforcement in the asphalt mat with the idea of allowing the mat to conform to major grade changes as a result of undercutting without breaking away entirely from the parent mass. Such uses of reinforcement should be considered in the light of a solution to a particular problem and not of a generally applicable nature, except in like installations.

For normal asphalt concrete erosion control on flood channels, etc., the use of wire reinforcing is not recommended unless severe scour and undercutting at the toe is considered highly probable. If used, various types of woven wire fencing will be found satisfactory. The wire should be galvanized, from 14 to 16 gauge and on about 4-inch spacings. As the asphalt concrete is laid over the wire, the wire should be pulled up slightly into the mix with long-handled hooks before the surface is rolled. The type of protection that is used against undercutting is a question of local conditions and engineering judgment.

14.18 GRADE OF ASPHALT CEMENT.—In normal practice wherein the asphalt concrete surfacing is laid initially in its final position, the grade of asphalt cement to use in the mix will be the same as for canal linings, i.e., 60 to 100 penetration. In special cases, however, such as prefabricated mats subject to rehandling after cooling, it may be advisable to use special asphalts, harder than above.

14.19 USE OF LOCAL AGGREGATES.—In the interest of economy it will be desirable to use local aggregate. Each such instance should be approached as a separate problem with complete engineering and laboratory studies of the aggregate in question being made. Many granular type materials regardless of size can be made usable by either directly determining the optimum amount and grade of asphalt cement or by blending with other granular materials and fillers. Thus, an infinite number of solutions are possible to the over-all problem of erosion control. Furthermore, the versatility of asphalt and asphalt mixes offers the engineer some solution to practically any phase of erosion control.

14.20 LAKE SHORES.—Installations similar to those used for streams can also be used to control erosion along lake shores. An engineering analysis should be made of existing conditions before selecting the type. One of the largest installations of this type was constructed at Lake Okeechobee, Florida by the Corps of Engineers. The paving mix consisted principally of a mixture of sand, shell, and soft limestone varying in size from 1½ inches to dust. The binder was liquid asphalt (Rapid-Curing Cutback) containing not more than 10 percent of solvent. It was found that an asphalt content between 9 percent and 10 percent was preferable for the mix. The mix was manufactured in a hot-mix plant and laid on the lake slopes with conventional paving equipment. The mix was cured and compacted after which it was sealed with RC-2 liquid (cutback) asphalt. The installation has proven to be very successful in the prevention of the lake shore erosion.

Figure XIV-9—Paving Shore Slope, Lake Okeechobee, Florida

G.—Asphalt Beach Erosion Control Structures

14.21 GENERAL.—Asphalt plays an important role in the growing science of erosion control of our ocean and inland beaches. The principal structures used for beach erosion control are sea walls, breakwaters, bulkheads, jetties and groins, each having its own differing function. Asphaltic materials are used in the construction of many of these installations; usually as part and parcel of a complex structure, but also as the material from which the entire structure is built. Asphalt concrete is used to pave or revet the slopes and tops of earth or sand sea walls; it is used to build low profile asphalt groins; and it is used to pave, or cap, the top surfaces of rock jetties, breakwaters, and groins. Asphalt grouting mixtures are used to consolidate and fill in the voids of stone or rock jetties and groins, and the rock riprap facing of sea walls.

These uses have evolved because of the excellent cementing and waterproofing qualities of asphalt; because of its durability; because dense asphalt mixes offer great resistance to marine borers; and because of the favorable economy of this type of construction.

14.22 ASPHALT GROUTING AND CAPPING OF ROCK AND STONE STRUCTURES.—Grouting and capping with asphaltic materials is a technique for making a stone or rock structure more effective and easier to construct and maintain. In brief, grouting consists of filling up the interstices in a stone structure with a pouring asphalt mastic; that is a very hot, rich mixture of asphalt cement, mineral filler, and fine aggregate, placed or poured in a near liquid state. Capping, which usually follows, need only be done when a traffic way is required on top of the structure.

Stone or rock breakwaters, sea walls, jetties and groins are very expensive to construct and to maintain. The stone is difficult to produce, usually has to be transported long distances to the sea coast, and the large sizes required are difficult to handle. Grouting with an asphalt hot mix has been developed to reduce the initial expense of such structures, to reduce the cost of maintaining them, and to increase their effectiveness and length of life. It acts to do this in several ways. It moves into and fills up the voids in the rock structure and hardens there. The

Figure XIV-10—Asphalt-Capped Sea Wall at Palos Verdes Estates, California

individual rock pieces, held together in a matrix of asphalt, then act as a whole to resist the heavy attack of the sea.

This whole mass has a measure of resilience to shock because of this inherent quality of asphalt. Because they can act together, the rock pieces in the mass can be smaller and less difficult to procure and handle. Because the voids are filled, the structure is relatively impermeable. In a stone jetty this prevents infiltration of sand into the protected channel. In a riprap revetment it prevents loss of material due to erosion and cavitation. And finally, because the integrity of the structure is preserved by this consolidation, its life is lengthened and the cost of maintaining it reduced.

The modern technique of grouting with asphaltic materials was initially used on European installations early in the 1930's. The first large scale construction of this type in the United States was the Galveston, Texas Jetty, started in 1935. Since these early beginnings there has been a gradual expansion of this type of construction, particularly in Europe. The usage is certain to grow in the

United States as suitable stone and rock become more difficult and expensive to procure.

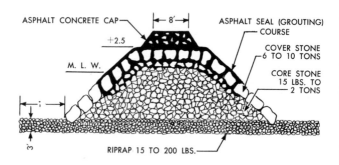

ASPHALT CONCRETE CAP
+2.5
M. L. W.
8'
ASPHALT SEAL (GROUTING) COURSE
COVER STONE 6 TO 10 TONS
CORE STONE 15 LBS. TO 2 TONS
RIPRAP 15 TO 200 LBS.

Figure XIV-11—Section, South Jetty, Galveston, Texas

14.23 ASPHALT GROINS.—A number of installations have been made using a hot-mix asphalt concrete for the complete construction of low profile, relatively short groins. A system of such groins has the function of holding a beach at the desired width and profile and preventing the constantly moving littoral currents from eroding it away. A beach so held at optimum width and profile is ample protection against storm, wave and wind both for itself and for the upland behind it. These low profile groin systems are not designed to reach out into the littoral drift and cause beaches to form by trapping material therefrom.

Some of the sand asphalt groins constructed to date have functioned successfully. Because of faults in mix and over-all structural design, others have only a limited success. The type of construction was initiated because of its extremely favorable economy, utilizing, as it does, locally available beach sand for the mix and not requiring expensive construction procedures. For this reason the development is likely to continue until design principles and construction methods are fully proven.

Figure XIV-12—Sand Asphalt Groin

14.24 ASPHALT SLOPE REVETMENTS.—Asphalt revetments may be used to protect the exposed seaside slopes of earth or sand structures (sea walls, breakwaters, natural slopes). These are similar to river bank revetments, though they are usually much thicker and heavier in order to resist the heavier attacks to which they are subjected. The use of asphaltic material on a sea wall slope is illustrated in Figure XIV-13. In this figure the underwater revetment is riprap, which has been consolidated and strengthened by the application of asphalt grout. The junction of the under- and above-water portion of the revetment is a critical point. It is protected by sheet piling driven five to six feet deep. The above-water revetment shown should be a dense-graded, hot-mix, asphalt concrete, high in mineral filler and asphalt cement content. This can be placed on most sea wall slopes by the use of conventional paving machines because the slopes are usually no steeper than 3:1.

The use of asphaltic materials for seaside revetments is much more common in Europe than in the United States.

One such use in the United States was the revetment of both sides of a road causeway as shown in Figure XIV-14. This long causeway with open water on both sides had been damaged by storms five times. A protective revetment was placed on both side slopes. First heavy treated timber sheeting was driven to protect the toe of the slope. On the more open side this sheeting was reinforced by twelve-inch timber piles, driven to ten-ton bearing capacity, on 20-foot centers. The 4:1 slopes were then paved with four inches of asphalt concrete, put down in two courses. Welded wire fabric reinforcing was placed between the two courses, being first anchored to the sheet piling by bolted timber wales. Paving was done with conventional paving equipment. After placing and compacting the base course of two inches, the wire fabric was ironed out on it with a small lawn roller. Then the surface course was placed on the wire and thoroughly compacted.

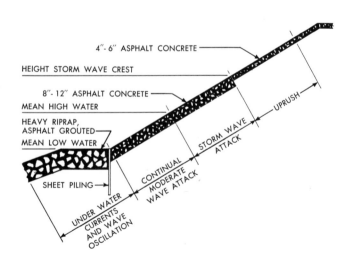

Figure XIV-13—Sea Wall Slope Revetment

Figure XIV-14—Asphalt Concrete Slope Protection, Causeway, Point Lookout, Maryland. (Chesapeake Bay is on right.)

H.—Asphalt Applications in Dam Construction

14.25 GENERAL.—Asphaltic materials have many important applications in the construction of dams. One is the use of heavy asphalt concrete facings on the upstream slopes of large earth-fill or rock-fill dams. These facings are designed to resist erosion and abrasion forces; in addition, they may act as an impervious screen to prevent leakage through the dam structure. Another is the application of an impervious asphalt layer in the core of the dam. In both methods, the impervious construction is generally continued vertically into the foundation of the dam in the form of a cut-off wall, which may also be constructed of asphaltic materials. Additionally, asphalt cut-off walls may be constructed in the abutment sections of dams to stop underflow, or flanking flow, through existing channels or fissures. And finally, hot asphalt may be injected under high pressure through pipes placed in drill holes to seal off leakage channels deep under dam structures.

The application of asphaltic materials to dam construction follows the principles and methods described in *Asphalt in Hydraulic Structures*, Manual Series No. 12 (MS-12), The Asphalt Institute. In fact, the construction of relatively thin asphalt sections for small dams and embankments does not differ in any important respect from the construction of linings, membranes, and revetments.

14.26 ASPHALT DAM FACINGS.—Asphalt mixes have been used for dam facings at several large installations in the United States and in foreign countries. They provide impervious layers at a most economical cost. One of the most recent of these types of installations is the Montgomery Dam in Colorado. Here a rockfill dam was faced with a layer of asphalt concrete approximately one foot thick. After the construction of the rockfill dam, a leveling course of mix was placed to fill the voids in the rock face and to provide a surface on which the asphalt facing was placed. This leveling course was from one to three inches thick. The facing was placed in three layers; the first four inches thick, the second 3½ inches, and the final layer was three inches. The mix was placed with modified conventional paving equipment in continuous layers and thoroughly compacted. The asphalt concrete mix contained approximately 8.5 percent of asphalt cement based on dry weight of the aggregate. Aggregate for the mixture came from glacial deposits occurring in the vicinity of the dam.

14.27 INJECTION OF ASPHALT INTO LEAKAGE CHANNELS UNDER DAMS AND ABUTMENT SECTIONS.—Leakage through the underlying strata of dams or abutment sections may be controlled by the pressure injection of hot fluid asphalt into the leakage channels. This use of asphalt is particularly important since it is effective even under conditions (such as appreciable heads and water velocities) that result in the carrying away of other types of grouting materials.

Relatively hard, high-softening-point asphalt cements are used for these purposes. The hot, fluid asphalt is usually pumped through heated pipes let down into drilled holes and having perforations at the leakage strata

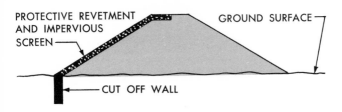

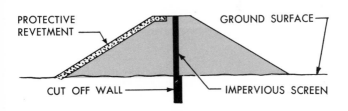

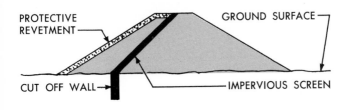

Figure XIV-15—Alternate Asphalt Courses for Dams

levels. Once in the leakage channel, the asphalt spreads out to a considerable extent and hardens into a tight plug, or water stop. Due to the inherent characteristics of asphalt these plugs can adapt to slight movements of the surrounding strata and changes in water pressure. Figure XIV-17 is a sketch showing the probable course of this process.

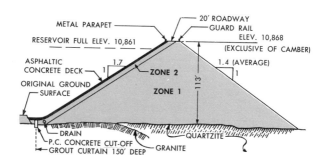

**Figure XIV-16—Montgomery Dam, Colorado—
Maximum Cross-Section**

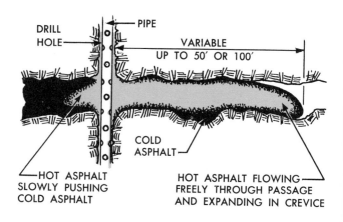

Figure XIV-17—Plugging a Leakage Channel with Asphalt

Though instances of such use are not frequent, they are extremely important because excessive leakage must be stopped once it has developed through the underlying strata of dam structures. It not only may be dangerous, but can result in an intolerable loss of water. In some cases it may be necessary to restore the bearing power of the strata underlying the dam. Asphalt is not a suitable material for this purpose. But it may be used first to stop the flow of water and then be followed by the installation of a portland cement or other type of grout curtain which will restore the foundation bearing power.

14.28 REFERENCES.—The following Asphalt Institute technical publication contains more detailed information about the use of asphalt in hydraulic structures:

(1) *Asphalt in Hydraulic Structures*, Manual Series No. 12 (MS-12).

Chapter XV

MISCELLANEOUS USES OF ASPHALT

15.01 GENERAL.—Some miscellaneous uses of asphalt are:

- A. Roofs
- B. Playgrounds
- C. Tennis Courts
- D. Swimming Pools
- E. On the Farm
- F. Drive-in Theaters
- G. Industrial Floors
- H. Pipe Coatings
- I. Sidewalks (See Chapter X)
- J. Mulch Treatments

A.—Asphalt Roofs

15.02 HISTORY.—Roofing was probably the world's first craft, for shelter has always been one of the primary material needs of man. From the beginning, he has had to protect himself against the relentless forces of nature: from extreme heat and cold, from rain, wind, hail, snow, and ice.

Asphalt, with its extraordinary combination of waterproofing, preservative, and cementing qualities, was an early discovery of ancient peoples. They used it extensively in the construction of their buildings and roads, many of which, after thousands of years of exposure to the elements, are still existing, well preserved.

Today, asphalt is recognized more than ever as the outstanding roofing material and it is used extensively to cover all kinds of buildings, from homes to factories. Asphalt roofing materials and construction methods are fully covered by specifications of the American Society for Testing and Materials and many government and private agencies. In addition, all types of asphalt roofing are sanctioned by Federal and other public agencies.

15.03 **TYPES OF ASPHALT ROOFING.**—Asphalt roofing is of two general types:

(1) **Prepared Roofing**

a. *Asphalt shingles.* This type is composed of three basic materials—asphalt, felt, and mineral granules. The felt is impregnated with an asphalt saturant. Both sides of the saturated felt are then covered with a harder, tougher coat of asphalt, in which are embedded mineral granules. This composition is then cut into individual shingles or strips.

b. *Asphalt roll roofing—smooth surfaced.* This type is made up of a single layer of roofing felt saturated with asphalt and coated on both sides with a harder asphalt.

c. *Asphalt roll roofing—mineral surfaced.* This type consists of smooth surfaced roll roofing in which mineral granules have been embedded on either one or both sides.

(2) **Asphalt built-up roofing.** An asphalt built-up roof is composed of several layers of asphalt-saturated felt applied to a flat or slightly sloped roof-deck. Asphalt is applied between the felt layers for adhesion. Over the top layer a flood coat of asphalt is then added and this is covered with gravel or slag.

Of the types listed the shingle roof has been the most common. Asphalt shingles are applied to the steep roofs of homes, barns, and similar structures. They fill the need for an attractive, efficient, and fire-resistant but low-cost roofing for residential construction.

The built-up roof is a contrasting type, constructed on the flat or nearly flat tops of very large buildings—industrial, public, and many others. These roofs are literally paved with asphalt, although in a manner quite different from the paving of roads.

15.04 **PREPARED PRODUCTS.**—Prepared roofings are those products which are manufactured and packaged ready to apply to the roof deck, usually by nailing only. Asphalt shingles and certain roll roofings are in this category. They consist of a base of saturated felt to which has been added an asphalt coating and, usually, a surfacing of mineral granules. For built-up roofing, only the components are manufactured and delivered to the job— the roofing itself being built up directly on the roof deck in a series of layers of plies.

Figure XV-1—Asphalt Shingles Cover More Homes Than All Other Types of Roofing Combined

15.05 SLOPE OF ROOF.—There are many roofs on which either prepared or built-up roofing can be used, but the choice is limited somewhat by the slope of the deck to which it is to be applied. Built-up roofs are usually applied only on the flatter slopes while the application of asphalt shingles and other prepared roofing is usually confined to the steeper slopes. However, with special techniques asphalt shingles are also often applied on slopes from two to four inches per foot.

15.06 WIND PROTECTION FOR ASPHALT SHINGLES.—In certain sections of the country subject to high winds, special techniques have been developed to protect conventional asphalt shingles against wind damage. One solution to this problem has been the fastening down of each of the shingle tabs with a small amount of asphalt cement placed under the tab after the shingles have been applied. Other approaches to this problem have been the development of shingles of special patterns which include slots or small tabs for locking the lower edge of the shingle in place, or which are designed to have the lower edge fastened down by a special corrosion resistant staple.

However, the latest development in wind protection for asphalt shingles is a special adhesive which does not take hold until it is exposed to heat of the sun. This adhesive is placed on the shingle in such a manner that, after the shingles have been applied to the roof and warmed by the sun, the adhesive firmly cements each tab to the roofing beneath it. No special application techniques are required, and in handling and storing only simple precautions must be taken to keep the shingles from being exposed to the sun for extended periods of time before application.

That this type of shingle has solved the problem of wind damage has been demonstrated by reports of recent hurricanes. Roofs sealed by this new principle have been virtually undamaged. In some cases, the asphalt shingles have remained intact, even though the entire roof structure was blown off.

15.07 COLOR-STYLED SHINGLES.—Asphalt shingles are available in almost any color from pastels to deep rich tones. Factory techniques of application of granules have improved with the development of new permanent colors, and granules may be applied in almost any blend or pattern of colors desired.

15.08 METHODS AND TYPES OF APPLICATION. —Methods of application and types of asphaltic materials used vary according to specifications. Often built-up roofs are of the cold-process type, which calls for a final coating of asphalt, applied by brush or spray, instead of slag or gravel. Yet whatever the method and type of asphalt, its use insures economy. Asphalt felts, manufactured at low cost and put up in rolls of a convenient size, are easily transported. Since they are flexible and pliable—

and thus conveniently handled—their application to the roof deck is simple and does not require highly-skilled labor.

The mopping on of the asphalt and the spreading of slag or gravel may be accomplished with the most readily available and simplest type of equipment. All operations can be performed quickly by the hand method of application, although for very large roofs mechanical felt-laying machines, hot-asphalt applicators, and gravel spreaders have been developed which will do the job more easily and rapidly. If properly constructed, an asphalt built-up roof will remain in top service condition for many years with little or no maintenance required. If it is found that occasional patching is necessary, it can be done at negligible cost.

15.09 INDUSTRIAL ROOFS.—Recent years also have seen changes in built-up roofing for industrial and commercial buildings, but these should more rightly be called changes in emphasis on the use of certain types of asphalt rather than changes in the materials themselves. Particularly in the West, there is evidence of a considerable shift of the construction of industrial and commercial buildings with flat, or nearly flat roofs. These flat decks allow the use of an asphalt with a considerably lower melting point than could be used on the steeper roofs. These softer asphalts usually have a longer life than the harder material which must be used to prevent flow during hot weather on the steeper slopes.

Also, they usually are manufactured with greater temperature susceptibility in order that any small cracks which may develop from contraction, expansion, or minor movements due to settling of the building may be healed by the softening and slight flowing which occurs in the asphalt on the roof during hot weather. This "healing" of cracks is of greater importance on flat slopes where water may remain for some time after a rain than it is on steeper slopes where water drains away at once.

The manufacture of low melt point asphalts for use specifically on flat decks highlights the many advantages of being able to "tailor make" asphalts with character-istics which best fit the intended service requirements. There is a roofing asphalt available for use in any climate and on any slope on which built-up roofing can be used.

Figure XV-2—Modern Industrial Building With Asphalt Built-Up Roof

15.10 ROOFING APPLICATION AUXILIARY EQUIPMENT.—It is safe to say that there has been greater progress made in the development of new equipment for the roofing applicator since 1950 than in the fifty years prior to that. And, what is more important, the acceptance and use of this equipment is beginning to keep pace with the development.

In the handling of asphalt shingles, pallets and fork lifts are almost universally used. On the job, many roofers now go one step further than the mere mechanical unloading of trucks—they place the shingles directly on the roof from the truck. Fork lifts, or, in some cases, lift-bed trucks are used for this purpose. On buildings too high for this type of equipment, there are a great variety of elevators and hoists available—from simple attachments for use with ladders to elaborate power-operated apparatus.

15.11 ASPHALT KETTLE.—The heart of the entire built-up roofing operation is the kettle for heating the asphalt to the proper temperature for application. For efficient operation the kettle must be able to bring the asphalt up to this temperature in a short period of time without overheating at the start, or at any time during the kettle's operation. Overheating may seriously damage the asphalt and considerably reduce the life expectancy of the roof.

Overheating may also cause the asphalt to be applied too thinly, resulting in poor adhesion between the roofing felts and possible later separation of the plies. It is likely that more failures in built-up roofing can be traced to overheating of the asphalt than to any other factor.

Most of these overheating problems can be solved by the use of the recently developed thermostatically controlled kettles. Standard temperature controls, similar to those used in the control of heating in the home, are adapted to this use. The thermostat is set to the desired temperature and the burner is shut off automatically when the asphalt reaches this temperature—not to be turned on again until the temperature drops below the established range.

The addition of a circulating pump to such a kettle results in an even temperature throughout and prevents local overheating. This recirculating of the asphalt may be done by a pump whose primary function is to raise the hot asphalt to the roof easily and quickly, thereby saving considerable labor and resulting in very little cooling of the asphalt before it is applied—a big improvement over the slow, inefficient methods of hoisting to the roof in buckets. Recent pump designs have proved to be practically fool-proof as far as plugged lines and breakdowns are concerned.

15.12 FELT LAYER.—The next step in the mechanization of the built-up roofing operation is the felt layer. This machine applies hot asphalt and a layer of felt in one uniform, continuous, controlled operation.

15.13 AGGREGATE SPREADER.—The spreading of roofing aggregate is also often done mechanically. The spreaders do a much more uniform and efficient job than can be done by hand with shovels. The felt layer, or a flood coater, may be used to apply the flood coat of asphalt, followed immediately by the aggregate spreader, thus assuring that the roofing aggregate is placed before the asphalt has a chance to cool.

The availability of such a wealth of new application equipment is both an opportunity and a challenge to the roofer. There is an opportunity for the production of a better roof at lower cost, but each job presents a challenge in engineering of the operation to make the best use of the equipment available. With the proper use of mechanized methods, nobody loses—the roofer can make greater profits and the owner gets a better, longer lasting roof.

B.—Playgrounds

15.14 PLAYGROUND SURFACING.—Pavement is, of course, not the immediate requirement for all playgrounds. Where it is, however, the following outline guide may help to shape the planning of those responsible.

Asphalt surface treatment, penetration macadam, and hot and cold mix surfacings have been used for playgrounds and, except for such modification as may be necessary because of restrictions due to area, the same procedure should be followed as when building a highway. For most situations a foundation thickness of from four to six inches will be ample. Properly graded, good quality crushed stone, slag, and gravel all make excellent bases and drain readily because of their porous nature. Foundations also may be constructed by stabilizing suitable natural soils with asphaltic products. Except for surface treatment, a surface course thickness of from 1½ to 2 inches is desirable, from the standpoint of durability. The surface texture as a rule should be fine grained. In addition to those types which use the usual mineral aggregates, experiments have been made with sawdust, cork, or rubber fillers.

Proprietary products have been developed and widely accepted using an emulsified asphalt base combined with selected pigments and fillers for squeegee application on asphalt concrete. These materials develop a tight seal with no loose material remaining. They permit easy cleaning and maintenance, and develop a smooth, non-skid surface.

15.15 ASPHALT-SAWDUST SURFACE.—For an asphalt-sawdust surface the procedure is essentially similar to surface treatment, and may be an original treatment over a waterbound surface course or a retreatment over an established surface. It may be either a light or heavy treatment. All the sawdust should pass a No. 4 sieve in the former and a ½ inch sieve in the latter and should not contain shavings or splinters. The surface should be thoroughly rolled with a light roller until the sawdust is well embedded. Emulsified asphalt or light, rapid-curing liquid asphalt may be used as a binder. For the heavy treatment, either heavy rapid-curing liquid asphalt, RC-800, or a hot asphalt cement may be used. The asphalt cement should have a penetration between 200 and 300, and be applied at a temperature between 275°F and 325°F.

After application of the asphaltic material, coarse sawdust should be spread and rolled until thoroughly embedded. The amount of asphalt should be about three-tenths gallon per square yard, with the sawdust added in thin applications and broomed about until no more will adhere.

15.16 ASPHALT CORK SURFACE.—For an asphalt cork surface the course is laid to a compacted depth of one to two inches, and usually upon an asphalt base or binder course. The mix should be composed of granulated cork, ¼ inch maximum diameter, sharp coarse sand, limestone dust, and an asphalt cement of 60-70 penetration. The following weight proportions have been used successfully in surfacing an exceptionally large municipal playground:

	PERCENT
Clean sharp sand	70 to 72
Ground cork	5 to 6
Limestone dust	7 to 8
Asphalt cement	15 to 17

Figure XV-3—Asphalt-Paved Playground, Washington, D.C.

15.17 PAVING DETAILS.—Full details on procedures involved in the paving of playgrounds, with the various asphalt types mentioned, are available upon request to the nearest Asphalt Institute Office. A list of Institute Offices and Member Companies will be found in the end papers.

C.—Tennis Courts

15.18 GENERAL.—Asphalt tennis courts are fast, true, and available for play immediately after rain. Where funds are limited, courts can be constructed on a sound base with an asphalt concrete leveling course, then finished with a fine-textured, enriched asphalt concrete. Proprietary products have been developed for multiple-layers constructed to very close tolerances and these courts, in color, are popular with players and athletic authorities.

15.19 SURFACE TYPES.—Surfaces should be made from sand asphalt mixtures such as Asphalt Institute mix types VII or VIII. See Asphalt Institute Specification Series No. 1, *Specifications and Construction Methods for Asphalt Concrete and Other Plant-Mix Types.*

The use of color on asphalt tennis courts is becoming increasingly popular. Favorite colors are grass-green and tile red, or a combination of both. A number of proprietary products are marketed for this purpose, but they must be tested to be sure they are compatible with asphalt and will weather without bleeding or discoloration. These special finishes are water-based materials and should be diluted to proper consistency before application. Best results are obtained by spreading with a long-handled hair broom in several applications.

15.20 DRAINAGE.—Proper drainage is of the utmost importance in the construction of a good court. Where funds are limited it is much better to place a low-cost surface than to neglect the foundation. In sandy or gravelly soil, underdrainage may not be required, but in heavy clay soils it is desirable to dig a ditch entirely around the court, with such bottom slope and outlet as will prevent accumulation of water. The ditch should be two or three feet in depth, with a perforated corrugated iron pipe, or open clay tile at the bottom, and should then be backfilled with broken stone or coarse gravel to within a few inches of the surface.

15.21 LAYOUT.—The paved area of a tennis court should be 60 by 120 feet, which gives ample room outside the limits of a doubles court, 36 feet by 78 feet for play.

It is preferable to have the entire surface in one plane but, where this is not practicable because of the topography, the slope may drop each way from the net. The usual gradient is one inch in 10 feet or, for a single plane, one end of the court is one foot lower than the other; while

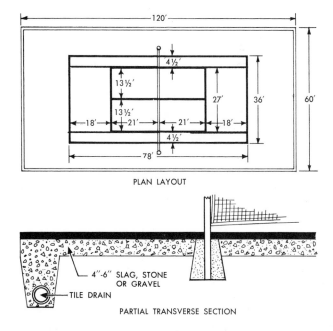

PLAN LAYOUT

PARTIAL TRANSVERSE SECTION

Figure XV-4—Design Layout for Tennis Court

for a slope either way from the net, each end is six inches lower than center. In the construction the subgrade should be leveled and finished to such an elevation that when the base and surface course are applied later the finished surface will be slightly above the adjacent sodded area. Where fills are made, they should be compacted thoroughly, and preferably allowed to stand under the weather until subjected to several heavy rains, before placing the surface.

15.22 BASE COURSE.—For the base course good quality steam cinders are quite satisfactory, and a compacted depth of four to six inches usually will be sufficient. Where crushed stone, slag or gravel base courses are constructed, it is desirable to place first a layer of screenings or sand, so as to consolidate and harden the subgrade and prevent the infiltration of earth into the coarser material. A one inch depth of screenings well worked into the earth will be sufficient, with three to six inches compacted depth of stone, slag or gravel. The base course should be rolled thoroughly and uniformly. Base courses also may be constructed by stabilizing suitable natural soils with asphaltic products. A superior type foundation may be obtained by placing asphalt base two to three inches in compacted depth.

15.23 ASPHALT MACADAM AND SURFACE TREATMENT.—Where funds are limited, macadam surfaces have been constructed using standard procedures. But, due to difficulty in obtaining surfaces smooth enough for good play, they are not widely accepted.

15.24 MULTIPLE-LAYER COLD MIX CONSTRUCTION.—Using proprietary products, a system of multi-layer construction provides a very high type weather-resistant surface. Layout is important, with an asphalt base and good drainage for sound foundation. These courts are constructed in one plane, sloped one inch in 15 feet from one end to the other. The four-inch minimum thickness base may be emulsified asphalt penetration construction, although other types of asphalt-treated base are acceptable. For the leveling and surface courses, cold mixes consisting of carefully blended aggregate and filler, with specially prepared emulsified asphalts and sufficient water, are prepared for proper placement by screed. The leveling course is 1½ inches thick, followed by a finer textured ½-inch surface course. After each course is dried, it is rolled to maximum compaction. The surface is checked with a 10-foot straightedge, permitting a maximum variation of ⅛ inch. Then the court is flooded, and low spots marked. Fine-textured mixes are applied, feather-edged, to fill the low spots.

Successive applications of factory-compounded products, containing the proper balance of emulsified asphalt binder, selected mineral fillers, and selected coloring are applied by squeegee to obtain a smooth, non-skid texture, and complete sealing action. Where color fastness is desired, special proprietary products are used in the final application. These special products contain no asphalt, but are compatible with asphalt surfacing and are applied at a rate of 10-15 gallons per 1,000 square feet, using long-handled hair brooms.

15.25 ASPHALT CONCRETE SURFACE.—Other high type surfaces are constructed with plant mixes. Coarse-graded mixtures are employed for the intermediate course, but the upper inch of surface course should be preferably a dense sand-asphalt mixture. Such mixtures may be accurately struck with a template to true cross section and profile, and will permit of slight adjustments to correct base irregularities. Because of the lighter traffic on a court as contrasted with a road or street, slightly more asphalt of somewhat softer consistency is recommended for the mix. Any cracking or drying out of surface with age can be remedied by light asphalt surface treatment at the rate of 0.1 gallon per square yard of cutback asphalt, RC-70, or quick-setting emulsified asphalt, RS-1 or RS-2K, and 10 pounds of sand cover. Proprietary products also have been developed for sealing cracked and weathered surfaces.

D.—Asphalt Swimming Pools

15.26 GENERAL CONSIDERATIONS.—Pools have various types of paved surfaces, but *asphalt* because of its superior waterproof characteristics is particularly well adapted for such use. The best asphalt construction calls for a dense-graded hot-laid surface course, although well sealed asphalt macadam has also been successfully used. It is important that the surface course be laid on a substantial well-drained base so as to eliminate any back pressure from ground water when the pool is periodically emptied for cleaning. In cold climates, depending upon the thickness of ice formation, the pool may be drained to any desired level to produce a skating rink.

All plans should be cleared with local authorities before construction begins.

15.27 ASPHALT POOL AT WALLINGFORD.—Wallingford, Connecticut, in 1960, completed a record size asphalt swimming pool. The pool has an over-all water surface area of more than 60,000 square feet and a depth ranging from three feet at the shallow end to nine feet, six inches in the diving pool.

For ten years the Wallingford pool was a community swimming pond, fed by a small brook. However, silt, filtering in with the flow from the stream, created a muddy bottom which, in turn, discolored the water. It was decided to line the pond with a dense asphalt concrete to permit periodic cleaning.

After removing about 500 cubic yards of accumulated silt, the engineer added some one thousand cubic yards of gravel to the natural sand foundation. On top of this was placed four to six inches of compacted stone base, gradation ranging from 1¼ inches down to ¾ inches. This base was surfaced with three inches of dense asphalt concrete, placed in two courses—two inches of intermediate mix and one inch of surface mix. After spray priming, this surface was treated with an emulsified filler before painting with an acrylic finish.

Figure XV-5—Asphalt-Paved Swimming Pool, Montpelier, Vt.

Figure XV-6—Asphalt-Paved Pool, Wallingford, Conn.

15.28 VERSATILITY IN USE.—Asphalt-paved pools can provide large swimming areas at relatively low cost. For example, the Wallingford pool is roped off into three areas. Approximately one-third of the pool, for tots and non-swimmers, slopes to a maximum depth of three feet. Beyond the guard rope is a full 50-meter racing pool ranging in depth from three to eight feet. Thereafter, the bottom slopes abruptly to a large diving area.

15.29 ADVANTAGES OF ASPHALT.—Superior qualities of asphalt-paved swimming pools include smoothness, pleasing appearance, and exceptionally good weathering qualities. These latter are based upon asphalt's resistance to water, sunlight, air, pressure, weight, freezing, thawing, chlorine, and abrasion.

15.30 RESURFACED SWIMMING POOL.—Another very large swimming pool, now asphalt-surfaced, is located at Crescent Hill, Louisville, Kentucky. This pool, 175 feet long by 150 feet wide, oval in shape, originally of rigid-type surface construction, had cracked and disintegrated so badly that it was decided to resurface with asphalt. Construction procedure consisted of patching, priming with a tack coat of a rapid-setting liquid asphalt, and resurfacing with one and one-half inches of asphalt concrete. After the bottom of the pool had been paved, using standard paving equipment and a 10-ton roller, the surface was coated lightly with aluminum paint, and two coats of white marine then applied.

15.31 REPAVING WITH ASPHALT.—The resurfacing of the large Crescent Hill swimming pool was so successful that a year later it was decided to repave the cracked and disintegrating surface of the nearby wading pool. This was effectively salvaged by patching, priming, and placing, over its approximately 2,000 square feet of worn out rigid-type paving, a smooth, waterproof surface of one and one-half inches of sheet asphalt.

15.32 ASPHALT WADING POOLS.—An asphalt wading pool may be visualized as a huge, shallow, waterproof platter, with a gradual slope to a suitable depth, possibly about eighteen inches. For this surface, three inches of hot-mix sheet asphalt or a fine-graded asphalt concrete, properly placed and compacted, on a well-drained foundation, will provide the necessary water-proofness and adequately smooth texture.

It is important that the foundation for the pool be carefully constructed by first shaping the earth subgrade to proper conformation and then densifying, by thorough compaction, at least eight or nine inches of the subgrade material. As there should be provision for draining, the bottom of the pool should be sloped slightly so that it may be quickly cleaned.

An asphalt wading pool, as the surface is not affected by freezing, will serve equally well for a skating rink in winter.

E.—Asphalt on the Farm

15.33 GENERAL.—Agricultural studies have shown that paved feed lots, barn lots, loafing areas, barn floors and similar areas are advantageous in livestock operations, especially dairy and beef cattle. As compared with muddy and dusty unpaved areas, the paved lots have many advantages to the livestock operator, such as:

(1) Faster rate of gain for beef stock
(2) Better milk production by dairy stock
(3) Better sanitation
(4) Ease of cleaning
(5) Better appearance

15.34 ADVANTAGES OF ASPHALT.—Asphalt pavement for livestock areas is not only lower in cost than other pavements, but also more durable, resistant to attack of animal wastes, and more resilient and thus easier on animal feet. Owing to its dark color, snow and ice melt faster. Also, it is quickly and easily laid and ready for use without a curing period.

15.35 REQUIREMENTS.—

(1) **Subgrade.** The natural soil foundation for livestock pavement should be cleared of debris, smoothed and sloped to proper line and grade, and compacted by

rolling to uniform supporting power. Thickness of pavement to be placed on the subgrade is indicated in Table XV-1.

Table XV-1—PAVEMENT THICKNESSES RECOMMENDED FOR LIVESTOCK USES

KIND OF SUBGRADE		THICKNESS REQUIREMENTS IN INCHES		
		Asphalt Concrete Surface	Base Course	Subbase Course
Good	Gravelly or sandy soils well drained and compacted	2 to 4	4	None
Fair	Average clay loam soils, not plastic when wet	2 to 4	4 to 6	0 to 4
Poor	Heavy clay soils, plastic when wet	2 to 4	4 to 6	4 to 8

(2) **Drainage.** Positive surface drainage is a must. A slope of not less than one inch in 10 feet is recommended, and even greater slope is desirable. Where the edge of pavement is in excavation or cut, a drainage channel (ditch or French drain) is necessary along the edge to carry drainage away quickly and to prevent it from seeping under the pavement.

(3) **Base and Subbase Courses.** Material for base and subbase courses should consist of good quality aggregates which meet local (county, city, or state) requirements for road and street construction. Materials should be well graded from coarse to fine, with not over eight percent passing a No. 200 sieve. These courses should be spread uniformly and well compacted.

(4) **Surface Course.** Acids in barnyard wastes do not affect asphalt, but they may affect and eventually erode certain types of aggregates such as the softer limestones or dolomites. Therefore, it is preferable to use aggregates in the surface course that will not react with acids. Also, it is necessary to make the surface course tight and dense to prevent infiltration of moisture into the pavement.

(5) **Sand Dressing.** After surface rolling is finished, the pavement should be uniformly covered with fine sand at the approximate rate of 10 pounds to the square yard.

CAUTION

Livestock operators are cautioned not to embark on a do-it-yourself effort to install paving for livestock. An experienced asphalt paving contractor should be engaged.

Figure XV-7—An Asphalt-Paved Farm Lot

15.36 PAVEMENT TYPE.—The concentrated loads of feet and the wheels of vehicles used for farm operations require a strong, durable pavement structure consisting of an asphalt course on top, supported by necessary base and subbase courses. Best results are normally obtained if the asphalt pavement is made of asphalt concrete.

15.37 MAINTENANCE.—See Chapter IX, Section B.

F.—Drive-in Theaters

15.38 GENERAL.—Asphalt is ideal for paving drive-in theaters because its dark surface has very low reflection of light, thus aiding vision of the screen.

15.39 TYPES OF PAVEMENTS.—Pavements for drive-in theaters are essentially the same as for parking lots carrying light passenger car traffic. (See Chapter XIII.)

G.—Industrial Floors

15.40 GENERAL.—Asphalt floors are admirably adapted for use in many factories and warehouses. They are ordinarily laid, if above ground level, on portland cement concrete decks but at or below ground level may be laid on any base course suitable for highway construction. Asphalt floors are waterproof, highly resistant to wear and, therefore, dustless and, by the selection of a highly silicious mineral aggregate for admixture with the asphalt cement, may be made acid-proof.

15.41 ASPHALT MASTIC FLOORS.—Originally asphalt mastic was prepared with crushed rock asphalt. The term is now, however, commonly applied to a mixture of graded sand, mineral filler, and asphalt cement quite similar in character to sheet asphalt paving. Factory and warehouse floors are frequently subjected to very heavy unit loads carried on small diameter narrow metal wheels. When this condition has to be met the regular sheet asphalt mixture is modified by using a harder asphalt cement of approximately 40 to 50 penetration and a higher proportion of very fine mineral filler. A maximum thickness of 1½ inches is recommended. Where acid-resistance is not required, but where high stability and shock resistance are needed for fork lift trucks, a proprietary product of specially prepared emulsified asphalt, portland cement, plaster sand and ⅜-inch rock may be used.

15.42 ASPHALT CONCRETE FLOORS.—Hot-laid dense-graded aggregate asphalt concrete such as used in paving highways and airports is particularly well adapted for paving warehouse and factory floors. Asphalt itself is unaffected by the various acids, but the mineral aggregate should be acid resistant and care should be taken to design and compact the mixture so as to produce very high density and imperviousness.

The thickness of the surface, base and subbase courses for warehouse floors should be designed as would highways for similar loadings. Refer to *Thickness Design —Asphalt Pavement Structures for Highways and Streets,* Manual Series No. 1 (MS-1), The Asphalt Institute.

15.43 ASPHALT BLOCK FLOORS.—Asphalt block type pavements have been widely and successfully used for heavy duty industrial floors, loading platforms, piers and ramps. They ordinarily are laid on a mortar bed with close joints and an emulsified asphalt joint filler applied with a squeegee machine.

H.—Asphalt Pipe Coatings

15.44 MAJOR TYPES.—Asphalt protective coatings for pipe lines* are of three major types as follows:
- (1) Wrapped Systems
- (2) Mastic Systems
- (3) Coatings for Interior Surfaces

15.45 WRAPPED SYSTEMS.—Asphalt wrapped systems for pipe lines consist of a prime coat followed by

---

* See also *Asphalt Institute Construction Series No. 96,* Asphalt Protective Coatings for Pipe Lines.

either one or two applications of asphalt enamel in conjunction with one or more layers of reinforcing and protective wrappings. An outer wrap may sometimes be applied in place of or in addition to the inner wrap. When extra protection* is required, additional layers or thicknesses of enamel and wrapping should be applied. When rock fill is encountered, extra protection* consisting of selected backfill or prefabricated rock shields may also be specified.

(1) SINGLE WRAP SYSTEM consists of the following:

    a. 1 coat of asphalt primer

    b. 1 coat of hot asphalt enamel 3/32 inch ± 1/32 inch

    c. 1 wrap of asphalt-saturated felt or asphalt-saturated glass wrap, completely bonded to the enamel

(or, where a more vulnerable, unshielded system is acceptable to the engineer, the following may be used):

    d. 1 coat of asphalt primer

    e. 1 coat of hot asphalt enamel 3/32 inch ± 1/32 inch—Grade B enamel only

    f. 1 wrap of glass mat (embedded in coating)

(2) DOUBLE WRAP SYSTEM consists of the following:

    a. 1 coat of asphalt primer

    b. 1 coat of hot asphalt enamel 3/32 inch ± 1/32 inch

    c. 1 wrap of glass mat (embedded in enamel)

    d. 1 wrap of asphalt-saturated felt or asphalt-saturated glass wrap, completely bonded to the enamel

(3) DOUBLE COAT—DOUBLE WRAP SYSTEM consists of the following:

---

* NOTE: *The Engineer shall specify the location and extent of extra protection required.*

a. 1 coat of asphalt primer

b. 1 coat of hot asphalt enamel 3/32 inch $\pm$ 1/32 inch

c. 1 wrap of asphalt-saturated felt, asphalt-saturated glass wrap, or glass mat, completely bonded to the enamel

d. 1 coat of hot asphalt enamel 2/32 inch minimum

e. 1 wrap of asphalt-saturated felt or asphalt-saturated glass wrap, completely bonded to the enamel

Where more than a double wrap is required, the procedure specified in either of the double wrap systems is modified to permit additional layers of hot asphalt enamel and wraps of asphalt-saturated felt, glass mat, or asphalt-saturated glass wrap.

15.46 MASTIC SYSTEMS.—Mastic systems for pipe lines consist of a prime coat followed by a coating of a dense, impervious, essentially voidless mixture of asphalt, mineral aggregate, and mineral filler, which may include asbestos fiber. The minimum permissible thickness usually is ¼ inch. The finished mastic coating should be painted with a whitewash.

Specifications and methods of testing for asphalt primer, asphalt binder, mineral aggregate, mineral filler, and asbestos filler are fully covered in Asphalt Institute Construction Series No. 96, *Asphalt Protective Coatings for Pipe Lines*, as are methods of constructing mastic systems for protective coatings for pipe lines.

15.47 COATINGS FOR INTERIOR SURFACES.— Asphalt coatings for interior surfaces of pipe lines consist of a prime coat followed by a centrifugally cast layer of asphalt enamel. The thickness usually is 3/32 inch $\pm$ 1/32 inch.

Specifications and methods of testing for asphalt primer and asphalt enamel for use on interior coatings of pipe lines are fully covered in Asphalt Institute Construction Series No. 96, *Asphalt Protective Coatings for Pipe Lines*, as are construction methods and tests of finished coating. Copies of this publication are available from Asphalt Institute Engineering offices as listed in the end papers.

I.—*Sidewalks*

(See Section G, Chapter X.)

J.—*Asphalt Mulch Treatment*

15.48 GENERAL.—Stabilizing slopes and flat areas adjacent to highways and other installations is a chronic problem for engineers, just as it has become a problem of national magnitude for farmers. Soil erosion, caused by wind and water, can be halted and prevented most effectively and economically by the establishment of vegetation which has the effect of anchoring the soil in place.

However, unless artificial methods are employed to maintain soil stability during the period of germination, the continuing destructive forces of nature may carry away the seed almost as rapidly as it is planted. To prevent this, mulching is employed to protect the seedlings in place until the plants are well started.

The application of a liquid asphalt spray in combination with the mulch locks the mulch in place and provides a thin film blanket which accelerates germination and assures a lush stand of vegetation.

15.49 METHOD OF USE.—There are two accepted methods for using asphalt in the mulching process. One is to apply the asphalt alone, in a spray film, on the seeded area. The other method is to employ the liquid asphalt as a tie-down for straw or hay. Established procedures have proved that asphalt can be used successfully in both types of treatment. The procedures will be discussed separately.

(1) **Asphalt Spray Mulch.** When using asphalt alone as a mulching spray, generally an asphalt emulsion is applied to the seeded area. This thin film of asphalt has three beneficial effects. First, it holds the seed in place against the eroding forces of wind and

rain. Secondly, by virtue of its dark color, it absorbs and conserves solar heat during the germination period. Finally, it tends to hold moisture in the soil, promoting rich and speedy plant growth. The asphalt film shrinks and cracks readily as the plantings emerge from the soil, permitting free plant growth. Eventually, after it has served its purpose, the asphalt film disintegrates.

The asphalt commonly used in film spray is asphalt emulsion (SS-1, SS-K, SM-K, or MS-2). This spray is applied at a rate of 0.15 to 0.30 gallon per square yard, depending upon the soil and slope of the area being treated. Care must be exercised in the rate of application. An excess of asphalt may seal the soil, delaying growth. Too little asphalt may not hold the soil against the erosive effects of wind and water.

The area should be properly prepared before seeding. No ridges or holes should be evident, otherwise distribution of the asphalt will not be uniform. Where there is a ridge, one side may receive a very heavy application while the far side may receive none. Where there are holes, the asphalt may flow and form puddles, slowing seed germination.

After the area has been prepared, seed and fertilizer are spread. This may be done by hand but several machines have been developed which apply seed, fertilizer and water in a single application. The machines can work from firm ground, blowing the mixture onto the seeding area without marring the prepared surface.

After seeding, the asphalt is sprayed on the area at the prescribed rate. The asphalt may be applied by hand-spray nozzle or with an offset distributor bar attached to an asphalt distributor truck.

(2) **Asphalt Mulch Tie-Down.** There are two methods in common use for anchoring straw or hay mulch with asphalt. One method is to spread the straw or hay over the area, then blanket it with a fog spray of asphalt. In the other method, employing a mechanical blower, the straw or hay is ejected simultaneously with the asphalt and the two ingredients are mixed in

Figure XV-8—Applying Asphalt to Straw-Mulched Slopes with Offset Spray Bar Attached to Distributor Truck

flight. Both methods will achieve excellent results if properly performed.

The tie-down method has many advantages over the old-style method of actually tying down the mulch with wooden pegs and twine. Very little hand labor is required and the seeded area is spared the damaging effect of men and machines tracking about on the slopes to leave miniature slides that may result in a washing out of top soil, seed, fertilizer, and mulch.

The two methods of using asphalt tie-down with mulch are discussed separately.

(3) **Method A.** After the area has been properly prepared, the straw or hay mulch is applied at a rate of approximately 1½ to 2 tons per acre. The mulch may be placed manually or with special blower developed for this purpose. With the mulch in place, the

seed is mixed with water and the mixture is sprayed by a hydraulic seed and fertilizer applicator. Borne in the watery mixture, the seed and fertilizer pass through the mulch and enter the soil. The liquid asphalt is then sprayed over the mulch, locking it in place.

The asphalt may be applied in a variety of patterns. Some prefer a saw-tooth pattern and there are some who use the checkerboard pattern, crossing evenly spaced perpendicular lines of asphalt with horizontal ones. The method most commonly used, and one which seems to perform most effectively—especially where wind velocity is high—is the application of the asphalt in a solid pattern.

When applying the asphalt in a solid pattern, a specially designed single-spray nozzle may be used or, in certain areas, a specially designed multiple-nozzle spray bar. The asphalt is usually applied at a rate of 0.10 gallon per square yard when the mulch is applied at the rate specified above. When a larger amount of

Figure XV-9—Mechanical Blower Ejecting Straw and Asphalt Simultaneously in a Single Efficient Operation

mulch is used the rate of application for the asphalt should be increased proportionately.

(4) **Method B.** After the area has been prepared for seeding, and after seed and fertilizer have been spread, the mulch and asphalt are placed in a single, blended application. Special blower equipment, with twin jets, ejects the asphalt and mulching material simultaneously. This method has two important advantages. It applies the two materials in a single operation, reducing the cost and speeding the work, and it results in a more complete bonding of the hay straw mulch.

Various agencies specify certain asphalt materials for use in the tie-down method but, generally, it has been found that any type of liquid asphalt thin enough to be blown from the spray equipment is satisfactory. Recommended for use are rapid curing (RC-70, RC-250 and RC-800), medium curing (MC-250 and MC-800), and emulsified asphalts (SS-1, SS-K, SM-K, MS-2, RS-1, RS-2, RS-2K, and RS-3K).

15.50 REFERENCES.—Additional information concerning the uses of asphalt discussed in this chapter will be found in the following Asphalt Institute technical publications:

(1) *Specifications and Construction Methods for Asphalt Concrete and Other Plant-Mix Types*, Specification Series No. 1 (SS-1)

(2) *Thickness Design—Asphalt Pavement Structures for Highways and Streets*, Manual Series No. 1 (MS-1)

(3) *Mix Design Methods for Asphalt Concrete and Other Hot-Mix Types*, Manual Series No. 2 (MS-2)

(4) *Asphalt Plant Manual*, Manual Series No. 3 (MS-3)

(5) *Asphalt Mulch Treatment*, Manual Series No. 7 (MS-7)

(6) *Asphalt Paving Manual*, Manual Series No. 8 (MS-8)

(7) *Asphalt in Hydraulic Structures*, Manual Series No. 12 (MS-12)

(8) *Asphalt Surface Treatments and Asphalt Penetration Macadam*, Manual Series No. 13 (MS-13)

(9) *Asphalt Protective Coatings for Pipe Lines*, Construction Series No. 96 (CS-96).

Chapter XVI

USEFUL TABLES AND
MISCELLANEOUS INFORMATION

16.01 GENERAL.—This chapter contains a collection of tables and miscellaneous information which is often helpful to users of asphaltic materials. Some of this material is in tabular form and some is in descriptive form. Information relative to the following is included: Instructions for Unloading Asphalt Tank Cars, Temperature-Volume Corrections for Asphaltic Materials, and useful tables.

16.02 INSTRUCTIONS FOR UNLOADING ASPHALT TANK CARS.—

WARNING

Keep lights and fires away. Do not use air or gas pressure in unloading tank cars.

---

(1) **Heating Equipment.** All asphalt tank cars are equipped with steam coils, some with a single unit coil and some with double unit coils.

Connections for steam inlet and steam outlet are identified on asphalt tank cars. It is important that the proper connection be made. Condensation may build up in the lines and prevent the free flow of steam if it is introduced into the coils at the outlet connection. When the proper connection is made, condensation will flow by gravity through the coils and discharge through the steam outlets.

The inlets to steam coils should be protected by a globe valve between the boiler and the tank car coil.

A ground joint union should be placed between the steam boiler and the tank car coils to expedite the assembly of the line and to provide a suitable place to break the line in case it is necessary to move the car.

The outlets from the steam coils should be reduced to ½ inch and a valve placed on the end of this coil so it can be adjusted to take care of condensation. With the double unit coil cars, a separate exhaust valve should be provided for each coil, so placed that if one coil leaks, the other coil may be used by closing the valve on the defective coil.

If at any time the stop cock on outlet valve has to be removed, the inlet valve should be closed first.

A union of some type should be placed in the unloading hose to facilitate easy connection or disconnection of the unloading line should the car be switched.

In heating all material it is essential that sufficient steam pressure be used. The time it takes to heat asphalt to a temperature so that it can be easily pumped depends entirely on the grade or penetration of the material, the pressure of steam used and weather conditions; from eight to twelve hours are sufficient under normal conditions.

Steam at a pressure of 90 pounds to 125 pounds should be used. The heat units are as follows: 90 pounds, 331°F; 100 pounds, 338°F; 110 pounds, 345°F; 125 pounds, 355°F. In order to pump readily, heavy paving asphalt of 45 to 60 penetration should be heated to around 240°F; 100 to 150 penetration to about 225°F; lighter grades should be heated to 200°F to 215°F.

(2) **Application of Steam.** Before turning steam into coils, be sure the outlet valves are wide open. Turn the steam into heater coils gradually until coil has been heated and steam shows at the outlet, after which steam can be turned on full.

After steam shows at the outlet, adjust outlet valve to take care of condensation.

Steam coils are easily broken by too rapid expansion unless this procedure is carefully followed.

During the first hour of steaming, it is desirable to open the steam outlet valve from time to time in order to blow out all surplus condensation, and thus insure more efficient heating.

The bubbling of steam through the asphalt is an indication of a break in the steam coil. Often rumbling will be heard.

If the car is equipped with double coils, turn off the steam from both coils and then determine which coil is defective by turning steam into each coil separately. Contents may then be heated by means of the good coil.

If both coils are defective, or a leak is found in the single coil type cars, the contents may be heated by the use of a portable coil inserted into the car through the dome.

If the contents of the car cannot be heated by methods described above, then notify shipper.

(3) **Placement and Unloading of Tank Cars.** Tank cars should be spotted on a level track with brakes set and the wheels blocked. The dome cover should be opened and the internal valve (see Figure XVI-3) inspected to be sure that it is in the closed position.

The unloading hose assembly should then be made ready for connection. The valve cap on the outlet leg should be eased off gradually, watching carefully for any indication of leakage. If leakage is apparent, tighten the cap and check the internal valve in the dome to be sure it is tightly closed. If there is no leakage, remove the cap and connect the unloading hose.

Before starting to unload, check all valves and lines leading to storage or to the truck to see that they are clear. Then open the internal valve and proceed with unloading.

If the outlet leg is plugged with asphalt, apply live steam. In no case should an open flame be used either on the outlet leg or under the tank car.

Whenever the unloading operation is discontinued, the internal valve should be closed before closing the valve on the hose assembly in order to allow the outlet leg to drain. Whenever the car is left unattended, pumping should be discontinued, the internal valve should be closed, dome cover replaced, hose assembly and steam lines disconnected, and outlet leg cap replaced.

After the tank car has been completely unloaded, close the internal valve and replace the dome cover, screwing down tight.

Outlet leg or cap should be left open until thoroughly drained, then closed.

Disconnect steam coil connections and permit coils to drain. DO NOT replace caps on steam coil outlets when returning the tank car, thereby insuring proper draining of the coils.

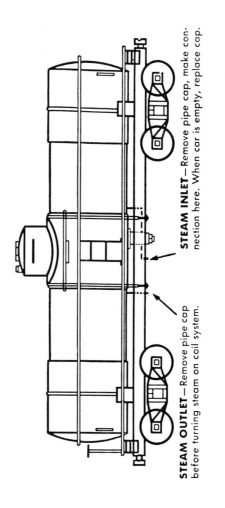

STEAM INLET—Remove pipe cap, make connection here. When car is empty, replace cap.

STEAM OUTLET—Remove pipe cap before turning steam on coil system.

Figure XVI-1—Single-Unit Coiled Car

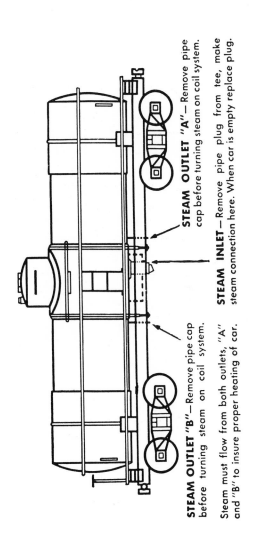

STEAM OUTLET "A" — Remove pipe cap before turning steam on coil system.

STEAM INLET — Remove pipe plug from tee, make steam connection here. When car is empty replace plug.

STEAM OUTLET "B" — Remove pipe cap before turning steam on coil system.

Steam must flow from both outlets, "A" and "B" to insure proper heating of car.

Figure XVI-2—Double-Unit Coiled Car

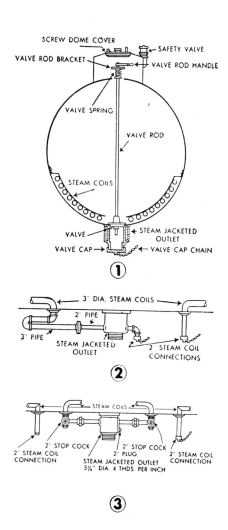

Figure XVI-3—(1) Internal Valve Assembly, (2) Steam and
Outlet Connections, Single Coil, (3) Steam and Outlet
Connections, Double Coil

16.03 TEMPERATURE-VOLUME CORRECTIONS FOR ASPHALTIC MATERIALS.

—Asphaltic products change in volume with change in temperature. Change in unit volume per degree change in temperature is termed "Coefficient of Expansion," a factor which varies with variations in the specific gravity of the asphaltic product. A temperature of 60°F is customarily used as the standard basis for volume determinations of asphalt and other petroleum products.

The American Society for Testing and Materials prepared and published extensive data tables on temperature-volume corrections of petroleum products. These tables appear in a book entitled *ASTM-IP Petroleum Measurement Tables,* published in January 1953 (ASTM designation D 1250). Temperature-Volume correction Tables XVI-1 and XVI-2, contained herein, have been extracted from this ASTM publication.

Temperature-Volume correction data are given in Table XVI-1 for asphaltic materials having a specific gravity at 60°F above 0.966 (designated by ASTM as Group 0 materials) and in Table XVI-2 for asphaltic materials having a specific gravity at 60°F of 0.850 to 0.966 inclusive (designated by ASTM as Group 1 materials).

Temperature-Volume corrections for emulsified asphalts are given in Table XVI-3.

Example of Use. Assume a specific gravity of an asphaltic product to be 0.985 at 60°F. Assume also that a volume of this material is measured to be 9,000 gallons at a temperature of 180°F. Determine the volume of this material at the standard temperature of 60°F.

Method. The specific gravity of 0.985 places the material in Group 0. Opposite a temperature of 180°F in the tabulation for Group 0 materials, the correction factor is determined to be 0.9587. Multiplying 0.9587 x 9000 gallons gives a volume at 60°F of 8628 gallons.

TABLE XVI-1—TEMPERATURE—VOLUME
CORRECTIONS FOR ASPHALTIC MATERIALS

GROUP 0—SPECIFIC GRAVITY AT 60°F ABOVE 0.966

LEGEND: t = observed temperature in degrees Fahrenheit
M = multiplier for correcting oil volumes to the basis of 60°F

t	M	t	M	t	M	t	M	t	M
0	1.0211	50	1.0035	100	0.9861	150	0.9689	200	0.9520
1	1.0208	51	1.0031	101	0.9857	151	0.9686	201	0.9516
2	1.0204	52	1.0028	102	0.9854	152	0.9682	202	0.9513
3	1.0201	53	1.0024	103	0.9851	153	0.9679	203	0.9509
4	1.0197	54	1.0021	104	0.9847	154	0.9675	204	0.9506
5	1.0194	55	1.0017	105	0.9844	155	0.9672	205	0.9503
6	1.0190	56	1.0014	106	0.9840	156	0.9669	206	0.9499
7	1.0186	57	1.0010	107	0.9837	157	0.9665	207	0.9496
8	1.0183	58	1.0007	108	0.9833	158	0.9662	208	0.9493
9	1.0179	59	1.0003	109	0.9830	159	0.9658	209	0.9489
10	1.0176	60	1.0000	110	0.9826	160	0.9655	210	0.9486
11	1.0172	61	0.9997	111	0.9823	161	0.9652	211	0.9483
12	1.0169	62	0.9993	112	0.9819	162	0.9648	212	0.9479
13	1.0165	63	0.9990	113	0.9816	163	0.9645	213	0.9476
14	1.0162	64	0.9986	114	0.9813	164	0.9641	214	0.9472
15	1.0158	65	0.9983	115	0.9809	165	0.9638	215	0.9469
16	1.0155	66	0.9979	116	0.9806	166	0.9635	216	0.9466
17	1.0151	67	0.9976	117	0.9802	167	0.9631	217	0.9462
18	1.0148	68	0.9972	118	0.9799	168	0.9628	218	0.9459
19	1.0144	69	0.9969	119	0.9795	169	0.9624	219	0.9456
20	1.0141	70	0.9965	120	0.9792	170	0.9621	220	0.9452
21	1.0137	71	0.9962	121	0.9788	171	0.9618	221	0.9449
22	1.0133	72	0.9958	122	0.9785	172	0.9614	222	0.9446
23	1.0130	73	0.9955	123	0.9782	173	0.9611	223	0.9442
24	1.0126	74	0.9951	124	0.9778	174	0.9607	224	0.9439
25	1.0123	75	0.9948	125	0.9775	175	0.9604	225	0.9436
26	1.0119	76	0.9944	126	0.9771	176	0.9601	226	0.9432
27	1.0116	77	0.9941	127	0.9768	177	0.9597	227	0.9429
28	1.0112	78	0.9937	128	0.9764	178	0.9594	228	0.9426
29	1.0109	79	0.9934	129	0.9761	179	0.9590	229	0.9422
30	1.0105	80	0.9930	130	0.9758	180	0.9587	230	0.9419
31	1.0102	81	0.9927	131	0.9754	181	0.9584	231	0.9416
32	1.0098	82	0.9923	132	0.9751	182	0.9580	232	0.9412
33	1.0095	83	0.9920	133	0.9747	183	0.9577	233	0.9409
34	1.0091	84	0.9916	134	0.9744	184	0.9574	234	0.9405
35	1.0088	85	0.9913	135	0.9740	185	0.9570	235	0.9402
36	1.0084	86	0.9909	136	0.9737	186	0.9567	236	0.9399
37	1.0081	87	0.9906	137	0.9734	187	0.9563	237	0.9395
38	1.0077	88	0.9902	138	0.9730	188	0.9560	238	0.9392
39	1.0074	89	0.9899	139	0.9727	189	0.9557	239	0.9389
40	1.0070	90	0.9896	140	0.9723	190	0.9553	240	0.9385
41	1.0067	91	0.9892	141	0.9720	191	0.9550	241	0.9382
42	1.0063	92	0.9889	142	0.9716	192	0.9547	242	0.9379
43	1.0060	93	0.9885	143	0.9713	193	0.9543	243	0.9375
44	1.0056	94	0.9882	144	0.9710	194	0.9540	244	0.9372
45	1.0053	95	0.9878	145	0.9706	195	0.9536	245	0.9369
46	1.0049	96	0.9875	146	0.9703	196	0.9533	246	0.9365
47	1.0046	97	0.9871	147	0.9699	197	0.9530	247	0.9362
48	1.0042	98	0.9868	148	0.9696	198	0.9526	248	0.9359
49	1.0038	99	0.9864	149	0.9693	199	0.9523	249	0.9356

TABLE XVI-1 (Continued)—TEMPERATURE—VOLUME CORRECTIONS FOR ASPHALTIC MATERIALS

GROUP 0—SPECIFIC GRAVITY AT 60°F ABOVE 0.966

LEGEND: t = observed temperature in degrees Fahrenheit
M = multiplier for correcting oil volumes to the basis of 60°F

t	M	t	M	t	M	t	M	t	M
250	0.9352	300	0.9187	350	0.9024	400	0.8864	450	0.8705
251	0.9349	301	0.9184	351	0.9021	401	0.8861	451	0.8702
252	0.9346	302	0.9181	352	0.9018	402	0.8857	452	0.8699
253	0.9342	303	0.9177	353	0.9015	403	0.8854	453	0.8696
254	0.9339	304	0.9174	354	0.9011	404	0.8851	454	0.8693
255	0.9336	305	0.9171	355	0.9008	405	0.8848	455	0.8690
256	0.9332	306	0.9167	356	0.9005	406	0.8845	456	0.8687
257	0.9329	307	0.9164	357	0.9002	407	0.8841	457	0.8683
258	0.9326	308	0.9161	358	0.8998	408	0.8838	458	0.8680
259	0.9322	309	0.9158	359	0.8995	409	0.8835	459	0.8677
260	0.9319	310	0.9154	360	0.8992	410	0.8832	460	0.8674
261	0.9316	311	0.9151	361	0.8989	411	0.8829	461	0.8671
262	0.9312	312	0.9148	362	0.8986	412	0.8826	462	0.8668
263	0.9309	313	0.9145	363	0.8982	413	0.8822	463	0.8665
264	0.9306	314	0.9141	364	0.8979	414	0.8819	464	0.8661
265	0.9302	315	0.9138	365	0.8976	415	0.8816	465	0.8658
266	0.9299	316	0.9135	366	0.8973	416	0.8813	466	0.8655
267	0.9296	317	0.9132	367	0.8969	417	0.8810	467	0.8652
268	0.9293	318	0.9128	368	0.8966	418	0.8806	468	0.8649
269	0.9289	319	0.9125	369	0.8963	419	0.8803	469	0.8646
270	0.9286	320	0.9122	370	0.8960	420	0.8800	470	0.8643
271	0.9283	321	0.9118	371	0.8957	421	0.8797	471	0.8640
272	0.9279	322	0.9115	372	0.8953	422	0.8794	472	0.8636
273	0.9276	323	0.9112	373	0.8950	423	0.8791	473	0.8633
274	0.9273	324	0.9109	374	0.8947	424	0.8787	474	0.8630
275	0.9269	325	0.9105	375	0.8944	425	0.8784	475	0.8627
276	0.9266	326	0.9102	376	0.8941	426	0.8781	476	0.8624
277	0.9263	327	0.9099	377	0.8937	427	0.8778	477	0.8621
278	0.9259	328	0.9096	378	0.8934	428	0.8775	478	0.8618
279	0.9256	329	0.9092	379	0.8931	429	0.8772	479	0.8615
280	0.9253	330	0.9089	380	0.8928	430	0.8768	480	0.8611
281	0.9250	331	0.9086	381	0.8924	431	0.8765	481	0.8608
282	0.9246	332	0.9083	382	0.8921	432	0.8762	482	0.8605
283	0.9243	333	0.9079	383	0.8918	433	0.8759	483	0.8602
284	0.9240	334	0.9076	384	0.8915	434	0.8756	484	0.8599
285	0.9236	335	0.9073	385	0.8912	435	0.8753	485	0.8596
286	0.9233	336	0.9070	386	0.8908	436	0.8749	486	0.8593
287	0.9230	337	0.9066	387	0.8905	437	0.8746	487	0.8590
288	0.9227	338	0.9063	388	0.8902	438	0.8743	488	0.8587
289	0.9223	339	0.9060	389	0.8899	439	0.8740	489	0.8583
290	0.9220	340	0.9057	390	0.8896	440	0.8737	490	0.8580
291	0.9217	341	0.9053	391	0.8892	441	0.8734	491	0.8577
292	0.9213	342	0.9050	392	0.8889	442	0.8731	492	0.8574
293	0.9210	343	0.9047	393	0.8886	443	0.8727	493	0.8571
294	0.9207	344	0.9044	394	0.8883	444	0.8724	494	0.8568
295	0.9204	345	0.9040	395	0.8880	445	0.8721	495	0.8565
296	0.9200	346	0.9037	396	0.8876	446	0.8718	496	0.8562
297	0.9197	347	0.9034	397	0.8873	447	0.8715	497	0.8559
298	0.9194	348	0.9031	398	0.8870	448	0.8712	498	0.8556
299	0.9190	349	0.9028	399	0.8867	449	0.8709	499	0.8552

TABLE XVI-2—TEMPERATURE—VOLUME
CORRECTIONS FOR ASPHALTIC MATERIALS

GROUP 1—SPECIFIC GRAVITY AT 60°F OF 0.850 TO 0.966

LEGEND: t = observed temperature in degrees Fahrenheit
M = multiplier for correcting oil volumes to the basis of 60°F

t	M	t	M	t	M	t	M	t	M
0	1.0241	50	1.0040	100	0.9842	150	0.9647	200	0.9456
1	1.0237	51	1.0036	101	0.9838	151	0.9643	201	0.9452
2	1.0233	52	1.0032	102	0.9834	152	0.9639	202	0.9448
3	1.0229	53	1.0028	103	0.9830	153	0.9635	203	0.9444
4	1.0225	54	1.0024	104	0.9826	154	0.9632	204	0.9441
5	1.0221	55	1.0020	105	0.9822	155	0.9628	205	0.9437
6	1.0217	56	1.0016	106	0.9818	156	0.9624	206	0.9433
7	1.0213	57	1.0012	107	0.9814	157	0.9620	207	0.9429
8	1.0209	58	1.0008	108	0.9810	158	0.9616	208	0.9425
9	1.0205	59	1.0004	109	0.9806	159	0.9612	209	0.9422
10	1.0201	60	1.0000	110	0.9803	160	0.9609	210	0.9418
11	1.0197	61	0.9996	111	0.9799	161	0.9605	211	0.9414
12	1.0193	62	0.9992	112	0.9795	162	0.9601	212	0.9410
13	1.0189	63	0.9988	113	0.9791	163	0.9597	213	0.9407
14	1.0185	64	0.9984	114	0.9787	164	0.9593	214	0.9403
15	1.0181	65	0.9980	115	0.9783	165	0.9589	215	0.9399
16	1.0177	66	0.9976	116	0.9779	166	0.9585	216	0.9395
17	1.0173	67	0.9972	117	0.9775	167	0.9582	217	0.9391
18	1.0168	68	0.9968	118	0.9771	168	0.9578	218	0.9388
19	1.0164	69	0.9964	119	0.9767	169	0.9574	219	0.9384
20	1.0160	70	0.9960	120	0.9763	170	0.9570	220	0.9380
21	1.0156	71	0.9956	121	0.9760	171	0.9566	221	0.9376
22	1.0152	72	0.9952	122	0.9756	172	0.9562	222	0.9373
23	1.0148	73	0.9948	123	0.9752	173	0.9559	223	0.9369
24	1.0144	74	0.9944	124	0.9748	174	0.9555	224	0.9365
25	1.0140	75	0.9940	125	0.9744	175	0.9551	225	0.9361
26	1.0136	76	0.9936	126	0.9740	176	0.9547	226	0.9358
27	1.0132	77	0.9932	127	0.9736	177	0.9543	227	0.9354
28	1.0128	78	0.9929	128	0.9732	178	0.9539	228	0.9350
29	1.0124	79	0.9925	129	0.9728	179	0.9536	229	0.9346
30	1.0120	80	0.9921	130	0.9725	180	0.9532	230	0.9343
31	1.0116	81	0.9917	131	0.9721	181	0.9528	231	0.9339
32	1.0112	82	0.9913	132	0.9717	182	0.9524	232	0.9335
33	1.0108	83	0.9909	133	0.9713	183	0.9520	233	0.9331
34	1.0104	84	0.9905	134	0.9709	184	0.9517	234	0.9328
35	1.0100	85	0.9901	135	0.9705	185	0.9513	235	0.9324
36	1.0096	86	0.9897	136	0.9701	186	0.9509	236	0.9320
37	1.0092	87	0.9893	137	0.9697	187	0.9505	237	0.9316
38	1.0088	88	0.9889	138	0.9693	188	0.9501	238	0.9313
39	1.0084	89	0.9885	139	0.9690	189	0.9498	239	0.9309
40	1.0080	90	0.9881	140	0.9686	190	0.9494	240	0.9305
41	1.0076	91	0.9877	141	0.9682	191	0.9490	241	0.9301
42	1.0072	92	0.9873	142	0.9678	192	0.9486	242	0.9298
43	1.0068	93	0.9869	143	0.9674	193	0.9482	243	0.9294
44	1.0064	94	0.9865	144	0.9670	194	0.9478	244	0.9290
45	1.0060	95	0.9861	145	0.9666	195	0.9475	245	0.9286
46	1.0056	56	0.9857	146	0.9662	196	0.9471	246	0.9283
47	1.0052	97	0.9854	147	0.9659	197	0.9467	247	0.9279
48	1.0048	98	0.9850	148	0.9655	198	0.9463	248	0.9275
49	1.0044	99	0.9846	149	0.9651	199	0.9460	249	0.9272

TABLE XVI-2 (Continued)—TEMPERATURE— VOLUME CORRECTIONS FOR ASPHALTIC MATERIALS

GROUP 1—SPECIFIC GRAVITY AT 60°F OF 0.850 TO 0.966

LEGEND: t = observed temperature in degrees Fahrenheit
M = multiplier for correcting oil volumes to the basis of 60°F

t	M	t	M	t	M	t	M	t	M
250	0.9268	300	0.9083	350	0.8902	400	0.8724	450	0.8550
251	0.9264	301	0.9080	351	0.8899	401	0.8721	451	0.8547
252	0.9260	302	0.9076	352	0.8895	402	0.8717	452	0.8543
253	0.9257	303	0.9072	353	0.8891	403	0.8714	453	0.8540
254	0.9253	304	0.9069	354	0.8888	404	0.8710	454	0.8536
255	0.9249	305	0.9065	355	0.8884	405	0.8707	455	0.8533
256	0.9245	306	0.9061	356	0.8881	406	0.8703	456	0.8529
257	0.9242	307	0.9058	357	0.8877	407	0.8700	457	0.8526
258	0.9238	308	0.9054	358	0.8873	408	0.8696	458	0.8522
259	0.9234	309	0.9050	359	0.8870	409	0.8693	459	0.8519
260	0.9231	310	0.9047	360	0.8866	410	0.8689	460	0.8516
261	0.9227	311	0.9043	361	0.8863	411	0.8686	461	0.8512
262	0.9223	312	0.9039	362	0.8859	412	0.8682	462	0.8509
263	0.9219	313	0.9036	363	0.8856	413	0.8679	463	0.8505
264	0.9216	314	0.9032	364	0.8852	414	0.8675	464	0.8502
265	0.9212	315	0.9029	365	0.8848	415	0.8672	465	0.8498
266	0.9208	316	0.9025	366	0.8845	416	0.8668	466	0.8495
267	0.9205	317	0.9021	367	0.8841	417	0.8665	467	0.8492
268	0.9201	318	0.9018	368	0.8838	418	0.8661	468	0.8488
269	0.9197	319	0.9014	369	0.8834	419	0.8658	469	0.8485
270	0.9194	320	0.9010	370	0.8831	420	0.8654	470	0.8481
271	0.9190	321	0.9007	371	0.8827	421	0.8651	471	0.8478
272	0.9186	322	0.9003	372	0.8823	422	0.8647	472	0.8474
273	0.9182	323	0.9000	373	0.8820	423	0.8644	473	0.8471
274	0.9179	324	0.8996	374	0.8816	424	0.8640	474	0.8468
275	0.9175	325	0.8992	375	0.8813	425	0.8637	475	0.8464
276	0.9171	326	0.8989	376	0.8809	426	0.8633	476	0.8461
277	0.9168	327	0.8985	377	0.8806	427	0.8630	477	0.8457
278	0.9164	328	0.8981	378	0.8802	428	0.8626	478	0.8454
279	0.9160	329	0.8978	379	0.8799	429	0.8623	479	0.8451
280	0.9157	330	0.8974	380	0.8795	430	0.8619	480	0.8447
281	0.9153	331	0.8971	381	0.8792	431	0.8616	481	0.8444
282	0.9149	332	0.8967	382	0.8788	432	0.8612	482	0.8440
283	0.9146	333	0.8963	383	0.8784	433	0.8609	483	0.8437
284	0.9142	334	0.8960	384	0.8781	434	0.8605	484	0.8433
285	0.9138	335	0.8956	385	0.8777	435	0.8602	485	0.8430
286	0.9135	336	0.8952	386	0.8774	436	0.8599	486	0.8427
287	0.9131	337	0.8949	387	0.8770	437	0.8595	487	0.8423
288	0.9127	338	0.8945	388	0.8767	438	0.8592	488	0.8420
289	0.9124	339	0.8942	389	0.8763	439	0.8588	489	0.8416
290	0.9120	340	0.8938	390	0.8760	440	0.8585	490	0.8413
291	0.9116	341	0.8934	391	0.8756	441	0.8581	491	0.8410
292	0.9113	342	0.8931	392	0.8753	442	0.8578	492	0.8406
293	0.9109	343	0.8927	393	0.8749	443	0.8574	493	0.8403
294	0.9105	344	0.8924	394	0.8746	444	0.8571	494	0.8399
295	0.9102	345	0.8920	395	0.8742	445	0.8567	495	0.8396
296	0.9098	346	0.8916	396	0.8738	446	0.8564	496	0.8393
297	0.9094	347	0.8913	397	0.8735	447	0.8560	497	0.8389
298	0.9091	348	0.8909	398	0.8731	448	0.8557	498	0.8386
299	0.9087	349	0.8906	399	0.8728	449	0.8554	499	0.8383

TABLE XVI-3—TEMPERATURE—VOLUME CORRECTIONS FOR EMULSIFIED ASPHALTS

LEGEND: t = observed temperature in degrees Fahrenheit
m = multiplier for correcting volumes to the basis of 60°F

t	M	t	M	t	M
60	1.00000	90	.99250	121	.98475
61	.99975	91	.99225	122	.98450
62	.99950	92	.99200	123	.98425
63	.99925	93	.99175	124	.98400
64	.99900	94	.99150	125	.98375
65	.99875	95	.99125	126	.98350
66	.99850	96	.99100	127	.98325
67	.99825	97	.99075	128	.98300
68	.99800	98	.99050	129	.98275
69	.99775	99	.99025	130	.98250
70	.99750	100	.99000	131	.98225
71	.99725	101	.98975	132	.98200
72	.99700	102	.98950	133	.98175
73	.99675	103	.98925	134	.98150
74	.99650	104	.98900	135	.98125
75	.99625	105	.98875	136	.98100
76	.99600	106	.98850	137	.98075
77	.99575	107	.98825	138	.98050
78	.99550	108	.98800	139	.98025
79	.99525	109	.98775	140	.98000
80	.99500	110	.98750	141	.97975
81	.99475	111	.98725	142	.97950
82	.99450	112	.98700	143	.97925
83	.99425	113	.98675	144	.97900
84	.99400	114	.98650	145	.97875
85	.99375	115	.98625	146	.97850
86	.99350	116	.98600	147	.97825
87	.99325	117	.98575	148	.97800
88	.99300	118	.98550	149	.97775
89	.99275	119	.98525	150	.97750
		120	.98500		

TABLE XVI-4—WEIGHT AND VOLUME RELATIONS OF ASPHALTIC MATERIALS AT 60°F

Sp. Gr. 60/60°F	Degrees A.P.I. *	Pounds** per Gallon	Gallons*** per Pound	Gallons *** per Ton
0.855	34.0	7.119	0.1405	280.9
60	33.0	.161	.1396	279.3
65	32.1	.203	.1388	277.7
70	31.1	.244	.1380	276.1
75	30.2	.286	.1372	274.5
80	29.3	.328	.1365	272.9
85	28.4	.369	.1357	271.4
90	27.5	.411	.1349	269.9
95	26.6	.453	.1342	268.4
0.900	25.7	.494	.1334	266.9
05	24.9	.536	.1327	265.4
10	24.0	.578	.1320	263.9
15	23.1	.620	.1312	262.5
20	22.3	.661	.1305	261.1
25	21.5	.703	.1298	259.6
30	20.7	.745	.1291	258.2
35	19.8	.786	.1284	256.9
40	19.0	.828	.1278	255.5
45	18.2	.870	.1271	254.1
50	17.5	.911	.1264	252.8
55	16.7	.953	.1257	251.5
60	15.9	.995	.1251	250.2
65	15.1	8.036	.1244	248.9
70	14.4	.078	.1238	247.6
75	13.6	.120	.1232	246.3
80	12.9	.162	.1225	245.0
85	12.2	.203	.1219	243.8
90	11.4	.245	.1213	242.6
95	10.7	.287	.1207	241.4
1.000	10.0	.328	.1201	240.2
05	9.3	.370	.1195	239.0
10	8.6	.412	.1189	237.8
15	7.9	.453	.1183	236.6
20	7.2	.495	.1177	235.4
25	6.6	.537	.1171	234.3
30	5.9	.578	.1166	233.1
35	5.2	.620	.1160	232.0
40	4.6	.662	.1154	230.9
45	3.9	.704	.1149	229.8
50	3.3	.745	.1143	228.7
55	2.6	.787	.1138	227.6
60	2.0	.829	.1133	226.5
65	1.4	.870	.1127	225.5
70	.7	.912	.1122	224.4
75	.1	.954	.1117	223.4
76	0.0	.962	.1116	223.2

* A. P. I. Gravity Degrees = $\dfrac{141.5}{\text{Sp. Gr. } 60°/60° \text{ F.}} - 131.5$

** For Lbs per Imperial Gallon multiply values in this column by 1.20094.

*** For Imperial Gallons per Lb or per Ton multiply values in these columns by 0.83268.

TABLE XVI-5—WEIGHTS AND VOLUMES OF ASPHALTIC MATERIALS (APPROXIMATE)

Type and Grade	Pounds per Gallon	Pounds per Barrels *	Gallons per Ton	Barrels * per Ton
MC-30....................	7.8	328	256	6.1
RC-, MC-, SC-70	7.9	332	253	6.0
RC-, MC-, SC-250	8.0	337	249	5.9
RC-, MC-, SC-800	8.2	343	245	5.8
RC-, MC-, SC-3000	8.3	349	241	5.7
40-50 Pen. A.C...........	8.6	361	233	5.5
60-70 Pen. A.C...........	8.5	357	235	5.6
85-100 Pen. A.C...........	8.5	357	235	5.6
120-150 Pen. A.C...........	8.5	357	235	5.6
200-300 Pen. A.C...........	8.4	353	238	5.7
Emulsified Asphalts	8.3	349	241	5.7

* A barrel equals 42 U.S. Gallons.
Notes: 1. Since the specific gravity of asphaltic materials varies, even for the same type and grade, the weight and volume relationships shown above are approximate and should be used only for general estimating purposes. Where more precise data are required, they must be computed on the basis of laboratory tests on the specific product.

2. The approximate data shown above are for materials at 60°F (15.6C).

MEMORANDUM OF CALL

Previous editions usable

TO:

☐ YOU WERE CALLED BY—   ☐ YOU WERE VISITED BY—

OF (Organization)

☐ PLEASE PHONE ▶   ☐ FTS   ☐ AUTOVON

☐ WILL CALL AGAIN   ☐ IS WAITING TO SEE YOU

☐ RETURNED YOUR CALL   ☐ WISHES AN APPOINTMENT

MESSAGE

RECEIVED BY	DATE	TIME

63-110   NSN 7540-00-634-4018   **STANDARD FORM 63 (Rev. 8-81)**
GPO : 1987 - 193-554   Prescribed by GSA
FPMR (41 CFR) 101—11.6

TABLE XVI-6—GALLONS OF ASPHALT REQUIRED PER 100 LINEAR FEET; VARIOUS WIDTHS AND GALLONS PER SQUARE YARD

Gals. per Sq. Yd.	WIDTH—FEET														
	1	2	6	7	8	9	10	11	12	14	16	18	20	22	24
0.10	1.1	2.2	6.7	7.8	8.9	10.0	11.1	12.2	13.3	15.6	17.8	20.0	22.2	24.4	26.7
0.15	1.7	3.3	10.0	11.7	13.3	15.0	16.7	18.3	20.0	23.3	26.7	30.0	33.3	36.7	40.0
0.20	2.2	4.4	13.3	15.6	17.8	20.0	22.2	24.4	26.7	31.1	35.6	40.0	44.4	48.9	53.3
0.25	2.8	5.6	16.7	19.4	22.2	25.0	27.8	30.6	33.3	38.9	44.4	50.0	55.6	61.1	66.7
0.30	3.3	6.7	20.0	23.3	26.7	30.0	33.3	36.7	40.0	46.7	53.3	60.0	66.7	73.3	80.0
0.35	3.9	7.8	23.3	27.2	31.1	35.0	38.9	42.8	46.7	54.4	62.2	70.0	77.8	85.5	93.3
0.40	4.4	8.9	26.7	31.1	35.6	40.0	44.4	48.9	53.3	62.2	71.1	80.0	88.9	97.8	107.
0.45	5.0	10.0	30.0	35.0	40.0	45.0	50.0	55.0	60.0	70.0	80.0	90.0	100.	110.	120.
0.50	5.6	11.1	33.3	38.9	44.4	50.0	55.6	61.1	66.7	77.8	88.9	100.	111.	122.	133.
0.55	6.1	12.2	36.7	42.8	48.9	55.0	61.1	67.2	73.3	85.5	97.8	110.	122.	134.	147.
0.60	6.7	13.3	40.0	46.7	53.3	60.0	66.7	73.4	80.0	93.3	107.	120.	133.	147.	160.
0.65	7.2	14.4	43.3	50.6	57.8	65.0	72.2	79.4	86.7	101.	116.	130.	144.	159.	173.
0.70	7.8	15.6	46.7	54.4	62.2	70.0	77.8	85.5	93.3	109.	124.	140.	156.	171.	187.
0.75	8.3	16.7	50.0	58.3	66.7	75.0	83.3	91.7	100.	117.	133.	150.	167.	183.	200.
0.80	8.9	17.8	53.3	62.2	71.1	80.0	88.9	97.8	107.	124.	142.	160.	178.	196.	213.
0.85	9.4	18.9	56.7	66.1	75.5	85.0	94.4	104.	113.	132.	151.	170.	189.	208.	227.
0.90	10.0	20.0	60.0	70.0	80.0	90.0	100.	110.	120.	140.	160.	180.	200.	220.	240.
0.95	10.6	21.1	63.3	73.9	84.4	95.0	106.	116.	127.	148.	169.	190.	211.	232.	253.
1.00	11.1	22.2	66.7	77.8	88.9	100.	111.	122.	133.	156.	178.	200.	222.	244.	267.
1.10	12.2	24.4	73.3	85.6	97.8	110.	122.	134.	147.	171.	196.	220.	244.	269.	293.
1.20	13.3	26.7	80.0	93.3	107.	120.	133.	147.	160.	187.	213.	240.	267.	293.	320.
1.25	13.9	27.8	83.3	97.2	111.	125.	139.	153.	167.	194.	222.	250.	278.	306.	333.
1.30	14.4	28.9	86.7	101.	116.	130.	144.	159.	173.	202.	230.	260.	289.	318.	347.
1.40	15.6	31.1	93.3	109.	124.	140.	156.	171.	187.	218.	249.	280.	311.	342.	373.
1.50	16.7	33.3	100.	117.	133.	150.	167.	183.	200.	233.	267.	300.	333.	367.	400.
1.75	19.4	38.9	117.	136.	156.	175.	194.	214.	233.	272.	311.	350.	389.	427.	467.
2.00	22.2	44.4	133.	156.	178.	200.	222.	244.	267.	311.	356.	400.	444.	489.	533.
2.25	25.0	50.0	150.	175.	200.	225.	250.	275.	300.	350.	400.	450.	500.	550.	600.
2.50	27.8	55.6	167.	194.	222.	250.	278.	306.	333.	389.	444.	500.	556.	611.	667.
2.75	30.6	61.1	183.	214.	244.	275.	306.	336.	367.	428.	489.	550.	611.	672.	733.
3.00	33.3	66.7	200.	233.	267.	300.	333.	367.	400.	467.	533.	600.	667.	733.	800.

Where: Q = Quantity of asphalt required, in gallons per station (100 ft.)
R = Rate of application in gallons per sq. yd.
W = Width of application, in feet

NOTE: Formula used for calculation:

$$Q = \frac{100\ W\ R}{9} = 11.11\ WR$$

TABLE XVI-7—GALLONS OF ASPHALT REQUIRED PER MILE FOR VARIOUS WIDTHS AND GALLONS PER SQUARE YARD

Gals. per Sq. Yd.	WIDTH—FEET														
	1	2	6	7	8	9	10	11	12	14	16	18	20	22	24
0.10	58.7	117	352	411	469	528	587	645	704	821	939	1056	1173	1291	1408
0.15	88.0	176	528	616	704	792	880	968	1056	1232	1408	1584	1760	1936	2112
0.20	117	235	704	821	939	1056	1173	1291	1408	1643	1877	2112	2347	2581	2816
0.25	147	293	880	1027	1173	1320	1467	1613	1760	2053	2347	2640	2933	3227	3520
0.30	176	352	1056	1232	1408	1584	1760	1936	2112	2464	2816	3168	3520	3872	4224
0.35	205	411	1232	1437	1643	1848	2053	2259	2464	2875	3285	3696	4107	4517	4928
0.40	235	469	1408	1643	1877	2112	2347	2581	2816	3285	3755	4224	4693	5163	5632
0.45	264	528	1584	1848	2112	2376	2640	2904	3168	3696	4224	4752	5280	5808	6336
0.50	293	587	1760	2053	2347	2640	2933	3227	3520	4107	4693	5280	5867	6453	7040
0.55	323	645	1936	2259	2581	2904	3227	3549	3872	4517	5163	5808	6453	7099	7744
0.60	352	704	2112	2464	2816	3168	3520	3872	4224	4928	5632	6336	7040	7744	8448
0.65	381	763	2288	2669	3051	3432	3813	4195	4576	5339	6101	6864	7627	8389	9152
0.70	411	821	2464	2875	3285	3696	4107	4517	4928	5749	6571	7392	8213	9035	9856
0.75	440	880	2640	3080	3520	3960	4400	4840	5280	6160	7040	7920	8800	9680	10560
0.80	469	939	2816	3285	3755	4224	4693	5163	5632	6571	7509	8448	9387	10325	11264
0.85	499	997	2992	3491	3989	4488	4987	5485	5984	6981	7979	8976	9973	10971	11968
0.90	528	1056	3168	3696	4224	4752	5280	5808	6336	7392	8448	9504	10560	11616	12672
0.95	557	1115	3344	3901	4459	5016	5573	6131	6688	7803	8917	10032	11147	12261	13376
1.00	587	1173	3520	4107	4693	5280	5867	6453	7040	8213	9387	10560	11733	12907	14080
1.25	733	1467	4400	5133	5867	6600	7333	8067	8800	10267	11733	13200	14667	16133	17600
1.50	880	1760	5280	6160	7040	7920	8800	9680	10560	12320	14080	15840	17600	19360	21120
1.75	1027	2053	6160	7187	8213	9240	10267	11293	12320	14373	16427	18480	20533	22587	24640
2.00	1173	2347	7040	8213	9387	10560	11733	12907	14080	16427	18773	21120	23467	25813	28160
2.25	1320	2640	7920	9240	10560	11880	13200	14520	15840	18480	21120	23760	26400	29040	31680
2.50	1467	2933	8800	10267	11733	13200	14667	16133	17600	20533	23467	26400	29333	32267	35200
2.75	1613	3227	9680	11293	12907	14520	16133	17747	19360	22587	25813	29040	32267	35493	38720
3.00	1760	3520	10560	12320	14080	15840	17600	19360	21120	24640	28160	31680	35200	38720	42240

NOTE: Formula used for calculation:

$$Q = \frac{5280\,W}{9}\,R = 586.67\,WR$$

Where: Q = Quantity of asphalt required, in gallons per mile
R = Rate of application, in gallons per sq. yd.
W = Width of application, in feet

TABLE XVI-8—LINEAR FEET COVERED BY 600-GALLON TANK OF ASPHALT FOR VARIOUS WIDTHS AND GALLONS PER SQUARE YARD

Gals. per Sq. Yd.	WIDTH—FEET														
	1	2	6	7	8	9	10	11	12	14	16	18	20	22	24
0.10	54000	27000	9000	7714	6750	6000	5400	4909	4500	3857	3375	3000	2700	2454	2250
0.15	36000	18000	6000	5143	4500	4000	3600	3272	3000	2571	2250	2000	1800	1636	1500
0.20	27000	13500	4500	3857	3375	3000	2700	2454	2250	1928	1687	1500	1350	1227	1125
0.25	21600	10800	3600	3096	2700	2400	2160	1963	1800	1543	1350	1200	1080	981	900
0.30	18000	9000	3000	2571	2250	2000	1800	1636	1500	1285	1125	1000	900	818	750
0.35	15429	7714	2572	2204	1928	1714	1543	1402	1286	1102	964	857	772	701	643
0.40	13500	6750	2250	1929	1688	1500	1350	1227	1125	964	844	750	675	613	562
0.45	12000	6000	2000	1714	1500	1333	1200	1091	1000	857	750	667	600	545	500
0.50	10800	5400	1800	1543	1350	1200	1080	982	900	771	675	600	540	491	450
0.55	9818	4909	1636	1403	1227	1091	982	893	818	702	614	546	491	446	409
0.60	9000	4500	1500	1286	1125	1000	900	818	750	643	562	500	450	409	375
0.65	8308	4154	1385	1187	1038	923	831	755	692	593	519	461	415	377	346
0.70	7714	3857	1286	1102	964	857	771	701	643	551	482	428	386	350	321
0.75	7200	3600	1200	1029	900	800	720	655	600	514	450	400	360	327	300
0.80	6750	3375	1125	964	844	750	675	613	562	482	422	375	338	306	281
0.85	6353	3176	1059	908	794	706	635	577	529	454	397	353	317	288	265
0.90	6000	3000	1000	857	750	667	600	545	500	428	375	333	300	272	250
0.95	5684	2842	947	812	710	632	568	517	473	406	355	316	284	258	236
1.00	5400	2700	900	771	675	600	540	491	450	385	337	300	270	245	225
1.10	4909	2455	818	701	614	545	491	446	409	351	307	273	245	223	204
1.20	4500	2250	750	643	562	500	450	409	375	321	281	250	225	204	187
1.25	4320	2160	720	617	540	480	432	393	360	308	270	240	216	196	180
1.30	4154	2077	692	593	519	461	415	377	346	296	260	231	207	188	173
1.40	3857	1929	643	551	482	428	386	350	321	275	241	214	193	175	160
1.50	3600	1800	600	514	450	400	360	327	300	257	225	200	180	163	150
1.75	3086	1543	514	441	386	343	309	280	257	220	193	171	154	140	128
2.00	2700	1350	450	386	338	300	270	245	225	193	169	150	135	122	112
2.25	2400	1200	400	343	300	267	240	218	200	171	150	133	120	109	100
2.50	2160	1080	360	309	270	240	216	197	180	154	135	120	108	98	90
2.75	1964	982	327	281	245	218	196	179	164	140	123	109	98	89	82
3.00	1800	900	300	257	225	200	180	164	150	128	112	100	90	82	75

NOTE: See Table XVI-15 for formula used for calculation.

TABLE XVI-9—LINEAR FEET COVERED BY 800-GALLON TANK OF ASPHALT FOR VARIOUS WIDTHS AND GALLONS PER SQUARE YARD

Gals. per Sq. Yd.	WIDTH—FEET														
	1	2	6	7	8	9	10	11	12	14	16	18	20	22	24
0.10	72000	36000	12000	10286	9000	8000	7200	6545	6000	5143	4500	4000	3600	3272	3000
0.15	48000	24000	8000	6857	6000	5333	4800	4364	4000	3429	3000	2667	2400	2182	2000
0.20	36000	18000	6000	5143	4500	4000	3600	3273	3000	2571	2250	2000	1800	1636	1500
0.25	28800	14400	4800	4114	3600	3200	2880	2618	2400	2057	1800	1600	1440	1309	1200
0.30	24000	12000	4000	3429	3000	2667	2400	2182	2000	1714	1500	1333	1200	1091	1000
0.35	20571	10286	3429	2939	2571	2286	2057	1870	1714	1469	1286	1143	1029	935	857
0.40	18000	9000	3000	2571	2250	2000	1800	1636	1500	1286	1125	1000	900	818	750
0.45	16000	8000	2667	2286	2000	1778	1600	1455	1333	1143	1000	889	800	727	667
0.50	14400	7200	2400	2057	1800	1600	1440	1309	1200	1029	900	800	720	654	600
0.55	13091	6545	2182	1870	1636	1455	1309	1190	1091	935	818	727	654	595	545
0.60	12000	6000	2000	1714	1500	1333	1200	1091	1000	857	750	667	600	545	500
0.65	11077	5538	1846	1582	1385	1231	1108	1007	923	791	692	615	554	504	461
0.70	10286	5143	1714	1469	1286	1143	1029	935	857	735	643	571	514	467	428
0.75	9600	4800	1600	1371	1200	1067	960	873	800	686	600	533	480	436	400
0.80	9000	4500	1500	1286	1125	1000	900	818	750	643	563	500	450	409	375
0.85	8471	4235	1412	1210	1059	941	847	770	706	605	529	471	423	385	353
0.90	8000	4000	1333	1143	1000	889	800	727	667	571	500	444	400	363	333
0.95	7579	3789	1263	1083	947	842	758	689	632	541	473	421	379	345	316
1.00	7200	3600	1200	1029	900	800	720	655	600	514	450	400	360	327	300
1.10	6545	3272	1091	935	818	727	655	595	546	467	409	364	327	298	273
1.25	5760	3000	1000	857	750	667	600	545	500	514	450	400	360	327	300
1.30	5538	2880	923	823	720	640	576	524	480	428	375	320	288	262	250
1.40	5143	2769	857	791	692	615	554	504	461	395	346	308	277	252	230
1.50	4800	2571	800	735	643	571	514	468	428	367	321	286	257	234	214
1.75	4114	2400	686	686	600	533	480	436	400	343	300	267	240	218	200
2.00	3600	2057	600	588	514	457	411	374	343	294	257	229	206	187	171
2.25	3200	1800	533	514	450	400	360	327	300	257	200	200	180	163	150
2.50	2880	1600	480	457	480	356	320	291	267	229	225	178	160	145	133
2.75	2618	1440	436	374	400	320	288	262	240	206	180	160	144	131	120
3.00	2400	1309	400	343	360	291	262	238	218	187	163	145	131	119	109

NOTE: See Table XVI-15 for formula used for calculation.

TABLE XVI-10—LINEAR FEET COVERED BY 1000-GALLON TANK OF ASPHALT FOR VARIOUS WIDTHS AND GALLONS PER SQUARE YARD

Gals. per Sq. Yd.	WIDTH—FEET														
	1	2	6	7	8	9	10	11	12	14	16	18	20	22	24
0.10	90000	45000	15000	12857	11250	10000	9000	8182	7500	6429	5625	5000	4500	4091	3750
0.15	60000	30000	10000	8571	7500	6667	6000	5455	5000	4286	3750	3333	3000	2727	2500
0.20	45000	22500	7500	6429	5625	5000	4500	4091	3750	3214	2813	2500	2250	2045	1875
0.25	36000	18000	6000	5143	4500	4000	3600	3273	3000	2571	2250	2000	1800	1636	1500
0.30	30000	15000	5000	4286	3750	3333	3000	2727	2500	2143	1875	1667	1500	1363	1250
0.35	25714	12857	4286	3673	3214	2857	2571	2338	2143	1837	1607	1429	1286	1169	1071
0.40	22500	11250	3750	3214	2813	2500	2250	2045	1875	1607	1406	1250	1125	1022	937
0.45	20000	10000	3333	2857	2500	2222	2000	1818	1667	1429	1250	1111	1000	909	833
0.50	18000	9000	3000	2571	2250	2000	1800	1636	1500	1286	1125	1000	900	818	750
0.55	16364	8182	2727	2338	2046	1818	1636	1488	1364	1169	1023	909	818	744	682
0.60	15000	7500	2500	2143	1875	1667	1500	1364	1250	1071	938	833	750	682	625
0.65	13846	6923	2308	1978	1731	1538	1385	1259	1154	989	865	769	692	629	577
0.70	12857	6429	2143	1837	1607	1429	1286	1169	1071	918	804	714	643	584	535
0.75	12000	6000	2000	1714	1500	1333	1200	1091	1000	857	750	667	600	545	500
0.80	11250	5625	1875	1607	1406	1250	1125	1023	938	804	703	625	563	511	469
0.85	10588	5294	1765	1513	1324	1176	1059	963	882	756	662	588	529	481	441
0.90	10000	5000	1667	1429	1250	1111	1000	909	833	714	625	556	500	454	416
0.95	9474	4737	1579	1353	1184	1053	947	861	789	676	592	526	473	430	394
1.00	9000	4500	1500	1286	1125	1000	900	818	750	643	563	500	450	409	375
1.10	8182	4091	1364	1169	1023	909	818	744	682	584	511	454	409	372	341
1.20	7500	3750	1250	1071	938	833	750	682	625	535	469	416	375	341	312
1.25	7200	3600	1200	1029	900	800	720	655	600	514	450	400	360	327	300
1.30	6923	3462	1154	989	866	769	692	629	577	494	433	384	346	314	288
1.40	6429	3215	1072	918	804	714	643	584	536	459	402	357	321	292	268
1.50	6000	3000	1000	857	750	667	600	545	500	429	375	333	300	272	250
1.75	5143	2571	857	735	643	571	514	468	429	367	321	286	257	234	214
2.00	4500	2250	750	643	563	500	450	409	375	321	281	250	225	204	187
2.25	4000	2000	667	571	500	444	400	364	333	286	250	222	200	182	166
2.50	3600	1800	600	514	450	400	360	327	300	257	225	200	180	163	150
2.75	3273	1636	545	468	409	364	327	298	272	234	204	182	163	149	136
3.00	3000	1500	500	429	375	333	300	273	250	214	187	167	150	136	125

NOTE: See Table XVI-15 for formula used for calculation.

TABLE XVI-11—LINEAR FEET COVERED BY 1200-GALLON TANK OF ASPHALT FOR VARIOUS WIDTHS AND GALLONS PER SQUARE YARD

Gals. per Sq. Yd.	WIDTH—FEET														
	1	2	6	7	8	9	10	11	12	14	16	18	20	22	24
0.10	108000	54000	18000	15429	13500	12000	10800	9818	9000	7714	6750	6000	5400	4909	4500
0.15	72000	36000	12000	10286	9000	8000	7200	6545	6000	5143	4500	4000	3600	3272	3000
0.20	54000	27000	9000	7714	6750	6000	5400	4909	4500	3857	3375	3000	2700	2454	2250
0.25	43200	21600	7200	6171	5400	4800	4320	3927	3600	3086	2700	2400	2160	1963	1800
0.30	36000	18000	6000	5143	4500	4000	3600	3273	3000	2571	2250	2000	1800	1636	1500
0.35	30858	15429	5143	4408	3857	3429	3086	2805	2571	2204	1929	1714	1543	1402	1286
0.40	27000	13500	4500	3857	3375	3000	2700	2455	2250	1929	1688	1500	1350	1227	1125
0.45	24000	12000	4000	3429	3000	2667	2400	2182	2000	1714	1500	1333	1200	1091	1000
0.50	21600	10800	3600	3086	2700	2400	2160	1964	1800	1543	1350	1200	1080	982	900
0.55	19636	9818	3273	2805	2454	2182	1965	1786	1636	1403	1227	1091	982	893	818
0.60	18000	9000	3000	2571	2250	2000	1800	1636	1500	1286	1125	1000	900	818	750
0.65	16616	8308	2769	2374	2077	1846	1662	1510	1385	1187	1038	923	831	755	692
0.70	15428	7714	2571	2204	1929	1714	1543	1403	1286	1102	964	857	771	701	643
0.75	14400	7200	2400	2057	1800	1600	1440	1309	1200	1029	900	800	720	655	600
0.80	13500	6750	2250	1929	1688	1500	1350	1227	1125	964	844	750	675	613	562
0.85	12706	6353	2118	1815	1588	1412	1271	1154	1059	908	794	706	635	577	529
0.90	12000	6000	2000	1714	1500	1333	1200	1091	1000	857	750	667	600	545	500
0.95	11368	5684	1895	1624	1421	1263	1137	1034	947	812	710	632	568	517	473
1.00	10800	5400	1800	1543	1350	1200	1080	982	900	771	675	600	540	491	450
1.10	9818	4909	1636	1403	1227	1091	982	893	818	701	614	545	491	446	409
1.20	9000	4500	1500	1286	1125	1000	900	818	750	643	562	500	450	409	375
1.25	8640	4320	1440	1234	1080	960	864	785	720	617	540	480	432	393	360
1.30	8308	4154	1385	1187	1038	923	831	755	692	593	519	461	415	377	346
1.40	7714	3857	1286	1102	964	857	771	701	643	551	482	428	386	350	321
1.50	7200	3600	1200	1029	900	800	720	655	600	514	450	400	360	327	300
1.75	6172	3086	1029	882	771	686	617	561	514	441	386	343	309	280	257
2.00	5400	2700	900	771	675	600	540	491	450	386	338	300	270	245	225
2.25	4800	2400	800	686	600	533	480	436	400	343	300	267	240	218	200
2.50	4320	2160	720	617	540	480	432	393	360	309	270	240	216	196	180
2.75	3927	1964	655	561	491	436	393	357	327	281	246	218	196	179	164
3.00	3600	1800	600	514	450	400	360	327	300	257	225	200	180	164	150

NOTE: See Table XVI-15 for formula used for calculation.

TABLE XVI-12—LINEAR FEET COVERED BY 1500-GALLON TANK OF ASPHALT FOR VARIOUS WIDTHS AND GALLONS PER SQUARE YARD

Gals. per Sq. Yd.	WIDTH—FEET														
	1	2	6	7	8	9	10	11	12	14	16	18	20	22	24
0.10	135000	67500	22500	19286	16875	15000	13500	12273	11250	9643	8438	7500	6750	6136	5625
0.15	90000	45000	15000	12857	11250	10000	9000	8182	7500	6429	5625	5000	4500	4091	3750
0.20	67500	33750	11250	9643	8438	7500	6750	6136	5625	4821	4219	3750	3375	3068	2812
0.25	54000	27000	9000	7714	6750	6000	5400	4909	4500	3857	3375	3000	2700	2455	2250
0.30	45000	22500	7500	6429	5625	5000	4500	4091	3750	3214	2812	2500	2250	2045	1875
0.35	38571	19286	6429	5510	4821	4286	3857	3507	3214	2755	2411	2143	1929	1753	1607
0.40	33750	16875	5625	4821	4219	3750	3375	3068	2812	2411	2109	1875	1688	1534	1406
0.45	30000	15000	5000	4286	3750	3333	3000	2727	2500	2143	1875	1667	1500	1364	1250
0.50	27000	13500	4500	3857	3375	3000	2700	2455	2250	1929	1688	1500	1350	1227	1125
0.55	24545	12273	4091	3507	3068	2727	2455	2231	2045	1754	1534	1364	1227	1116	1023
0.60	22500	11250	3750	3214	2812	2500	2250	2045	1875	1607	1406	1250	1125	1023	938
0.65	20769	10385	3462	2967	2596	2308	2077	1888	1731	1484	1298	1154	1038	944	865
0.70	19286	9643	3214	2755	2411	2143	1929	1753	1607	1378	1205	1071	964	877	804
0.75	18000	9000	3000	2571	2250	2000	1800	1636	1500	1286	1125	1000	900	818	750
0.80	16875	8437	2812	2411	2109	1875	1688	1534	1406	1205	1055	938	844	767	703
0.85	15882	7941	2647	2269	1985	1765	1588	1444	1324	1134	992	882	794	722	662
0.90	15000	7500	2500	2143	1875	1667	1500	1364	1250	1071	938	834	750	682	625
0.95	14210	7105	2368	2030	1776	1579	1421	1292	1184	1015	888	790	710	646	592
1.00	13500	6750	2250	1929	1688	1500	1350	1227	1125	964	844	750	675	614	562
1.10	12273	6136	2045	1753	1534	1364	1227	1116	1022	877	768	682	614	558	511
1.20	11250	5625	1875	1607	1406	1250	1125	1023	938	803	703	625	562	511	469
1.25	10800	5400	1800	1543	1350	1200	1080	982	900	771	675	600	540	491	450
1.30	10385	5192	1731	1484	1298	1154	1038	944	865	742	649	577	519	472	433
1.40	9643	4821	1607	1378	1205	1071	964	877	804	689	603	536	482	438	402
1.50	9000	4500	1500	1286	1125	1000	900	818	750	643	562	500	450	409	375
1.75	7714	3857	1286	1102	964	857	675	701	643	551	482	429	386	351	321
2.00	6750	3375	1125	964	844	750	600	614	562	482	422	375	338	307	281
2.25	6000	3000	1000	857	750	667	540	545	500	429	375	334	300	273	250
2.50	5400	2700	900	771	675	600	491	491	450	385	338	300	270	246	225
2.75	4909	2455	818	701	614	545	450	446	409	351	307	273	245	223	205
3.00	4500	2250	750	643	562	500	450	409	375	321	281	250	225	204	188

NOTE: See Table XVI-15 for formula used for calculation.

TABLE XVI-13—LINEAR FEET COVERED BY 2000-GALLON TANK OF ASPHALT FOR VARIOUS WIDTHS AND GALLONS PER SQUARE YARD

Gals. per Sq. Yd.	24	22	20	18	16	14	12	11	10	9	8	7	6	2	1
0.10	7500	8182	9000	10000	11250	12857	15000	16364	18000	20000	22500	25714	30000	90000	180000
0.15	5000	5455	6000	6667	7500	8571	10000	10909	12000	13333	15000	17142	20000	60000	120000
0.20	3750	4091	4500	5000	5625	6429	7500	8182	9000	10000	11250	12857	15000	45000	90000
0.25	3000	3273	3600	4000	4500	5143	6000	6545	7200	8000	9000	10286	12000	36000	72000
0.30	2500	2727	3000	3333	3750	4286	5000	5455	6000	6667	7500	8571	10000	30000	60000
0.35	2143	2338	2571	2857	3214	3673	4286	4675	5143	5714	6428	7346	8571	25714	51428
0.40	1875	2045	2250	2500	2813	3214	3750	4091	4500	5000	5625	6428	7500	22500	45000
0.45	1667	1818	2000	2222	2500	2857	3333	3636	4000	4444	5000	5714	6667	20000	40000
0.50	1500	1636	1800	2000	2250	2571	3000	3273	3600	4000	4500	5143	6000	18000	36000
0.55	1364	1488	1636	1818	2046	2338	2727	2975	3273	3636	4091	4676	5455	16364	32728
0.60	1250	1364	1500	1667	1875	2143	2500	2727	3000	3333	3750	4286	5000	15000	30000
0.65	1154	1259	1385	1538	1731	1978	2308	2517	2769	3077	3462	3956	4615	13846	27692
0.70	1071	1169	1286	1429	1607	1837	2143	2338	2571	2857	3214	3673	4286	12857	25714
0.75	1000	1091	1200	1333	1500	1714	2000	2182	2400	2667	3000	3429	4000	12000	24000
0.80	938	1023	1125	1250	1406	1607	1875	2045	2250	2500	2812	3214	3750	11250	22500
0.85	882	963	1059	1176	1324	1513	1765	1925	2118	2353	2647	3026	3529	10588	21176
0.90	833	909	1000	1111	1250	1429	1667	1818	2000	2222	2500	2857	3333	10000	20000
0.95	789	861	947	1053	1184	1353	1579	1722	1895	2105	2368	2706	3158	9474	18946
1.00	750	818	900	1000	1125	1286	1500	1636	1800	2000	2250	2572	3000	9000	18000
1.10	682	744	818	909	1023	1169	1364	1488	1636	1818	2046	2338	2727	8182	16364
1.20	625	682	750	833	938	1071	1250	1364	1500	1667	1875	2143	2500	7500	15000
1.25	600	655	720	800	900	1029	1200	1309	1440	1600	1800	2057	2400	7200	14400
1.30	577	629	692	769	866	989	1154	1259	1385	1538	1732	1978	2308	6923	13848
1.40	536	584	643	714	804	918	1071	1169	1286	1429	1607	1836	2143	6429	12858
1.50	500	545	600	667	750	857	1000	1091	1200	1333	1500	1714	2000	6000	12000
1.75	429	467	514	571	643	735	857	935	1029	1143	1286	1469	1714	5143	10286
2.00	375	409	450	500	563	643	750	818	900	1000	1125	1286	1500	4500	9000
2.25	333	364	400	444	500	571	667	727	800	889	1000	1143	1333	4000	8000
2.50	300	327	360	400	450	514	600	655	720	800	900	1028	1200	3600	7200
2.75	272	298	327	364	409	468	545	595	655	727	818	935	1091	3273	6546
3.00	250	273	300	333	375	429	500	545	600	667	750	857	1000	3000	6000

WIDTH—FEET

NOTE: See Table XVI-15 for formula used for calculation.

Gals. per Sq. Yd.	WIDTH—FEET														
	1	2	6	7	8	9	10	11	12	14	16	18	20	22	24
0.10	225000	112500	37500	32143	28125	25000	22500	20455	18750	16072	14062	12500	11250	10227	9375
0.15	150000	75000	25000	21429	18750	16667	15000	13637	12500	10714	9375	8333	7500	6818	6250
0.20	112500	56250	18750	16071	14062	12500	11250	10227	9375	8036	7031	6250	5625	5113	4687
0.25	90000	45000	15000	12857	11250	10000	9000	8182	7500	6428	5625	5000	4500	4091	3750
0.30	75000	37500	12500	10714	9375	8333	7500	6818	6250	5357	4688	4167	3750	3409	3125
0.35	64286	32143	10714	9184	8036	7143	6429	5844	5357	4592	4018	3571	3214	2922	2678
0.40	56250	28125	9375	8036	7031	6250	5625	5114	4688	4018	3515	3125	2812	2557	2344
0.45	50000	25000	8333	7143	6250	5556	5000	4546	4166	3571	3125	2778	2500	2273	2083
0.50	45000	22500	7500	6429	5625	5000	4500	4091	3750	3214	2812	2500	2250	2045	1875
0.55	40909	20455	6818	5844	5114	4545	4091	3719	3409	2922	2557	2273	2045	1859	1704
0.60	37500	18750	6250	5357	4688	4167	3750	3409	3125	2678	2344	2083	1875	1705	1562
0.65	34615	17308	5769	4945	4327	3846	3462	3147	2884	2472	2163	1923	1731	1573	1442
0.70	32143	16071	5357	4592	4018	3571	3214	2922	2678	2296	2009	1786	1607	1461	1339
0.75	30000	15000	5000	4286	3750	3333	3000	2727	2500	2143	1875	1667	1500	1364	1250
0.80	28125	14062	4687	4018	3516	3125	2812	2557	2344	2009	1758	1562	1406	1278	1172
0.85	26470	13235	4412	3782	3309	2941	2647	2406	2206	1891	1654	1470	1323	1203	1103
0.90	25000	12500	4167	3571	3125	2778	2500	2273	2083	1786	1562	1389	1250	1136	1041
0.95	23684	11842	3947	3383	2960	2632	2368	2153	1974	1692	1480	1316	1184	1076	987
1.00	22500	11250	3750	3214	2812	2500	2250	2046	1875	1607	1406	1250	1125	1023	937
1.05	21428	10714	3571	3061	2679	2381	2143	1948	1786	1531	1339	1190	1071	974	893
1.10	20455	10227	3409	2922	2557	2273	2046	1860	1705	1461	1278	1136	1023	930	852
1.15	19565	9783	3261	2795	2446	2174	1957	1779	1630	1398	1223	1087	978	889	815
1.20	18750	9375	3125	2679	2344	2083	1875	1705	1562	1339	1172	1041	937	852	781
1.25	18000	9000	3000	2571	2250	2000	1800	1636	1500	1286	1125	1000	900	818	750
1.30	17308	8654	2885	2473	2163	1923	1731	1573	1442	1236	1082	961	865	786	721
1.35	16667	8333	2778	2381	2083	1852	1667	1515	1389	1190	1042	926	833	758	694
1.40	16071	8036	2679	2296	2009	1786	1607	1461	1339	1148	1004	893	804	730	669
1.50	15000	7500	2500	2143	1875	1667	1500	1364	1250	1071	937	833	750	682	625
1.75	12857	6429	2143	1837	1607	1429	1286	1169	1071	918	803	714	643	584	536
2.00	11250	5625	1875	1607	1406	1250	1125	1023	938	803	703	625	562	511	469
2.25	10000	5000	1667	1429	1250	1111	1000	909	833	714	625	556	500	454	417
2.50	9000	4500	1500	1286	1125	1000	900	818	750	643	562	500	450	409	375
2.75	8182	4091	1364	1169	1023	909	818	744	682	584	511	454	409	372	341
3.00	7500	3750	1250	1071	938	833	750	682	625	535	469	417	375	341	312

NOTE: See Table XVI-15 for formula used for calculation.

TABLE XVI-15—LINEAR FEET COVERED BY TANK OF ANY CAPACITY FOR VARIOUS WIDTHS AND GALLONS PER SQ. YD.

To compute the number of linear feet which will be covered by a tank of any capacity, for various widths and rates of application, use the following formula:

$$L = \frac{9C}{RW}$$

Where:

L = No. of linear feet which will be covered.

C = Capacity of tank in gallons (or quantity of asphalt in tank).

R = Rate of application in gallons per sq. yd.

W = Width of application in feet.

NOTE

In many instances it will be easier to make such computations from data contained in Tables XVI-8 through 14, using appropriate multiplying factors. For example, it is apparent that the number of linear feet covered by a 4000-gallon tank, for a given width, would be twice that covered by a 2000-gallon tank for the same width. If the tank capacity is not in some convenient multiple, such as a 3300-gallon tank, the data contained in Table XVI-10 for the 1000-gallon tank may be multiplied by an appropriate factor. For the 3300-gallon tank, the multiplying factor would be 3300 ÷ 1000 = 3.3. An example of such a computation for the 3300-gallon tank is as follows:

1. Table XVI-10 indicates that a 1000-gallon tank will cover 3750 linear feet when applied to a strip 12 feet wide and at a rate of 0.20 gallons per sq. yd.
2. A 3300-gallon tank would cover 3.3 times this distance or 3.3 × 3750 = 12,375 linear feet.

TABLE XVI-16—QUANTITIES FOR VARIOUS DEPTHS OF CYLINDRICAL TANKS IN HORIZONTAL POSITION

% Depth Filled	% of Capacity	% Depth Filled	% of Capacity	% Depth Filled	% of Capacity	% Depth Filled	% of Capacity
1	0.20	26	20.73	51	51.27	76	81.50
2	0.50	27	21.86	52	52.55	77	82.60
3	0.90	28	23.00	53	53.81	78	83.68
4	1.34	29	24.07	54	55.08	79	84.74
5	1.87	30	25.31	55	56.34	80	85.77
6	2.45	31	26.48	56	57.60	81	86.77
7	3.07	32	27.66	57	58.86	82	87.76
8	3.74	33	28.84	58	60.11	83	88.73
9	4.45	34	30.03	59	61.36	84	89.68
10	5.20	35	31.19	60	62.61	85	90.60
11	5.98	36	32.44	61	63.86	86	91.50
12	6.80	37	33.66	62	65.10	87	92.36
13	7.64	38	34.90	63	66.34	88	93.20
14	8.50	39	36.14	64	67.56	89	94.02
15	9.40	40	37.39	65	68.81	90	94.80
16	10.32	41	38.64	66	69.97	91	95.55
17	11.27	42	39.89	67	71.16	92	96.26
18	12.24	43	41.14	68	72.34	93	96.93
19	13.23	44	42.40	69	73.52	94	97.55
20	14.23	45	43.66	70	74.69	95	98.13
21	15.26	46	44.92	71	75.93	96	98.66
22	16.32	47	46.19	72	77.00	97	99.10
23	17.40	48	47.45	73	78.14	98	99.50
24	18.50	49	48.73	74	79.27	99	99.80
25	19.61	50	50.00	75	80.39		

Full capacity of tank in U. S. gallons $= \dfrac{0.7854 \times D^2 \times L}{231}$

Note: The formula for direct computation of quantity when tank is less than half full is shown below. When more than half full, compute the full capacity of the tank as noted above; consider the shaded portion to represent the unfilled portion at the top of the tank and compute its volume as indicated below; then, deduct the volume determined for the unfilled portion from the total volume of the tank to arrive at the volume of the filled portion.

First, compute θ where $\cos\theta = \dfrac{d}{R} = \dfrac{R-h}{R}$

Then $A = \pi R^2 \dfrac{\theta}{180} - R \sin\theta\,(R-h)$

And $V = L \left[\dfrac{\pi R^2 \dfrac{\theta}{180} - R \sin\theta\,(R-h)}{231} \right]$

Where A = Cross section area of filled portion of tank in sq in
V = Volume of filled portion of tank in U.S. gallons
L = Length of interior of tank in inches
D = Diameter of interior of tank in inches
R = Radius of interior of tank in inches
h = Depth of liquid in inches
d = R − h, inches

Note: The volume occupied by any piping, fittings or other material inside the tank must be deducted from the volume computed by use of the table or formula.

TABLE XVI-17—TEMPERATURE CONVERSIONS
°F to °C and °C to °F

The formula for converting °F to °C is: $°C = \frac{5}{9}(°F - 32)$

The formula for converting °C to °F is: $°F = \frac{9}{5}(°C) + 32$

To use the following table, locate the temperature to be converted in the center column which is in boldface type. If the temperature to be converted is in °C, the temperature in °F will be found in the column to the right. If the temperature to be converted is in °F, the temperature in °C will be found in the column to the left. For example, to convert 25°C to °F, locate 25 in the center (**boldface**) column. In the column to the right, under °F, it is found that 25°C = 77°F.

° C	Temp. to Convert	° F	° C	Temp. to Convert	° F	° C	Temp. to Convert	° F
−45.6	**−50**	−58.0	−23.3	**−10**	+14.0	−1.1	**+30**	+86.0
45.0	**49**	56.2	22.8	**9**	15.8	0.6	**31**	87.8
44.4	**48**	54.4	22.2	**8**	17.6	0.0	**32**	89.6
43.9	**47**	52.6	21.7	**7**	19.4	+0.6	**33**	91.4
43.3	**46**	50.8	21.1	**6**	21.2	1.1	**34**	93.2
42.8	**45**	49.0	20.6	**5**	23.0	1.7	**35**	95.0
42.2	**44**	47.2	20.0	**4**	24.8	2.2	**36**	96.8
41.7	**43**	45.4	19.4	**3**	26.6	2.8	**37**	98.6
41.1	**42**	43.6	18.9	**2**	28.4	3.3	**38**	100.4
40.6	**41**	41.8	18.3	**−1**	30.2	3.9	**39**	102.2
−40.0	**−40**	−40.0	−17.8	**0**	+32.0	+4.4	**+40**	+104.0
39.4	**39**	38.2	17.2	**+1**	33.8	5.0	**41**	105.8
38.9	**38**	36.4	16.7	**2**	35.6	5.6	**42**	107.6
38.3	**37**	34.6	16.1	**3**	37.4	6.1	**43**	109.4
37.8	**36**	32.8	15.6	**4**	39.2	6.7	**44**	111.2
37.2	**35**	31.0	15.0	**5**	41.0	7.2	**45**	113.0
36.7	**34**	29.2	14.4	**6**	42.8	7.8	**46**	114.8
36.1	**33**	27.4	13.9	**7**	44.6	8.3	**47**	116.6
35.6	**32**	25.6	13.3	**8**	46.4	8.9	**48**	118.4
35.0	**31**	23.8	12.8	**9**	48.2	9.4	**49**	120.2
−34.4	**−30**	−22.0	−12.2	**+10**	+50.0	+10.0	**+50**	+122.0
33.9	**29**	20.2	11.7	**11**	51.8	10.6	**51**	123.8
33.3	**28**	18.4	11.1	**12**	53.6	11.1	**52**	125.6
32.8	**27**	16.6	10.6	**13**	55.4	11.7	**53**	127.4
32.2	**26**	14.8	10.0	**14**	57.2	12.2	**54**	129.2
31.7	**25**	13.0	9.4	**15**	59.0	12.8	**55**	131.0
31.1	**24**	11.2	8.9	**16**	60.8	13.3	**56**	132.8
30.6	**23**	9.4	8.3	**17**	62.6	13.9	**57**	134.6
30.0	**22**	7.6	7.8	**18**	64.4	14.4	**58**	136.4
29.4	**21**	5.8	7.2	**19**	66.2	15.0	**59**	138.2
−28.9	**−20**	−4.0	−6.7	**+20**	+68.0	+15.6	**+60**	+140.0
28.3	**19**	2.2	6.1	**21**	69.8	16.1	**61**	141.8
27.8	**18**	0.4	5.6	**22**	71.6	16.7	**62**	143.6
27.2	**17**	+1.4	5.0	**23**	73.4	17.2	**63**	145.4
26.7	**16**	3.2	4.4	**24**	75.2	17.8	**64**	147.2
26.1	**15**	5.0	3.9	**25**	77.0	18.3	**65**	149.0
25.6	**14**	6.8	3.3	**26**	78.8	18.9	**66**	150.8
25.0	**13**	8.6	2.8	**27**	80.6	19.4	**67**	152.6
24.4	**12**	10.4	2.2	**28**	82.4	20.0	**68**	154.4
23.9	**11**	12.2	1.7	**29**	84.2	20.6	**69**	156.2

TABLE XVI-17 (Continued)—TEMPERATURE CONVERSIONS °F to °C and °C to °F

°C	Temp. to Convert	°F	°C	Temp. to Convert	°F	°C	Temp. to Convert	°F
+21.1	+70	+158.0	+48.9	+120	+248.0	+76.7	+170	+338.0
21.7	71	159.8	49.4	121	249.8	77.2	171	339.8
22.2	72	161.6	50.0	122	251.6	77.8	172	341.6
22.8	73	163.4	50.6	123	253.4	78.3	173	343.4
23.3	74	165.2	51.1	124	255.2	78.9	174	345.2
23.9	75	167.0	51.7	125	257.0	79.4	175	347.0
24.4	76	168.8	52.2	126	258.8	80.0	176	348.8
25.0	77	170.6	52.8	127	260.6	80.6	177	350.6
25.6	78	172.4	53.3	128	262.4	81.1	178	352.4
26.1	79	174.2	53.9	129	264.2	81.7	179	354.2
+26.7	+80	+176.0	+54.4	+130	+266.0	+82.2	+180	+356.0
27.2	81	177.8	55.0	131	267.8	82.8	181	357.8
27.8	82	179.6	55.6	132	269.6	83.3	182	359.6
28.3	83	181.4	56.1	133	271.4	83.9	183	361.4
28.9	84	183.2	56.7	134	273.2	84.4	184	363.2
29.4	85	185.0	57.2	135	275.0	85.0	185	365.0
30.0	86	186.8	57.8	136	276.8	85.6	186	366.8
30.6	87	188.6	58.3	137	278.6	86.1	178	368.6
31.1	88	190.4	58.9	138	280.4	86.7	188	370.4
31.7	89	192.2	59.4	139	282.2	87.2	189	372.2
+32.2	+90	+194.0	+60.0	+140	+284.0	+87.8	+190	+374.0
32.8	91	195.8	60.6	141	285.8	88.3	191	375.8
33.3	92	197.6	61.1	142	287.6	88.9	192	377.6
33.9	93	199.4	61.7	143	289.4	89.4	193	379.4
34.4	94	201.2	62.2	144	291.2	90.0	194	381.2
35.0	95	203.0	62.8	145	293.0	90.6	195	383.0
35.6	96	204.8	63.3	146	294.8	91.1	196	384.8
36.1	97	206.6	63.9	147	296.6	91.7	197	386.6
36.7	98	208.4	64.4	148	298.4	92.2	198	388.4
37.2	99	210.2	65.0	149	300.2	92.8	199	390.2
+37.8	+100	+212.0	+65.6	+150	+302.0	+93.3	+200	+392.0
38.3	101	213.8	66.1	151	303.8	93.9	201	393.8
38.9	102	215.6	66.7	152	305.6	94.4	202	395.6
39.4	103	217.4	67.2	153	307.4	95.0	203	397.4
40.0	104	219.2	67.8	154	309.2	95.6	204	399.2
40.6	105	221.0	68.3	155	311.0	96.1	205	401.0
41.1	106	222.8	68.9	156	312.8	96.7	206	402.8
41.7	107	224.6	69.4	157	314.6	97.2	207	404.6
42.2	108	226.4	70.0	158	316.4	97.8	208	406.4
42.8	109	228.2	70.6	159	318.2	98.3	209	408.2
+43.3	+110	+230.0	+71.1	+160	+320.0	+98.9	+210	+410.0
43.9	111	231.8	71.7	161	321.8	99.4	211	411.8
44.4	112	233.6	72.2	162	323.6	100.0	212	413.6
45.0	113	235.4	72.8	163	325.4	100.6	213	415.4
45.6	114	237.2	73.3	164	327.2	101.1	214	417.2
46.1	115	239.0	73.9	165	329.0	101.7	215	419.0
46.7	116	240.8	74.4	166	330.8	102.2	216	420.8
47.2	117	242.6	75.0	167	332.6	102.8	217	422.6
47.8	118	244.4	75.6	168	334.4	103.3	218	424.4
48.3	119	246.2	76.1	169	336.2	103.9	219	426.2

TABLE XVI-17 (Continued)—TEMPERATURE
CONVERSIONS °F to °C and °C to °F

° C	Temp. to Convert	° F	° C	Temp. to Convert	° F	° C	Temp. to Convert	° F
+104.4	+220	+428.0	+132.2	+270	+518.0	+160.0	+320	+608.0
105.0	221	429.8	132.8	271	519.8	160.6	321	609.8
105.6	222	431.6	133.3	272	521.6	161.1	322	611.6
106.1	223	433.4	133.9	273	523.4	161.7	323	613.4
106.7	224	435.2	134.4	274	525.2	162.2	324	615.2
107.2	225	437.0	135.0	275	527.0	162.8	325	617.0
107.8	226	438.8	135.6	276	528.8	163.3	326	618.8
108.3	227	440.6	136.1	277	530.6	163.9	327	620.6
108.9	228	442.4	136.7	278	532.4	164.4	328	622.4
109.4	229	444.2	137.2	279	534.2	165.0	329	624.2
+110.0	+230	+446.0	+137.8	+280	+536.0	+165.6	+330	+626.0
110.6	231	447.8	138.3	281	537.8	166.1	331	627.8
111.1	232	449.6	138.9	282	539.6	166.7	332	629.6
111.7	233	451.4	139.4	283	541.4	167.2	333	631.4
112.2	234	453.2	140.0	284	543.2	167.8	334	633.2
112.8	235	455.0	140.6	285	545.0	168.3	335	635.0
113.3	236	456.8	141.1	286	546.8	168.9	336	636.8
113.9	237	458.6	141.7	287	548.6	169.4	337	638.6
114.4	238	460.4	142.2	288	550.4	170.0	338	640.4
115.0	239	462.2	142.8	289	552.2	170.6	339	642.2
+115.6	+240	+464.0	+143.3	+290	+554.0	+171.1	+340	+644.0
116.1	241	465.8	143.9	291	555.8	171.7	341	645.8
116.7	242	467.6	144.4	292	557.6	172.2	342	647.6
117.2	243	469.4	145.0	293	559.4	172.8	343	649.4
117.8	244	471.2	145.6	294	561.2	173.3	344	651.2
118.3	245	473.0	146.1	295	563.0	173.9	345	653.0
118.9	246	474.8	146.7	296	564.8	174.4	346	654.8
119.4	247	476.6	147.2	297	566.6	175.0	347	656.6
120.0	248	478.4	147.8	298	568.4	175.6	348	658.4
120.6	249	480.2	148.3	299	570.2	176.1	349	660.2
+121.1	+250	+482.0	+148.9	+300	+572.0	+176.7	+350	+662.0
121.7	251	483.8	149.4	301	573.8	177.2	351	663.8
122.2	252	485.6	150.0	302	575.6	177.8	352	665.6
122.8	253	487.4	150.6	303	577.4	178.3	353	667.4
123.3	254	489.2	151.1	304	579.2	178.9	354	669.2
123.9	255	491.0	151.7	305	581.0	179.4	355	671.0
124.4	256	492.8	152.2	306	582.8	180.0	356	672.8
125.0	257	494.6	152.8	307	584.6	180.6	357	674.6
125.6	258	496.4	153.3	308	586.4	181.1	358	676.4
126.1	259	498.2	153.9	309	588.2	181.7	359	678.2
+126.7	+260	+500.0	+154.4	+310	+590.0	+182.2	+360	+680.0
127.2	261	501.8	155.0	311	591.8	182.8	361	681.8
127.8	262	503.6	155.6	312	593.6	183.3	362	683.6
128.3	263	505.4	156.1	313	595.4	183.9	363	685.4
128.9	264	507.2	156.7	314	597.2	184.4	364	687.2
129.4	265	509.0	157.2	315	599.0	185.0	365	689.0
130.0	266	510.8	157.8	316	600.8	185.6	366	690.8
130.6	267	512.6	158.3	317	602.6	186.1	367	692.6
131.1	268	514.4	158.9	318	604.4	186.7	368	694.4
131.7	269	516.2	159.4	319	606.2	187.2	369	696.2

TABLE XVI-17 (Continued)—TEMPERATURE
CONVERSIONS °F to °C and °C to °F

° C	Temp. to Con-vert	° F	° C	Temp. to Con-vert	° F	° C	Temp. to Con-vert	° F
+187.8	+370	+698.0	+215.6	+420	+788.0	+243.3	+470	+878.0
188.3	371	699.8	216.1	421	789.8	243.9	471	879.8
188.9	372	701.6	216.7	422	791.6	244.3	472	881.6
189.4	373	703.4	217.2	423	793.4	245.0	473	883.4
190.0	374	705.2	217.8	424	795.2	245.6	474	885.2
190.6	375	707.0	218.3	425	797.0	246.1	475	887.0
191.1	376	708.8	218.9	426	798.8	246.7	476	888.8
191.7	377	710.6	219.4	427	800.6	247.2	477	890.6
192.2	378	712.4	220.0	428	802.4	247.8	478	892.4
192.8	379	714.2	220.6	429	804.2	248.3	479	894.2
+193.3	+380	+716.0	+221.1	+430	+806.0	+248.9	+480	+896.0
193.9	381	717.8	221.7	431	807.8	249.4	481	897.8
194.4	382	719.6	222.2	432	809.6	250.0	482	899.6
195.0	383	721.4	222.8	433	811.4	250.6	483	901.4
195.6	384	723.2	223.3	434	813.2	251.1	484	903.2
196.1	385	725.0	223.9	435	815.0	251.7	485	905.0
196.7	386	726.8	224.4	436	816.8	252.2	486	906.8
197.2	387	728.6	225.0	437	818.6	252.8	487	908.6
197.8	388	730.4	225.6	438	820.4	253.3	488	910.4
198.3	389	732.2	226.1	439	822.2	253.9	489	912.2
+198.9	+390	+734.0	+226.7	+440	+824.0	+254.4	+490	+914.0
199.4	391	735.8	227.2	441	825.8	255.0	491	915.8
200.0	392	737.6	227.8	442	827.6	255.6	492	917.6
200.6	393	739.4	228.3	443	829.4	256.1	493	919.4
201.1	394	741.2	228.9	444	831.2	256.7	494	921.2
201.7	395	743.0	229.4	445	833.0	257.2	495	923.0
202.2	396	744.8	230.0	446	834.8	257.8	496	924.8
202.8	397	746.6	230.6	447	836.6	258.3	497	926.6
203.3	398	748.4	231.1	448	838.4	258.9	498	928.4
203.9	399	750.2	231.7	449	840.2	259.4	499	930.2
+204.4	+400	+752.0	+232.2	+450	+842.0	+260.0	+500	+932.0
205.0	401	753.8	232.8	451	843.8	260.6	501	933.8
205.6	402	755.6	233.3	452	845.6	261.1	502	935.6
206.1	403	757.4	233.9	453	847.4	261.7	503	937.4
206.7	404	759.2	234.4	454	849.2	262.2	504	939.2
207.2	405	761.0	235.0	455	851.0	262.8	505	941.0
207.8	406	762.8	235.6	456	852.8	263.3	506	942.8
208.3	407	764.6	236.1	457	854.6	263.9	507	944.6
208.9	408	766.4	236.7	458	856.4	264.4	508	946.4
209.4	409	768.2	237.2	459	858.2	265.0	509	948.2
+210.0	+410	+770.0	+237.8	+460	+860.0	+265.6	+510	+950.0
210.6	411	771.8	238.3	461	861.8	266.1	511	951.8
211.1	412	773.6	238.9	462	863.6	266.7	512	953.6
211.7	413	775.4	239.4	463	865.4	267.2	513	955.4
212.2	414	777.2	240.0	464	867.2	267.8	514	957.2
212.8	415	779.0	240.6	465	869.0	268.3	515	959.0
213.3	416	780.8	241.1	466	870.8	268.9	516	960.8
213.9	417	782.6	241.7	467	872.6	269.4	517	962.6
214.4	418	784.4	242.2	468	874.4	270.0	518	964.4
215.0	419	786.2	242.8	469	876.2	270.6	519	966.2

TABLE XVI-17 *(Continued)*—TEMPERATURE
CONVERSIONS °F to °C and °C to °F

° C	Temp. to Convert	° F	° C	Temp. to Convert	° F	° C	Temp. to Convert	° F
+271.1	+520	+968.0	+282.2	+540	+1004.0	+293.3	+560	+1040.0
271.7	521	969.8	282.8	541	1005.8	293.9	561	1041.8
272.2	522	971.6	283.3	542	1007.6	294.4	562	1043.6
272.8	523	973.4	283.9	543	1009.4	295.0	563	1045.4
273.3	524	975.2	284.4	544	1011.2	295.6	564	1047.2
273.9	525	977.0	285.0	545	1013.0	296.1	565	1049.0
274.4	526	978.8	285.6	546	1014.8	296.7	566	1050.8
275.0	527	980.6	286.1	547	1016.6	297.2	567	1052.6
275.6	528	982.4	286.7	548	1018.4	297.8	568	1054.4
276.1	529	984.2	287.2	549	1020.2	298.3	569	1056.2
+276.7	+530	+986.0	+287.8	+550	+1022.0	298.9	+570	1058.0
277.2	531	987.8	288.3	551	1023.8	299.4	571	1059.8
277.8	532	989.6	288.9	552	1025.6	300.0	572	1061.0
278.3	533	991.4	289.4	553	1027.4	300.6	573	1063.4
278.9	534	993.2	290.0	554	1029.2	301.1	574	1065.2
279.4	535	995.0	290.6	555	1031.0	301.7	575	1067.0
280.0	536	996.8	291.1	556	1032.8	302.2	576	1068.8
280.6	537	998.6	291.7	557	1034.6	302.8	577	1070.6
281.1	538	1000.4	292.2	558	1036.4	303.3	578	1072.4
281.7	539	1002.2	292.8	559	1038.2	303.9	579	1074.4

TABLE XVI-18—TEMPERATURE OF LIQUIDS HEATED BY STEAM AT VARIOUS GAUGE PRESSURES

Gauge Pressure in Lbs Per Square Inch	Temperature of Saturated Steam Degrees Fahrenheit	Highest Temp. a Liquid Can be Heated in a Vessel With Heating Equipment 85% Efficient
50	297	253
55	302	257
60	307	261
65	312	265
70	316	269
75	320	272
80	324	275
85	327	278
90	331	281
95	334	284
100	338	287
105	341	290
110	344	292
115	347	295
120	350	298
125	353	300
130	355	302
135	358	304
140	361	307
145	363	309
150	366	311

TABLE XVI-19—WEIGHT PER CUBIC FOOT AND PER CUBIC YARD OF DRY MINERAL AGGREGATES FOR AGGREGATES OF DIFFERENT SPECIFIC GRAVITY AND VARIOUS VOID CONTENTS

	Specific Gravity	VOIDS—PERCENT								
		15	20	25	30	35	40	45	50	55
POUNDS PER CUBIC FOOT	2.0	106.1	99.8	93.6	87.4	81.1	74.9	68.6	62.4	56.2
	2.1	111.4	104.8	98.3	91.7	85.2	78.6	72.1	65.5	59.0
	2.2	116.7	109.8	103.0	96.1	89.2	82.4	75.5	68.6	61.8
	2.3	122.0	114.8	107.6	100.5	93.3	86.1	78.9	71.8	64.6
	2.4	127.3	119.8	112.3	104.8	97.3	89.9	82.4	74.9	67.4
	2.5	132.6	124.8	117.0	109.2	101.4	93.6	85.8	78.0	70.2
	2.6	137.9	129.8	121.7	113.6	105.5	97.3	89.2	81.1	73.0
	2.7	143.2	134.8	126.4	117.9	109.5	101.1	92.7	84.2	75.8
	2.8	148.5	139.8	131.0	122.3	113.6	104.8	96.1	87.4	78.6
	2.9	153.8	144.8	135.7	126.7	117.6	108.6	99.5	90.5	81.4
	3.0	159.1	149.8	140.4	131.0	121.7	112.3	103.0	93.6	84.2
	3.1	164.4	154.8	145.1	135.4	125.7	116.1	106.4	96.7	87.0
	3.2	169.7	159.7	149.8	139.8	129.8	119.8	109.8	99.8	89.9
POUNDS PER CUBIC YARD	2.0	2860	2700	2530	2360	2190	2020	1850	1680	1520
	2.1	3010	2830	2650	2480	2300	2120	1950	1770	1590
	2.2	3150	2970	2780	2590	2410	2220	2040	1850	1670
	2.3	3290	3100	2910	2710	2520	2330	2130	1940	1740
	2.4	3440	3240	3030	2830	2630	2430	2220	2020	1820
	2.5	3580	3370	3160	2950	2740	2530	2320	2110	1900
	2.6	3720	3500	3290	3070	2850	2630	2410	2190	1970
	2.7	3870	3640	3410	3180	2960	2730	2500	2270	2050
	2.8	4010	3770	3540	3300	3070	2830	2590	2360	2120
	2.9	4150	3910	3660	3420	3180	2930	2690	2440	2200
	3.0	4300	4040	3790	3540	3290	3030	2780	2530	2270
	3.1	4440	4180	3920	3660	3400	3130	2870	2610	2350
	3.2	4580	4310	4040	3770	3500	3230	2970	2700	2430

1. The Specific Gravity of commonly used road construction aggregates normally is within the following ranges:
   Granite 2.6-2.9   Sand (Quartzite) 2.5-2.7   Blast Furnace
   Gravel 2.5-2.7   Sandstone 2.0-2.7   Slag 2.0-2.5
   Limestone 2.1-2.8   Traprock 2.7-3.2

2. Data contained in this table are applicable to dry mineral aggregates in either the loose or compacted state, and the void content should be selected accordingly. Preferably, both the void content and specific gravity should be determined in the laboratory.

3. The formulas for computation of data in table above are as follows:
   Per Cu Ft

   $$W = 62.4 \times \frac{G(100 - V)}{100} = 0.624 \, G(100 - V)$$

   and
   Per Cu Yd

   $$W = 27 \times 62.4 \times \frac{G(100 - V)}{100} = 16.85 \, G(100 - V)$$

Where: W = Wt. per cu ft
   W = Wt. per cu yd
   G = Specific gravity
   V = Air void content, percent

TABLE XVI-20—WEIGHT AND VOLUME RELATIONS FOR VARIOUS TYPES OF COMPACTED ASPHALT PAVEMENTS

Note:

Because of the considerable variations of specific gravity, gradation, and other characteristics of mineral aggregates, weight per unit volume of compacted asphalt pavement varies considerably. Exact weights per unit volume should be determined in the laboratory from samples taken from the pavement or prepared in the laboratory with the same materials as used in the field.

Pounds Per Cubic Foot	Pounds Per Cubic Yard	Pounds Per Square Yard Per 1 Inch Depth
100	2700	75
105	2835	79
110	2970	82
115	3105	86
120	3240	90
125	3375	94
130	3510	97
135	3645	101
140	3780	105
145	3915	109
150	4050	112
155	4185	116
160	4320	120

	Pounds Per Cubic Foot	Pounds Per Cubic Yard	Pounds Per Square Yard Per 1 Inch Depth	
	Range	Range	Range	Frequently Used for Preliminary Estimate
Macadam—A.I. Type I or Penetration Macadam	110-135	2970-3645	82-101	95
Open Graded—A.I. Type II	115-140	3105-3780	86-105	100
Coarse Graded—A.I. Type III	130-155	3510-4050	97-112	105
Dense Graded—A.I. Type IV	135-155	3645-4185	101-116	110
Fine Graded—A.I. Type V	130-150	3510-4050	97-112	105
Stone Sheet—A.I. Type VI	130-150	3510-4050	97-112	105
Sand Sheet—A.I. Type VII	120-140	3240-3780	90-105	100
Fine Sheet—A.I. Type VIII	110-135	2970-3645	90-105	100
Mixed-In-Place Macadam—A.I. Spec. RM-1	110-135	2970-3645	82-101	95
Mixed-In-Place Dense Graded—A.I. Spec. RM-2	110-135	2970-3645	82-101	95
Mixed-In-Place Sand Asphalt—A.I. Spec. RM-3	100-125	2700-3375	75-94	85

TABLE XVI-21—POUNDS PER SQUARE YARD OF MATERIAL REQUIRED FOR VARIOUS DEPTHS AND WEIGHTS OF MATERIALS IN POUNDS PER CUBIC YARD

Lbs Per Cu Yd	Depth—Inches											
	1	2	3	4	5	6	7	8	9	10	11	12
10	0.3	0.6	0.8	1.1	1.4	1.7	1.9	2.2	2.5	2.8	3.1	3.3
20	0.6	1.1	1.7	2.2	2.8	3.3	3.9	4.4	5.0	5.6	6.1	6.7
30	0.8	1.7	2.5	3.3	4.2	5.0	5.8	6.7	7.5	8.3	9.2	10.0
40	1.1	2.2	3.3	4.4	5.6	6.7	7.8	8.9	10.0	11.1	12.2	13.3
50	1.4	2.8	4.2	5.6	6.9	8.3	9.7	11.1	12.5	13.9	15.3	16.7
60	1.7	3.3	5.0	6.7	8.3	10.0	11.7	13.3	15.0	16.7	18.3	20.0
70	1.9	3.9	5.8	7.8	9.7	11.7	13.6	15.6	17.5	19.4	21.4	23.3
80	2.2	4.4	6.7	8.9	11.1	13.3	15.6	17.8	20.0	22.2	24.4	26.7
90	2.5	5.0	7.5	10.0	12.5	15.0	17.5	20.0	22.5	25.0	27.5	30.0
100	2.8	5.6	8.3	11.1	13.9	16.6	19.4	22.2	25.0	27.8	30.5	33.3
200	5.6	11.1	16.7	22.2	27.8	33.3	38.9	44.4	50.0	55.5	61.1	66.6
300	8.3	16.7	25.0	33.3	41.7	50.0	58.3	66.6	75.0	83.3	91.6	100.0
400	11.1	22.2	33.3	44.4	55.5	66.6	77.8	88.9	100.0	111.1	122.2	133.3
500	13.9	27.8	41.7	55.5	69.4	83.3	97.2	111.1	125.0	138.8	152.7	166.6
600	16.7	33.3	50.0	66.6	83.3	100.0	116.6	133.3	150.0	166.6	183.3	199.9
700	19.4	38.9	58.3	77.8	97.2	116.6	136.1	155.5	175.0	194.4	213.8	233.3
800	22.2	44.4	66.6	88.9	111.1	133.3	155.5	177.7	199.9	222.2	244.4	266.6
900	25.0	50.0	75.0	100.0	125.0	150.0	175.0	200.0	224.9	250.0	274.9	299.9
1000	27.8	55.5	83.3	111.1	138.8	166.6	194.4	222.2	249.9	277.7	305.5	333.2
2000	55.5	111.1	166.6	222.2	277.7	333.2	388.8	444.3	499.9	555.4	610.9	666.5
3000	83.3	166.6	250.0	333.2	416.6	500.0	583.2	666.5	749.8	833.1	916.4	999.7
4000	111.1	222.2	333.2	444.3	555.4	666.5	777.6	888.6	999.7	1110.8	1221.9	1333.0
5000	138.8	277.7	416.6	555.4	694.2	833.1	972.0	1110.8	1249.6	1388.5	1527.4	1666.2

Where: q = Quantity of material in lbs per sq yd
D = Depth in inches
W = Weight of material in lbs per cu yd

Note: Formula used for calculations: $q = \dfrac{(D)}{(36)} W = 0.02777\ D\ W$

TABLE XVI-22—TONS OF MATERIAL REQUIRED PER 100 LINEAR FEET FOR VARIOUS WIDTHS AND POUNDS PER SQUARE YARD

Lbs Per Sq Yd	Width—Feet														
	1	2	3	4	5	6	7	8	9	10	20	30	40	50	60
1	0.01	0.01	0.02	0.02	0.03	0.03	0.04	0.04	0.05	0.06	0.11	0.17	0.22	0.28	0.33
2	0.01	0.02	0.03	0.04	0.06	0.07	0.08	0.09	0.10	0.11	0.22	0.33	0.44	0.56	0.67
3	0.02	0.03	0.05	0.07	0.08	0.10	0.12	0.13	0.15	0.17	0.33	0.50	0.67	0.83	1.00
4	0.02	0.04	0.07	0.09	0.11	0.13	0.16	0.18	0.20	0.22	0.44	0.67	0.89	1.11	1.33
5	0.03	0.06	0.08	0.11	0.14	0.17	0.19	0.22	0.25	0.28	0.56	0.83	1.11	1.39	1.67
6	0.03	0.07	0.10	0.13	0.17	0.20	0.23	0.27	0.30	0.33	0.67	1.00	1.33	1.67	2.00
7	0.04	0.08	0.12	0.16	0.19	0.23	0.27	0.31	0.35	0.39	0.78	1.17	1.56	1.94	2.33
8	0.04	0.09	0.13	0.18	0.22	0.27	0.31	0.36	0.40	0.44	0.89	1.33	1.78	2.22	2.67
9	0.05	0.10	0.15	0.20	0.25	0.30	0.35	0.40	0.45	0.50	1.00	1.50	2.00	2.50	3.00
10	0.06	0.11	0.17	0.22	0.28	0.33	0.39	0.44	0.50	0.56	1.11	1.67	2.22	2.78	3.33
20	0.11	0.22	0.33	0.44	0.56	0.67	0.78	0.89	1.00	1.11	2.22	3.33	4.44	5.56	6.67
30	0.17	0.33	0.50	0.67	0.83	1.00	1.17	1.33	1.50	1.67	3.33	5.00	6.67	8.33	10.00
40	0.22	0.44	0.67	0.89	1.11	1.33	1.56	1.78	2.00	2.22	4.44	6.67	8.89	11.11	13.33
50	0.28	0.56	0.83	1.11	1.39	1.67	1.94	2.22	2.50	2.78	5.56	8.33	11.11	13.89	16.67
60	0.33	0.67	1.00	1.33	1.67	2.00	2.33	2.67	3.00	3.33	6.67	10.00	13.33	16.67	20.00
70	0.39	0.78	1.17	1.56	1.94	2.33	2.72	3.11	3.50	3.89	7.78	11.67	15.56	19.44	23.33
80	0.44	0.89	1.33	1.78	2.22	2.67	3.11	3.56	4.00	4.44	8.89	13.33	17.78	22.22	26.67
90	0.50	1.00	1.50	2.00	2.50	3.00	3.50	4.00	4.50	5.00	10.00	15.00	20.00	25.00	30.00
100	0.56	1.11	1.67	2.22	2.78	3.33	3.89	4.44	5.00	5.56	11.11	16.67	22.22	27.78	33.33
200	1.11	2.22	3.33	4.44	5.56	6.67	7.78	8.89	10.00	11.11	22.22	33.33	44.44	55.56	66.67
300	1.67	3.33	5.00	6.67	8.33	10.00	11.67	13.33	15.00	16.67	33.33	50.00	66.67	83.33	100.00
400	2.22	4.44	6.67	8.89	11.11	13.33	15.56	17.78	20.00	22.22	44.44	66.67	88.89	111.11	133.33
500	2.78	5.56	8.33	11.11	13.89	16.67	19.44	22.22	25.00	27.78	55.56	83.33	111.11	138.89	166.67
600	3.33	6.67	10.00	13.33	16.67	20.00	23.33	26.67	30.00	33.33	66.67	100.00	133.33	166.67	200.00
700	3.89	7.78	11.67	15.56	19.44	23.33	27.22	31.11	35.00	38.89	77.78	116.69	155.56	194.44	233.33
800	4.44	8.89	13.33	17.78	22.22	26.67	31.11	35.56	40.00	44.44	88.89	133.33	177.78	222.22	266.67
900	5.00	10.00	15.00	20.00	25.00	30.00	35.00	40.00	45.00	50.00	100.00	150.00	200.00	250.00	300.00
1000	5.56	11.11	16.67	22.22	27.78	33.33	38.89	44.44	50.00	55.56	111.11	166.67	222.22	277.78	333.33

Note: Formula used for calculation:

$$w = \left(\frac{W}{3}\right)\left(\frac{R}{3}\right)\left(\frac{R}{2000}\right) = 0.005556\ RW$$

Where w = Weight of material in tons per 100 feet
R = Rate of application in lbs per sq yd
W = Width of application in feet

TABLE XVI-23—TONS OF MATERIAL REQUIRED PER MILE FOR VARIOUS WIDTHS AND POUNDS PER SQUARE YARD

Lbs Per Sq Yd	Width—Feet														
	1	2	3	4	5	6	7	8	9	10	20	30	40	50	60
1	0.3	0.6	0.9	1.2	1.5	1.8	2.1	2.3	2.6	2.9	5.9	8.8	11.7	14.7	17.6
2	0.6	1.2	1.8	2.3	2.9	3.5	4.1	4.7	5.3	5.9	11.7	17.6	23.5	29.3	35.2
3	0.9	1.8	2.6	3.5	4.4	5.3	6.2	7.0	7.9	8.8	17.6	26.4	35.2	44.0	52.8
4	1.2	2.3	3.5	4.7	5.9	7.0	8.2	9.4	10.6	11.7	23.5	35.2	46.9	58.7	70.4
5	1.5	2.9	4.4	5.9	7.3	8.8	10.3	11.7	13.2	14.7	29.3	44.0	58.7	73.3	88.0
6	1.8	3.5	5.3	7.0	8.8	10.6	12.3	14.1	15.8	17.6	35.2	52.8	70.4	88.0	105.6
7	2.1	4.1	6.2	8.2	10.3	12.3	14.4	16.4	18.5	20.5	41.1	61.6	82.1	102.7	123.2
8	2.3	4.7	7.0	9.4	11.7	14.1	16.4	18.8	21.1	23.5	46.9	70.4	93.9	117.3	140.8
9	2.6	5.3	7.9	10.6	13.2	15.8	18.5	21.1	23.8	26.4	52.8	79.2	105.6	132.0	158.4
10	2.9	5.9	8.8	11.7	14.7	17.6	20.5	23.5	26.4	29.3	58.7	88.0	117.3	146.7	176.0
20	5.9	11.7	17.6	23.5	29.3	35.2	41.1	46.9	52.8	58.7	117.3	176.0	234.7	293.3	352.0
30	8.8	17.6	26.4	35.2	44.0	52.8	61.6	70.4	79.2	88.0	176.0	264.0	352.0	440.0	528.0
40	11.7	23.5	35.2	46.9	58.7	70.4	82.1	93.9	105.6	117.3	234.7	352.0	469.3	586.7	704.0
50	14.7	29.3	44.0	58.7	73.3	88.0	102.7	117.3	132.0	146.7	293.3	440.0	586.7	733.3	880.0
60	17.6	35.2	52.8	70.4	88.0	105.6	123.2	140.8	158.4	176.0	352.0	528.0	704.0	880.0	1056.0
70	20.5	41.1	61.6	82.1	102.7	123.2	143.7	164.3	184.8	205.3	410.7	616.0	821.3	1026.7	1232.0
80	23.5	46.9	70.4	93.9	117.3	140.8	164.3	187.7	211.2	234.7	469.3	704.0	938.7	1173.3	1408.0
90	26.4	52.8	79.2	105.6	132.0	158.4	184.8	211.2	237.6	264.0	528.0	792.0	1056.0	1320.0	1584.0
100	29.3	58.7	88.0	117.3	146.7	176.0	205.3	234.7	264.0	293.3	586.7	880.0	1173.3	1466.7	1760.0
200	58.7	117.3	176.0	234.7	293.3	352.0	410.7	469.3	528.0	586.7	1173.3	1760.0	2346.7	2933.3	3520.0
300	88.0	176.0	264.0	352.0	440.0	528.0	616.0	704.0	792.0	880.0	1760.0	2640.0	3520.0	4400.0	5280.0
400	117.3	234.7	352.0	469.3	586.7	704.0	821.3	938.7	1056.0	1173.3	2346.7	3520.0	4693.3	5866.7	7040.0
500	146.7	293.3	440.0	586.7	733.3	880.0	1026.7	1173.3	1320.0	1466.7	2933.3	4400.0	5866.7	7333.3	8800.0
600	176.0	352.0	528.0	704.0	880.0	1056.0	1232.0	1408.0	1584.0	1760.0	3520.0	5280.0	7040.0	8800.0	10560.0
700	205.3	410.7	616.0	821.3	1026.7	1232.0	1437.3	1642.7	1848.0	2053.3	4106.7	6160.0	8213.3	10266.7	12320.0
800	234.7	469.3	704.0	938.7	1173.3	1408.0	1642.7	1877.3	2112.0	2346.7	4693.3	7040.0	9386.7	11733.3	14080.0
900	264.0	528.0	792.0	1056.0	1320.0	1584.0	1848.0	2112.0	2376.0	2640.0	5280.0	7920.0	10560.0	13200.0	15840.0
1000	293.3	586.7	880.0	1173.3	1466.7	1760.0	2053.3	2346.7	2640.0	2933.3	5866.7	8800.0	11733.3	14666.7	17600.0

Note: Formula used for calculation is as follows:

$$w = \left(\frac{W}{3}\right)\left(\frac{5280}{3}\right)\left(\frac{R}{2000}\right) = 0.2933\ RW$$

Where w = Weight of material in tons per mile
R = Rate of application in lbs per sq yd
W = Width of application in feet

TABLE XVI-24—LINEAR FEET COVERED BY ONE TON OF MATERIAL FOR VARIOUS WIDTHS AND POUNDS PER SQUARE YARD

Lbs Per Sq Yd	Width—Feet									
	8	9	10	11	12	13	14	15	16	17
4	563	500	450	409	375	346	321	300	281	265
6	375	333	300	273	250	231	214	200	188	176
8	281	250	225	205	188	173	161	150	141	132
10	225	200	180	164	150	138	129	120	113	106
15	150	133	120	109	100	92.3	85.7	80.0	75.0	70.6
20	113	100	90.0	81.8	75.0	69.2	64.3	60.0	56.3	52.9
25	90.0	80.0	72.0	65.5	60.0	55.4	51.4	48.0	45.0	42.4
30	75.0	66.7	60.0	54.5	50.0	46.2	42.9	40.0	37.5	35.3
35	64.3	57.1	51.4	46.8	42.9	39.6	36.7	34.3	32.1	30.3
40	56.3	50.0	45.0	40.9	37.5	34.6	32.1	30.0	28.1	26.5
45	50.0	44.4	40.0	36.4	33.3	30.8	28.6	26.7	25.0	23.5
50	45.0	40.0	36.0	32.7	30.0	27.7	25.7	24.0	22.5	21.2
60	37.5	33.3	30.0	27.3	25.0	23.1	21.4	20.0	18.8	17.6
70	32.1	28.6	25.7	23.4	21.4	19.8	18.4	17.1	16.1	15.1
80	28.1	25.0	22.5	20.5	18.8	17.3	16.1	15.0	14.1	13.2
90	25.0	22.2	20.0	18.2	16.7	15.4	14.3	13.3	12.5	11.8
100	22.5	20.0	18.0	16.4	15.0	13.8	12.9	12.0	11.3	10.6
120	18.8	16.7	15.0	13.6	12.5	11.5	10.7	10.0	9.4	8.8
140	16.1	14.3	12.9	11.7	10.7	9.9	9.2	8.6	8.0	7.6
160	14.1	12.5	11.3	10.2	9.4	8.7	8.0	7.5	7.0	6.6

180	12.5	11.1	10.0	9.1	8.3	7.7	7.1	6.7	6.3	5.9
200	11.3	10.0	9.0	8.2	7.5	6.9	6.4	6.0	5.6	5.3
220	10.2	9.1	8.2	7.4	6.8	6.3	5.8	5.5	5.1	4.8
240	9.4	8.3	7.5	6.8	6.3	5.8	5.4	5.0	4.7	4.4
260	8.7	7.7	6.9	6.3	5.8	5.3	4.9	4.6	4.3	4.1
280	8.0	7.1	6.4	5.8	5.4	4.9	4.6	4.3	4.0	3.8
300	7.5	6.7	6.0	5.5	5.0	4.6	4.3	4.0	3.8	3.5
320	7.0	6.3	5.6	5.1	4.7	4.3	4.0	3.8	3.5	3.3
340	6.6	5.9	5.3	4.8	4.4	4.1	3.8	3.5	3.3	3.1
360	6.3	5.6	5.0	4.5	4.2	3.8	3.6	3.3	3.1	2.9
380	5.9	5.3	4.7	4.3	3.9	3.6	3.4	3.2	3.0	2.8
400	5.6	5.0	4.5	4.1	3.8	3.5	3.2	3.0	2.8	2.6
420	5.4	4.8	4.3	3.9	3.6	3.3	3.1	2.9	2.7	2.5
440	5.1	4.5	4.1	3.7	3.4	3.1	2.9	2.7	2.6	2.4
460	4.9	4.3	3.9	3.6	3.3	3.0	2.8	2.6	2.4	2.3
480	4.7	4.2	3.8	3.4	3.1	2.9	2.7	2.5	2.3	2.2
500	4.5	4.0	3.6	3.3	3.0	2.8	2.6	2.4	2.2	2.1
520	4.3	3.8	3.5	3.1	2.9	2.7	2.5	2.3	2.2	2.0
540	4.2	3.7	3.3	3.0	2.8	2.6	2.4	2.2	2.1	2.0
560	4.0	3.6	3.2	2.9	2.7	2.5	2.3	2.1	2.0	1.9
580	3.9	3.4	3.1	2.8	2.6	2.4	2.2	2.1	1.9	1.8
600	3.8	3.3	3.0	2.7	2.5	2.3	2.1	2.0	1.9	1.8

Note: Formula used for calculation:

$$L = \frac{2000(9)}{R \; W} = \frac{18000}{R \; W}$$

Where:
L = Lineal feet covered by one ton of material
R = Rate of spread in lbs per sq. yd.
W = Width of spread in feet

TABLE XVI-25—CUBIC YARDS OF MATERIAL REQUIRED FOR VARIOUS WIDTHS AND DEPTHS PER 100 LINEAR FEET AND PER MILE

Width, Feet	Depth—Inches											
	1	2	3	4	5	6	7	8	9	10	11	12
1	0.31	0.62	0.93	1.23	1.54	1.85	2.16	2.47	2.78	3.09	3.40	3.70
2	0.62	1.23	1.85	2.47	3.09	3.70	4.32	4.94	5.56	6.17	6.79	7.41
3	0.93	1.85	2.78	3.70	4.63	5.56	6.48	7.41	8.33	9.26	10.2	11.1
4	1.23	2.47	3.70	4.94	6.17	7.41	8.64	9.88	11.1	12.3	13.6	14.8
5	1.54	3.09	4.63	6.17	7.72	9.26	10.8	12.3	13.9	15.4	17.0	18.5
6	1.85	3.70	5.56	7.41	9.26	11.1	13.0	14.8	16.7	18.5	20.4	22.2
7	2.16	4.32	6.48	8.64	10.8	13.0	15.1	17.3	19.4	21.6	23.8	25.9
8	2.47	4.94	7.41	9.88	12.3	14.8	17.3	19.8	22.2	24.7	27.2	29.6
9	2.78	5.56	8.33	11.1	13.9	16.7	19.4	22.2	25.0	27.8	30.6	33.3
10	3.09	6.17	9.26	12.3	15.4	18.5	21.6	24.7	27.8	30.9	34.0	37.0
20	6.17	12.3	18.5	24.7	30.9	37.0	43.2	49.4	55.6	61.7	67.9	74.1
30	9.26	18.5	27.8	37.0	46.3	55.6	64.8	74.1	83.3	92.6	102	111
40	12.3	24.7	37.0	49.4	61.7	74.1	86.4	98.8	111	123	136	148
50	15.4	30.9	46.3	61.7	77.2	92.6	108	123	139	154	170	185
60	18.5	37.0	55.6	74.1	92.6	111	130	148	167	185	204	222
70	21.6	43.2	64.8	86.4	108	130	151	173	194	216	238	259
80	24.7	49.4	74.1	98.8	123	148	173	198	222	247	272	296
90	27.8	55.6	83.3	111	139	167	194	222	250	278	306	333
100	30.9	61.7	92.6	123	154	185	216	247	278	309	340	370

PER 100 LINEAR FEET

W												
1	16.3	32.6	48.9	65.2	81.5	97.8	114	130	147	163	179	196
2	32.6	65.2	97.8	130	163	196	228	261	293	326	359	391
3	48.9	97.8	147	196	244	293	342	391	440	489	538	587
4	65.2	130	196	261	326	391	456	521	587	652	717	782
5	81.5	163	244	326	407	489	570	652	733	815	896	978
6	97.8	196	293	391	489	587	684	782	880	978	1076	1173
7	114	228	342	456	570	684	799	913	1027	1141	1255	1369
8	130	261	391	521	652	782	913	1043	1173	1304	1434	1564
9	147	293	440	587	733	880	1027	1173	1320	1467	1613	1760
10	163	326	489	652	815	978	1141	1304	1467	1630	1793	1956
20	326	652	978	1304	1630	1956	2281	2607	2933	3259	3585	3911
30	489	978	1467	1956	2444	2933	3422	3911	4440	4889	5378	5867
40	652	1304	1956	2607	3259	3911	4563	5215	5867	6519	7170	7822
50	815	1630	2444	3259	4074	4889	5704	6519	7333	8148	8963	9778
60	978	1956	2933	3911	4889	5867	6844	7822	8800	9778	10756	11733
70	1141	2281	3422	4563	5704	6844	7985	9126	10267	11407	12548	13689
80	1304	2607	3911	5215	6519	7822	9126	10430	11733	13037	14341	15644
90	1467	2933	4400	5867	7333	8800	10267	11733	13200	14667	16133	17600
100	1630	3259	4889	6519	8148	9778	11407	13037	14667	16296	17926	19556

Note: Formulas used for calculation:

Per 100 Lin Ft: $q = \left(\dfrac{D}{36}\right)\left(\dfrac{W}{3}\right)\left(\dfrac{100}{3}\right) = 0.3086DW$

Per Mile: $q = \left(\dfrac{D}{36}\right)\left(\dfrac{W}{3}\right)\left(\dfrac{5280}{3}\right) = 16.2963DW$

Where: q = Quantity of material in cubic yards
D = Depth in inches
W = Width in feet

— 325 —

TABLE XVI-26—SPECIFIC GRAVITY AND DENSITY OF MISCELLANEOUS SOLIDS AND LIQUIDS

Important Note

The specific gravity and density of most materials included in this table will vary through a range of values. Accordingly, ranges are indicated. Such ranges, however, are not necessarily all-inclusive as values will occasionally be encountered which will fall outside the indicated range.

Where solids are concerned, the specific gravity and density shown are for the material in solid form. To determine the density or unit weight of the material in crushed or granular form, it is also necessary to know the void content which, in turn, depends upon the gradation and degree of compaction of such materials. Knowing the void content and specific gravity, the bulk density or unit weight of the material in crushed or granular form may be obtained from Table XVI-19.

It is preferable to determine both the specific gravity and the void content by appropriate test. The data provided below should therefore be used only for estimating purposes.

Specific Gravities and Densities of Miscellaneous Solid and Liquid Materials

Material	Sp Gr	Weight lbs/cu ft
Alcohol, ethyl, pure	0.79	49.2
Aluminum	2.55–2.80	159–175
Aluminum oxide	3.95–4.00	
Asbestos	2.1–2.8	131–175
Asbestos paper		13.0–22.0
Asbestos sheet		53–56
Asphalt cement	0.99–1.04	61.8–64.9
Asphalt, liquid	0.92–1.01	57.4–63.0
Asphalt, natural	1.00–1.42	62.4–88.6
Basalt	2.7–3.2	168–200
Benzene	0.73–0.75	45.6–46.8
Brass	8.4–8.7	524–543
Brick, building	1.4–1.9	87–119
Brick, paving	1.8–2.3	112–114
Bronze	7.4–8.9	462–556
Calcium carbonate, pure	2.71	
Calcium chloride (anhydrous)	2.15	
Carbon, amorphous (carbon black)	1.8–2.1	
Carbon disulphide	1.26	78.7
Carbon tetrachloride	1.59	99.5
Cement, portland	3.1–3.2	
Cement, portland, loose		94
Cement mortar, portland		130–140
Cinders		40–45
Clay	2.5–2.7	
Coal	1.2–1.5	75–93
Concrete, asphalt	2.16–2.48	135–155
Concrete, portland cement	2.2–2.4	137–150
Copper	8.8–8.95	549–559
Cork	0.22–0.26	13–16
Creosote	1.03–1.08	64.3–67.4
Dolomite	2.8–2.9	174–181
Earth, loamy, dry		100–118
Feldspar	2.5–2.7	156–168

TABLE XVI-26 (Continued)—SPECIFIC GRAVITY AND DENSITY OF MISCELLANEOUS SOLIDS AND LIQUIDS

Material	Sp Gr	Weight lbs/cu ft
Felt.................................		16–21
Gasoline............................	0.70–0.75	43.7–46.8
Glass...............................	2.4–2.8	150–175
Granite..............................	2.6–2.9	162–181
Graphite............................	2.3–2.7	143–168
Gravel..............................	2.50–2.70	
Gypsum, calcined....................	1.81	
Ice.................................	0.88–0.92	55–58
Iron, cast, pig......................	7.2	450
Iron, wrought.......................	7.6–7.9	474–493
Kerosene............................	0.78–0.82	48.7–51.2
Lead................................	11.34	707.9
Leather.............................	0.86–1.02	53–64
Limestone...........................	2.1–2.8	131–175
Lime, quick (calcium oxide)...........	2.62	
Lime, hydrated or slaked (calcium hydroxide)................	2.20	
Lubricating oil......................	0.86–0.94	53.7–58.7
Mercury at 20°C.....................	13.546	845.65
Mica, muscovite.....................	2.7–3.1	168–194
Naphtha, petroleum ether.............	0.63–0.66	39.3–41.2
Paraffin wax	0.85–0.95	53.0–59.3
Peat................................		20–40
Petroleum..........................	0.91–1.04	56.8–64.9
Pitch...............................	1.07–1.15	67–72
Quartz, flint........................	2.5–2.8	156–175
Rubber.............................	0.92–0.96	57–60
Salt (sodium chloride)	2.16	134.8
Sand...............................	2.5–2.7	
Sandstone...........................	2.0–2.7	125–168
Slate...............................	2.6–2.9	162–181
Slag, granulated.....................	1.4–1.6	
Slag, blast furnace..................	2.0–2.5	
Steel...............................	7.8–7.9	487–493
Tar.................................	0.95–1.25	59–78
Timber (air dry)		
Fir, Douglas........................	0.48–0.55	30–34
Oak, Chestnut......................	0.74	46.2
Pine, Southern.....................	0.61–0.67	38–42
Redwood, California................	0.42	26.1
Trap Rock...........................	2.7–3.2	168–200
Water, distilled, 39.2°F (+4°C)........	1.00	62.43
Water, sea..........................	1.02–1.04	63.6–64.9

TABLE XVI-27—CONVERSION OF LINEAR MEASUREMENTS FEET TO MILES AND MILES TO FEET

FEET TO MILES

Feet	1	2	3	4	5	6	7	8	9
Miles	0.00019	0.00038	0.00057	0.00076	0.00095	0.00114	0.00133	0.00152	0.00171
Feet	10	20	30	40	50	60	70	80	90
Miles	0.00189	0.00379	0.00568	0.00758	0.00947	0.01136	0.01326	0.01515	0.01705
Feet	100	200	300	400	500	600	700	800	900
Miles	0.01894	0.03788	0.05682	0.07576	0.09470	0.11364	0.13258	0.15152	0.17046
Feet	1000	2000	3000	4000	5000	6000	7000	8000	9000
Miles	0.18939	0.37879	0.56818	0.75758	0.94697	1.13636	1.32576	1.51515	1.70455
Feet	10000	20000	30000	40000	50000	60000	70000	80000	90000
Miles	1.8939	3.7879	5.6818	7.5758	9.4697	11.3636	13.2576	15.1515	17.0455

MILES TO FEET

Miles	0.1	1.0	1.1	1.2	1.3	1.4	1.5	1.6	1.7	1.8	1.9
Feet	528	5280	5808	6336	6864	7392	7920	8448	8976	9504	10032
Miles	0.2	2.0	2.1	2.2	2.3	2.4	2.5	2.6	2.7	2.8	2.9
Feet	1056	10560	11088	11616	12144	12672	13200	13728	14256	14784	15312
Miles	0.3	3.0	3.1	3.2	3.3	3.4	3.5	3.6	3.7	3.8	3.9
Feet	1584	15840	16368	16896	17424	17952	18480	19008	19536	20064	20592
Miles	0.4	4.0	4.1	4.2	4.3	4.4	4.5	4.6	4.7	4.8	4.9
Feet	2112	21120	21648	22176	22704	23232	23760	24288	24816	25344	25872
Miles	0.5	5.0	5.1	5.2	5.3	5.4	5.5	5.6	5.7	5.8	5.9
Feet	2640	26400	26928	27456	27984	28512	29040	29568	30096	30624	31152
Miles	0.6	6.0	6.1	6.2	6.3	6.4	6.5	6.6	6.7	6.8	.9
Feet	3168	31680	32208	32736	33264	33792	34320	34848	35376	35904	36432
Miles	0.7	7.0	7.1	7.2	7.3	7.4	7.5	7.6	7.7	7.8	7.9
Feet	3696	36960	37488	38016	38544	39072	39600	40128	40656	41184	41712
Miles	0.8	8.0	8.1	8.2	8.3	8.4	8.5	8.6	8.7	8.8	8.9
Feet	4224	42240	42768	43296	43824	44352	44880	45408	45936	46464	46992
Miles	0.9	9.0	9.1	9.2	9.3	9.4	9.5	9.6	9.7	9.8	9.9
Feet	4752	47520	48048	48576	49104	49632	50160	50688	51216	51744	52272

TABLE XVI-28—CONVERSION OF LINEAR MEASUREMENTS DECIMALS OF AN INCH FOR EACH $\frac{1}{64}$ INCH

Fraction	⅟₆₄ths	Decimal	Millimeters (approx.)	Fraction	⅟₆₄ths	Decimal	Millimeters (approx.)
. .	1	.015625	0.397	. .	33	.515625	13.097
$\frac{1}{32}$	2	.03125	0.794	$\frac{17}{32}$	34	.53125	13.494
. .	3	.046875	1.191	. .	35	.546875	13.891
$\frac{1}{16}$	4	.0625	1.588	$\frac{9}{16}$	36	.5625	14.288
. .	5	.078125	1.984	. .	37	.578125	14.684
$\frac{3}{32}$	6	.09375	2.381	$\frac{19}{32}$	38	.59375	15.081
. .	7	.109375	2.778	. .	39	.609375	15.478
$\frac{1}{8}$	8	.125	3.175	$\frac{5}{8}$	40	.625	15.875
. .	9	.140625	3.572	. .	41	.640625	16.272
$\frac{5}{32}$	10	.15625	3.969	$\frac{21}{32}$	42	.65625	16.669
. .	11	.171875	4.366	. .	43	.671875	17.066
$\frac{3}{16}$	12	.1875	4.763	$\frac{11}{16}$	44	.6875	17.463
. .	13	.203125	5.159	. .	45	.703125	17.859
$\frac{7}{32}$	14	.21875	5.556	$\frac{23}{32}$	46	.71875	18.256
. .	15	.234375	5.953	. .	47	.734375	18.653
$\frac{1}{4}$	16	.250	6.350	$\frac{3}{4}$	48	.750	19.050
. .	17	.265625	6.747	. .	49	.765625	19.447
$\frac{9}{32}$	18	.28125	7.144	$\frac{25}{32}$	50	.78125	19.844
. .	19	.296875	7.541	. .	51	.796875	20.241
$\frac{5}{16}$	20	.3125	7.938	$\frac{13}{16}$	52	.8125	20.638
. .	21	.328125	8.334	. .	53	.828125	21.034
$\frac{11}{32}$	22	.34375	8.731	$\frac{27}{32}$	54	.84375	21.431
. .	23	.359375	9.128	. .	55	.859375	21.828
$\frac{3}{8}$	24	.375	9.525	$\frac{7}{8}$	56	.875	22.225
. .	25	.390625	9.922	. .	57	.890625	22.622
$\frac{13}{32}$	26	.40625	10.319	$\frac{29}{32}$	58	.90625	23.019
. .	27	.421875	10.716	. .	59	.921875	23.416
$\frac{7}{16}$	28	.4375	11.113	$\frac{15}{16}$	60	.9375	23.813
. .	29	.453125	11.509	. .	61	.953125	24.209
$\frac{15}{32}$	30	.46875	11.906	$\frac{31}{32}$	62	.96875	24.606
. .	31	.484375	12.303	. .	63	.984375	25.003
$\frac{1}{2}$	32	.500	12.700	1	64	1.000	25.400

TABLE XVI-29—CONVERSION OF LINEAR MEASUREMENTS DECIMALS OF A FOOT FOR EACH $\frac{1}{32}$ INCH TO 12 INCHES

Inch	0″	1″	2″	3″	4″	5″
0	0	.0833	.1667	.2500	.3333	.4167
$\frac{1}{32}$	.0026	.0859	.1693	.2526	.3359	.4193
$\frac{1}{16}$	.0052	.0885	.1719	.2552	.3385	.4219
$\frac{3}{32}$	.0078	.0911	.1745	.2578	.3411	.4245
$\frac{1}{8}$	.0104	.0938	.1771	.2604	.3438	.4271
$\frac{5}{32}$	.0130	.0964	.1797	.2630	.3464	.4297
$\frac{3}{16}$	.0156	.0990	.1823	.2656	.3490	.4323
$\frac{7}{32}$	.0182	.1016	.1849	.2682	.3516	.4349
$\frac{1}{4}$	.0208	.1042	.1875	.2708	.3542	.4375
$\frac{9}{32}$	.0234	.1068	.1901	.2734	.3568	.4401
$\frac{5}{16}$	.0260	.1094	.1927	.2760	.3594	.4427
$\frac{11}{32}$	.0286	.1120	.1953	.2786	.3620	.4453
$\frac{3}{8}$	.0313	.1146	.1979	.2812	.3646	.4479
$\frac{13}{32}$	.0339	.1172	.2005	.2839	.3672	.4505
$\frac{7}{16}$	.0365	.1198	.2031	.2865	.3698	.4531
$\frac{15}{32}$	.0391	.1224	.2057	.2891	.3724	.4557
$\frac{1}{2}$	.0417	.1250	.2083	.2917	.3750	.4583
$\frac{17}{32}$	.0443	.1276	.2109	.2943	.3776	.4609
$\frac{9}{16}$	.0469	.1302	.2135	.2969	.3802	.4635
$\frac{19}{32}$	.0495	.1328	.2161	.2995	.3828	.4661
$\frac{5}{8}$	.0521	.1354	.2188	.3021	.3854	.4688
$\frac{21}{32}$	.0547	.1380	.2214	.3047	.3880	.4714
$\frac{11}{16}$	.0573	.1406	.2240	.3073	.3906	.4740
$\frac{23}{32}$	.0599	.1432	.2266	.3099	.3932	.4766
$\frac{3}{4}$	.0625	.1458	.2292	.3125	.3958	.4792
$\frac{25}{32}$	.0651	.1484	.2318	.3151	.3984	.4818
$\frac{13}{16}$	.0677	.1510	.2344	.3177	.4010	.4844
$\frac{27}{32}$	.0703	.1536	.2370	.3203	.4036	.4870
$\frac{7}{8}$	.0729	.1563	.2396	.3229	.4063	.4896
$\frac{29}{32}$	.0755	.1589	.2422	.3255	.4089	.4922
$\frac{15}{16}$	.0781	.1615	.2448	.3281	.4115	.4948
$\frac{31}{32}$	.0807	.1641	.2474	.3307	.4141	.4974

Inch	6″	7″	8″	9″	10″	11″
0	.5000	.5833	.6667	.7500	.8333	.9167
$\frac{1}{32}$	.5026	.5859	.6693	.7526	.8359	.9193
$\frac{1}{16}$	.5052	.5885	.6719	.7552	.8385	.9219
$\frac{3}{32}$	.5078	.5911	.6745	.7578	.8411	.9245
$\frac{1}{8}$	.5104	.5938	.6771	.7604	.8438	.9271
$\frac{5}{32}$	.5130	.5964	.6797	.7630	.8464	.9297
$\frac{3}{16}$	.5156	.5990	.6823	.7656	.8490	.9323
$\frac{7}{32}$	.5182	.6016	.6849	.7682	.8516	.9349
$\frac{1}{4}$	.5208	.6042	.6875	.7708	.8542	.9375
$\frac{9}{32}$	.5234	.6068	.6901	.7734	.8568	.9401
$\frac{5}{16}$	.5260	.6094	.6927	.7760	.8594	.9427
$\frac{11}{32}$	.5286	.6120	.6953	.7786	.8620	.9453
$\frac{3}{8}$	.5313	.6146	.6979	.7813	.8646	.9479
$\frac{13}{32}$	.5339	.6172	.7005	.7839	.8672	.9505
$\frac{7}{16}$	.5365	.6198	.7031	.7865	.8698	.9531
$\frac{15}{32}$	.5391	.6224	.7057	.7891	.8724	.9557
$\frac{1}{2}$	.5417	.6250	.7083	.7917	.8750	.9583
$\frac{17}{32}$	.5443	.6276	.7109	.7943	.8776	.9609
$\frac{9}{16}$	.5469	.6302	.7135	.7969	.8802	.9635
$\frac{19}{32}$	.5495	.6328	.7161	.7995	.8828	.9661
$\frac{5}{8}$	.5521	.6354	.7188	.8021	.8854	.9688
$\frac{21}{32}$	.5547	.6380	.7214	.8047	.8880	.9714
$\frac{11}{16}$	.5573	.6406	.7240	.8073	.8906	.9740
$\frac{23}{32}$	.5599	.6432	.7266	.8099	.8932	.9766
$\frac{3}{4}$	.5625	.6458	.7292	.8125	.8958	.9792
$\frac{25}{32}$	.5651	.6484	.7318	.8151	.8984	.9818
$\frac{13}{16}$	.5677	.6510	.7344	.8177	.9010	.9844
$\frac{27}{32}$	.5703	.6536	.7370	.8203	.9036	.9870
$\frac{7}{8}$	.5729	.6563	.7396	.8229	.9063	.9896
$\frac{29}{32}$	.5755	.6589	.7422	.8255	.9089	.9922
$\frac{15}{16}$	.5781	.6615	.7448	.8281	.9115	.9948
$\frac{31}{32}$	.5807	.6641	.7474	.8307	.9141	.9974

TABLE XVI-30—CONVERSION FACTORS—LENGTH MEASUREMENTS

Units	Inches	Feet	Yards	Rods	Miles	Meters
1 Inch	1	0.08333	0.027778	0.005051	0.0000157828	0.0254
1 Foot	12	1	0.3333	0.060606	0.000018939	0.304801
1 Yard	36	3	1	0.181818	0.000568182	0.914402
1 Rod (Surveyor's Measure)	198	16.5	5.5	1	0.003125	5.029216
1 Mile (U.S. Statute)	63360	5280	1760	320	1	1609.347
1 Meter	39.37	3.280833	1.093611	0.198838	0.00062137	1
1 Link	7.92	0.66	0.22	0.04	0.000125	0.201168
1 Chain (Surveyor's)	792	66	22	4	0.0125	20.117
1 Station	1200	100	33.33	6.060606	0.0189394	30.4801
1 Furlong	7920	660	220	40	0.125	201.168
1 Mile (Int. Nautical)	72913	6076.103	2025.366	368.248	1.15078	1852
1 Millimeter	0.03937	0.003281	0.001094	0.000199	—	0.001
1 Centimeter	0.3937	0.032808	0.010936	0.001988	—	0.01
1 Kilometer	—	3280.833	1093.611	198.836	0.621370	1000

TABLE XVI-31—CONVERSION FACTORS—AREA MEASUREMENTS

Units	Square Inches	Square Feet	Square Yards	Square Rods	Acres	Square Miles	Square Meters
1 Square Inch	1	0.006944	0.0007716	—	—	—	0.00064516
1 Square Foot	144	1	0.11111	0.0036731	—	—	0.09290341
1 Square Yard	1296	9	1	0.033058	0.0002066	—	0.8361307
1 Square Rod	39204	272.25	30.25	1	0.00625	—	25.29295
1 Acre	—	43560	4840	160	1	0.0015625	4046.873
1 Square Mile	—	—	3097600	102400	640	1	2589998
1 Square Meter	1550	10.76387	1.195985	0.0393367	0.0002471	—	1
1 Square Link	62.7264	0.4356	0.0484	0.0016	0.00001	—	0.040468
1 Square Chain	627264	4356	484	16	0.1	—	404.689
1 Square	14400	100	11.1111	0.367309	0.0022956	—	9.29034
1 Section	—	—	3097600	102400	640	1	2589998
1 Square Centimeter	0.1549997	0.0010764	0.0001196	—	—	—	0.0001
1 Hectare	—	107638.7	11959.85	395.367	2.471044	0.003861	10000
1 Square Kilometer	—	—	1195985	39536.7	247.1044	0.3861006	1000000

TABLE XVI-32—CONVERSION FACTORS—VOLUME MEASUREMENTS

Units	Cubic Inches	Cubic Feet	Cubic Yards	Pints (Liquid)	Quarts (Liquid)	Gallons (U.S.)	Liters (1000 cc)
1 Cubic Inch	1	0.000579	0.0000214	0.034632	0.017316	0.004329	0.016387
1 Cubic Foot	1728	1	0.037037	59.844	29.922	7.4805	28.31625
1 Cubic Yard	46656	27	1	1615.8	807.9	201.975	764.54
1 Pint (Liquid)	28.875	0.016710	0.000619	1	0.5	0.125	0.473168
1 Quart (Liquid)	57.75	0.033420	0.001238	2	1	0.25	0.946333
1 Gallon (U.S.)	231	0.1336805	0.004951	8	4	1	3.78533
1 Liter (1000 cc)	61.025	0.035316	0.001308	2.11336	1.056682	0.264178	1
1 Gil	7.21876	0.004177	0.000155	0.25	0.125	0.03125	0.118292
1 Pint (Dry)	33.6003	0.019445	0.000720	1.163647	0.581823	0.145456	0.550599
1 Quart (Dry)	67.200625	0.038889	0.001440	2.32730	1.163646	0.290912	1.10120
1 Quart (Imperial)	69.35503	0.040135	0.001486	2.4019	1.200953	0.302238	1.13650
1 Gallon (Imperial)	277.4201	0.16054	0.0059457	9.60762	4.80381	1.20095	4.54609
1 Peck	537.605	0.311114	0.011523	18.61835	9.309177	2.327294	8.809586
1 Bushel (US)	2150.42	1.2444	0.046089	74.47341	37.23670	9.3092	35.238329
1 Board Foot	144	0.08333	0.003086	4.987012	2.493506	0.623376	2.3597
1 Cord	221184	128	4.74074	7660.051	3830.025	957.506	3624.48
1 Petroleum Barrel	9701.975	5.614569	0.207947	336	168	42	158.9839
1 Barrel (U.S. Liquid)	7276.370	4.21086	0.15596	252	126	31.5	119.237895
1 Cubic Meter	61023.38	35.314445	1.307943	2113.4	1056.7	264.178	1000
1 Cubic Centimeter	0.061024	0.0000353	—	0.002113	0.001057	0.0002642	0.001

TABLE XVI-33—CONVERSION FACTORS—WEIGHT MEASUREMENTS

Units	Ounces	Pounds	Tons (Short)	Tons (Long)	Kilograms	Tons (Metric)
1 Ounce	1	0.0625	—	—	0.028349	—
1 Pound	16	1	0.0005	0.0004464	0.4535924	0.00045359
1 Ton (Short)	32000	2000	1	0.892857	907.18486	0.907185
1 Ton (Long)	35840	2240	1.12	1	1016.047	1.016047
1 Kilogram	35.27396	2.204622	0.0011023	0.0009842	1	0.001
1 Ton (Metric)	35273.96	2204.62	1.102231	0.98421	1000	1
1 Hundredweight (Short)	1600	100	0.05	0.044643	45.3592	0.045359
1 Hundredweight (Long)	1792	112	0.056	0.05	50.8023	0.050802
1 Grain	0.0022857	—	—	—	—	—
1 Gram	0.0352739	0.002204	—	—	0.001	—
1 Milligram	—	—	—	—	0.000001	—

TABLE XVI-34—MISCELLANEOUS CONVERSION FACTORS

Multiply	By	To Obtain
Pounds per foot	1.48816	Kilograms per meter
Pounds per square foot	4.88241	Kilograms per square meter
Pounds per square inch	0.07031	Kilograms per square cm.
Pounds per square inch	0.0007031	Kilograms per square mm.
Pounds per cubic foot	16.0184	Kilograms per cubic meter
Radians	57.29578	Degrees, angular
Horsepower	550	Ft-Lbs per second
Horsepower	2544	B.T.U.'s per hour
Horsepower	745.5	Watts
B.T.U.	251.98	Calories, gram
B.T.U.	777.98	Ft-Lbs
Feet per second	0.68182	Miles per hour
Miles per hour	88	Feet per minute
Miles per hour	1.46667	Feet per second
Pounds	444822	Dynes
Kilograms	980665	Dynes
Atmosphere	1.0333	Kilograms per square cm.
Atmosphere	14.697	Pounds per square inch
Atmosphere	29.921	Inches of mercury (0°C. at sea level)
Atmosphere	0.76	Meters of mercury (0°C. at sea level)
Atmosphere	33.9	Feet of water (4°C. at sea level)
Pounds of water per minute	0.016021	Cubic feet per minute
Cubic feet per minute	0.12468	Gallons per second
Fathoms	6	Feet
Degrees per foot	0.00057261	Radians per centimeter
Centimeters of mercury (at 20°C.)	5.34	Inches of water (at 20°C.)

TABLE XVI-35—SQUARE YARDS OF ROAD SURFACE FOR VARIOUS ROAD WIDTHS

Road Width	Per Lineal Foot	Per 100 Ft.	Per Mile	Road Width	Per Lineal Foot	Per 100 Ft.	Per Mile
6'	0.67	66.67	3,520	24'	2.67	266.67	14,080
7'	0.78	77.78	4,107	25'	2.78	277.78	14,667
8'	0.89	88.89	4,693	26'	2.89	288.89	15,253
9'	1.00	100.00	5,280	28'	3.11	311.11	16,427
10'	1.11	111.11	5,867	30'	3.33	333.33	17,600
11'	1.22	122.22	6,453	32'	3.56	355.56	18,773
12'	1.33	133.33	7,040	34'	3.78	377.78	19,947
13'	1.44	144.44	7,627	36'	4.00	400.00	21,120
14'	1.56	155.56	8,213	38'	4.22	422.22	22,293
15'	1.67	166.67	8,800	40'	4.44	444.44	23,467
16'	1.78	177.78	9,387	50'	5.56	555.56	29,333
17'	1.89	188.89	9,973	60'	6.67	666.67	35,200
18'	2.00	200.00	10,560	70'	7.78	777.78	41,067
20'	2.22	222.22	11,733	75'	8.33	833.33	44,000
22'	2.44	244.44	12,907	80'	8.89	888.89	46,933

TABLE XVI-36—DENSITY AND VISCOSITY OF WATER AT VARIOUS TEMPERATURES

Temperature		Density gm/ml	Density in lbs/cu ft	Viscosity in Centipoises
°C	°F			
−10	+14	0.99815	62.3128	2.60
−5	23	0.99930	62.3846	2.13
0	32	0.99987	62.4201	1.7921
+4	39.20	1.00000	62.4283	1.5674
5	41	0.99999	62.4276	1.5188
10	50	0.99973	62.4114	1.3077
15	59	0.99913	62.3739	1.1404
20	68	0.99823	62.3178	1.0050
20.2	68.36	0.99819	62.3153	1.0000
25	77	0.99707	62.2453	0.8937
30	86	0.99567	62.1579	0.8007
35	95	0.99406	62.0574	0.7225
40	104	0.99224	61.9438	0.6560
45	113	0.99025	61.8196	0.5988
50	122	0.98807	61.6835	0.5494
55	131	0.98573	61.5374	0.5064
60	140	0.98324	61.3820	0.4688
65	149	0.98059	61.2165	0.4355
70	158	0.97781	61.0430	0.4061
75	167	0.97489	60.8607	0.3799
80	176	0.97183	60.6697	0.3565
85	185	0.96865	60.4711	0.3355
90	194	0.96534	60.2645	0.3165
95	203	0.96192	60.0510	0.2994
100	212	0.95838	59.8300	0.2838

TABLE XVI-37—AREAS OF PLANE FIGURES

Square

Diagonal $= d = s\sqrt{2}$.
Area $= s^2 = 4b^2 = 0.5d^2$.
Example. $s = 6$; $b = 3$. Area $= (6)^2 = 36$ Ans.
$\quad\quad\quad d = 6 \times 1.414 = 8.484$ Ans.

Rectangle and Parallelogram

Area $= ab$ or $b\sqrt{d^2 - b^2}$
Example. $a = 6$; $b = 3$.
Area $= 3 \times 6 = 18$ Ans

Trapezoid

Area $= \frac{1}{2}h(a + b)$
Example. $a = 2$; $b = 4$; $h = 3$.
$\quad\quad$ Area $= \frac{1}{2} \times 3(2 + 4) = 9$. Ans.

Trapezium

Area $= \frac{1}{2}[a(h + h^1) + bh^1 + ch]$
Example. $a = 4$; $b = 2$; $c = 2$; $h = 3$; $h^1 = 2$.
Area $= \frac{1}{2}[4(3 + 2) + (2 \times 2) + (2 \times 3)] = 15$.
$\quad\quad\quad\quad\quad\quad\quad\quad\quad\quad\quad\quad\quad\quad$ Ans.

Triangles

Both formulas apply to both figures
Area $= \frac{1}{2}bh$.
Example. $h = 3$; $b = 5$.
$\quad\quad$ Area $= \frac{1}{2}(3 \times 5) = 7\frac{1}{2}$. Ans.

Area $= \sqrt{S(S - a)(S - b)(S - c)}$ when $S = \dfrac{a + b + c}{2}$

Example. $a = 2$; $b = 3$; $c = 4$.
$$S = \frac{2 + 3 + 4}{2} = 4.5$$
Area $= \sqrt{4.5(4.5 - 2)(4.5 - 3)(4.5 - 4)} = 2.9$.
$\quad\quad\quad\quad\quad\quad\quad\quad\quad\quad\quad\quad\quad\quad$ Ans.

Regular Polygons

Area $\begin{cases} 5 \text{ sides} = 1.720477\ S^2 = 3.63271\ r^2 \\ 6\ \text{"}\quad = 2.598150\ S^2 = 3.46410\ r^2 \\ 7\ \text{"}\quad = 3.633875\ S^2 = 3.37101\ r^2 \\ 8\ \text{"}\quad = 4.828427\ S^2 = 3.31368\ r^2 \\ 9\ \text{"}\quad = 6.181875\ S^2 = 3.27573\ r^2 \\ 10\ \text{"}\quad = 7.694250\ S^2 = 3.24920\ r^2 \\ 11\ \text{"}\quad = 9.365675\ S^2 = 3.22993\ r^2 \\ 12\ \text{"}\quad = 11.196300\ S^2 = 3.21539\ r^2 \end{cases}$

n = number of sides; r = short radius;
S = length of side; R = long radius.

Area $= \dfrac{n}{4} S^2 \cot \dfrac{180°}{n} = \dfrac{n}{2} R^2 \sin \dfrac{360°}{n}$

$\quad\quad = nr^2 \tan \dfrac{180°}{n}$

TABLE XVI-37 *(continued)*

Circle

$\pi = 3.1416$; A = area; d = diameter; p = circumference or periphery; r = radius.

$$p = \pi d = 3.1416d. \qquad p = 2\sqrt{\pi A} = 3.54\sqrt{A}$$

$$p = 2\pi r = 6.2832r. \qquad p = \frac{2A}{r} = \frac{4A}{d}$$

$$d = \frac{p}{\pi} = \frac{p}{3.1416} \qquad d = 2\sqrt{\frac{A}{\pi}} = 1.128\sqrt{A}$$

$$r = \frac{p}{2\pi} = \frac{p}{6.2832} \qquad r = \sqrt{\frac{A}{\pi}} = 0.564\sqrt{A}$$

$$A = \frac{\pi d^2}{4} = 0.7854d^2 \qquad A = \frac{p^2}{4\pi} = \frac{p^2}{12.57}$$

$$A = \pi r^2 = 3.1416r^2 \qquad A = \frac{pr}{2} = \frac{pd}{4}$$

Circular Ring

Area $= \pi(R^2 - r^2) = 3.1416(R^2 - r^2)$
Area $= 0.7854(D^2 - d^2) = 0.7854(D - d)(D + d)$
Area = difference in areas between the inner and outer circles.
Example. $R = 4$; $r = 2$.
Area $= 3.1416(4^2 - 2^2) = 37.6992$. Ans.

Quadrant

Area $= \frac{\pi r^2}{4} = 0.7854r^2 = 0.3927c^2$.

Example. $r = 3$. c = chord.
Area $= .7854 \times 3^2 = 7.0686$. Ans.

Segment

b = length of arc. θ = angle in degrees
c = chord $= \sqrt{4(2hr - h^2)}$
Area $= \frac{1}{2}[br - c(r - h)]$
$\qquad = \pi r^2 \dfrac{\theta}{360} - \dfrac{c(r - h)}{2}$

When θ is greater than $180°$ then $\dfrac{c}{2} \times$ difference

between r and h is added to the fraction $\dfrac{\pi r^2 \theta}{360}$

Example. $r = 3$; $\theta = 120°$; $h = 1.5$
Area $= 3.1416 \times 3^2 \times \dfrac{120}{360} - \dfrac{5.196(3 - 1.5)}{2}$

$= 5.5278$. Ans.

Sector

Area $= \dfrac{br}{2} = \pi r^2 \dfrac{\theta}{360°}$

θ = angle in degrees; b = length of arc.
Example. $r = 3$; $\theta = 120°$
Area $= 3.1416 \times 3^2 \times \dfrac{120}{360} = 9.4248$. Ans.

TABLE XVI-37 *(continued)*

Spandrel

Area $= 0.2146r^2 = 0.1073c^2$
Example. $r = 3$
Area $= 0.2146 \times 3^2 = 1.9314$. Ans

Parabola

$l =$ length of curved line = periphery $- s$

$l = \dfrac{s^2}{8h}[\sqrt{c(1+c)} + 2.0326 \times \log(\sqrt{c}+\sqrt{1+c})]$

in which $c = \left(\dfrac{4h}{s}\right)^2$

Area $= \dfrac{2}{3}sh$

Example. $s = 3$; $h = 4$

Area $= \dfrac{2}{3} \times 3 \times 4 = 8$. Ans.

Ellipse

Area $= \pi\, ab = 3.1416ab$

Circum. $= 2\pi \sqrt{\dfrac{a^2 + b^2}{2}}$ (close approximation)

Example. $a = 3$; $b = 4$.

Area $= 3.1416 \times 3 \times 4 = 37.6992$. Ans.

Circum. $= 2 \times 3.1416 \sqrt{\dfrac{(3)^2 + (4)^2}{2}}$

$= 6.2832 \times 3.5355 = 22.21$ Ans.

TABLE XVI-38—VOLUME AND SURFACE AREA OF SOLIDS

Symbols

$V =$ Volume
$S =$ Lateral Surface Area
$T =$ Total Surface Area
$B =$ Area of Base
$P =$ Perimeter Perpendicular to Sides
$P_b =$ Perimeter of Base
$A =$ Area of Section Perpendicular to Sides
$l =$ Lateral Length
$h =$ Perpendicular Height
$d =$ Diagonal Length

Cube

$V = h^3$
$T = 6h^2$
$S = 4h^2$
$d = h\sqrt{3}$

TABLE XVI-38 *(continued)*

Rectangular Prism

$$V = abh$$
$$T = 2(ab + ah + bh)$$
$$S = 2(ah + bh)$$
$$d = \sqrt{a^2 + b^2 + h^2}$$

Prism or Cylinder, Right or Oblique, Parallel Ends

$$V = Al$$
$$S = Pl$$
$$T = Pl + 2B$$

(Note $A = B$, $P = P_b$ and $l = h$ for right cylinders and prisms

Cylinder, Right or Oblique, Circular or Otherwise, Parallel Ends

$$V = Bh \text{ (Right Cylinder)}$$
$$V = Al \text{ (Oblique Cylinder)}$$
$$S = P_bh \text{ (Right Cylinder)}$$
$$S = Pl \text{ (Oblique Cylinder)}$$
$$T = P_bh + 2B \text{ (Right Cylinder)}$$
$$T = Pl + 2B \text{ (Oblique Cylinder)}$$

Frustrum of Prism or Cylinder

$$V = Bh_1 \text{ (where } h_1 \text{ is perpendicular height from base to c.g. of top)}$$
or, for cylinder
$$V = \frac{A}{2}(l_1 + l_2)$$

Pyramid or Cone, Right and Regular

$$V = \frac{Bh}{3}$$
$$S = \frac{P_bl}{2}$$
$$T = \frac{P_bl}{2} + B$$

Pyramid or Cone, Right or Oblique, Regular or Irregular

$$V = \frac{Bh}{3}$$

TABLE XVI-38 *(continued)*

Frustrum of Pyramid or Cone, Right and Regular, Parallel Ends

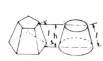

$$V = \frac{h}{3}(B + B_1 + \sqrt{BB_1})$$

$$S = \frac{l}{2}(P_b + P_T)$$

$$T = \frac{l}{2}(P_b + P_T) + B + B_1$$

where: B_1 = Area of Top
P_T = Perimeter of To**p**

Frustrum of Any Pyramid or Cone, Parallel Ends

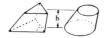

$$V^* = \frac{h}{3}(B + B_1 + \sqrt{BB_1})$$

where: B_1 = Area of Top

Wedge, Regular

$$V = \frac{ch}{6}(2a + b)$$

Sphere

$$V = \frac{4\pi r^3}{3}$$

$$S = 4\pi r^2$$

Spherical Sector

$$S = \frac{1}{2}\pi r(4b + c)$$

$$V = \frac{2}{3}\pi r^2 b$$

Spherical Segment

$$S = 2\pi rb = \frac{1}{4}\pi(4b^2 + c^2)$$

$$V = \frac{1}{3}\pi b^2(3r - b)$$

$$= \frac{1}{24}\pi b(3c^2 + 4b^2)$$

TABLE XVI-38 (continued)

Spherical Zone

$$S = 2\pi rb$$
$$V = \frac{1}{24}\pi b(3a^2 + 3c^2 + 4b^2)$$

Circular Ring

$$S = 4\pi^2 Rr$$
$$V = 2\pi^2 Rr^2$$

Ellipsoid

$$V = \frac{1}{3}\pi rab$$

Paraboloid

$$V = \frac{1}{2}\pi r^2 h$$

TABLE XVI-39—TRIGONOMETRIC RELATIONS AND SOLUTIONS OF RIGHT ANGLE TRIANGLES

As shown in the illustration, the sides of the right angled triangle are designated a, b and c. The angles opposite each of these sides are designated A, B and C respectively.

Angle A, opposite the hypotenuse a is the right angle and is therefore always one of the known quantities.

Sides and Angles Known	Formulas for Sides and Angles to be Found		
Sides a and b.....	$c = \sqrt{a^2 - b^2}$	$\sin B = \dfrac{b}{a}$	$C = 90° - B$
Sides a and c.....	$b = \sqrt{a^2 - c^2}$	$\sin C = \dfrac{c}{a}$	$B = 90° - C$
Sides b and c.....	$a = \sqrt{b^2 + c^2}$	$\tan B = \dfrac{b}{c}$	$C = 90° - B$
Side a; angle B....	$b = a \times \sin B$	$c = a \times \cos B$	$C = 90° - B$
Side a; angle C....	$b = a \times \cos C$	$c = a \times \sin C$	$B = 90° - C$
Side b; angle B....	$a = \dfrac{b}{\sin B}$	$c = b \times \cot B$	$C = 90° - B$
Side b; angle C....	$a = \dfrac{b}{\cos C}$	$c = b \times \tan C$	$B = 90° - C$
Side c; angle B....	$a = \dfrac{c}{\cos B}$	$b = c \times \tan B$	$C = 90° - B$
Side c; angle C....	$a = \dfrac{c}{\sin C}$	$b = c \times \cot C$	$B = 90° - C$

TABLE XVI-40—TRIGONOMETRIC FUNCTIONS

Angle	Sin	Cos	Tan	Angle	Sin	Cos	Tan
0	0.000	1.000	0.000	46	0.719	0.695	1.04
1	0.017	0.999	0.017	47	0.731	0.682	1.07
2	0.035	0.999	0.035	48	0.743	0.669	1.11
3	0.052	0.999	0.052	49	0.755	0.656	1.15
4	0.070	0.998	0.070	50	0.766	0.643	1.19
5	0.087	0.996	0.087	51	0.777	0.629	1.23
6	0.105	0.995	0.105	52	0.788	0.616	1.28
7	0.122	0.993	0.123	53	0.799	0.602	1.33
8	0.139	0.990	0.141	54	0.809	0.588	1.38
9	0.156	0.988	0.158	55	0.819	0.574	1.43
10	0.174	0.985	0.176				
				56	0.829	0.559	1.48
11	0.191	0.982	0.194	57	0.839	0.545	1.54
12	0.208	0.978	0.213	58	0.848	0.530	1.60
13	0.225	0.974	0.231	59	0.857	0.515	1.66
14	0.242	0.970	0.249	60	0.866	0.500	1.73
15	0.259	0.966	0.268				
				61	0.875	0.485	1.80
16	0.276	0.961	0.287	62	0.883	0.469	1.88
17	0.292	0.956	0.306	63	0.891	0.454	1.96
18	0.309	0.951	0.325	64	0.899	0.438	2.05
19	0.326	0.946	0.344	65	0.906	0.423	2.14
20	0.342	0.940	0.364				
				66	0.914	0.407	2.25
21	0.358	0.934	0.384	67	0.921	0.391	2.36
22	0.375	0.927	0.404	68	0.927	0.375	2.48
23	0.391	0.921	0.424	69	0.934	0.358	2.61
24	0.407	0.914	0.445	70	0.940	0.342	2.75
25	0.423	0.906	0.466				
				71	0.946	0.326	2.90
26	0.438	0.899	0.488	72	0.951	0.309	3.08
27	0.454	0.891	0.510	73	0.956	0.292	3.27
28	0.469	0.883	0.532	74	0.961	0.276	3.49
29	0.485	0.875	0.554	75	0.966	0.259	3.73
30	0.500	0.866	0.577				
				76	0.970	0.242	4.01
31	0.515	0.857	0.601	77	0.974	0.225	4.33
32	0.530	0.848	0.625	78	0.978	0.208	4.70
33	0.545	0.839	0.649	79	0.982	0.191	5.14
34	0.559	0.829	0.675	80	0.985	0.174	5.67
35	0.574	0.819	0.700				
				81	0.988	0.156	6.31
36	0.588	0.809	0.727	82	0.990	0.139	7.12
37	0.602	0.799	0.754	83	0.993	0.122	8.14
38	0.616	0.788	0.781	84	0.995	0.105	9.51
39	0.629	0.777	0.810	85	0.996	0.087	11.43
40	0.643	0.766	0.839				
				86	0.998	0.070	14.30
41	0.656	0.755	0.869	87	0.999	0.052	19.08
42	0.669	0.743	0.900	88	0.999	0.035	28.64
43	0.682	0.731	0.933	89	0.999	0.017	57.29
44	0.695	0.719	0.966	90	1.000	0.000	Infinity
45	0.707	0.707	1.000				

TABLE XVI-41—ASPHALT BLOCK RECOMMENDED THICKNESSES FOR TYPICAL APPLICATIONS

Typical Applications	Thickness of Unit Recommended
Industrial Floors	1½″, 2″ or 2½″
Warehouse, Baggage and Express Room Floors	1½″ or 2″
Traffic Aisles and Loading Platforms	1½″ or 2″
Piers and Docks	1½″ or 2″
Roof Decks—Parking or Storage	1½″
Roof Decks and Balconies—Recreational	1¼″ or 1½″
Airport, Hangars, Runways, Aprons	1½″, 2″ or 2½″
Ramps and Bridge Approaches	2½″ or 3″
Streets, Roads, Bridges, Viaducts	2½″ or 3″
Waterproofing Protection Courses	1¼″
Estate, Residential and Institutional Driveways	2″ {Hexagonal or Rectangular
Walks, Courts, Plazas and Terraces	2″ {Hexagonal or Rectangular

TABLE XVI-42—ASPHALT BLOCK WEIGHT AND QUANTITY RELATIONSHIPS

Size	Pounds per Block	Pounds per Sq Ft	Pounds per Sq Yd	Net Tons per Thousand Blocks	Number of Blocks per Sq Ft	Number of Blocks per Sq Yd	Per M Blocks Sq Ft	Per M Blocks Sq Yd
5″ x 12″ x 2″	10.5	25.2	227	5.25	2.4	21.6	417	46
5″ x 12″ x 2½″	12.9	31.0	279	6.45	2.4	21.6	417	46
5″ x 12″ x 3″	16.1	38.6	347	8.05	2.4	21.6	417	46
4″ x 8″ x 1¼″	3.4	15.3	138	1.70	4.50	40.5	222	25
4″ x 8″ x 1½″	4.1	18.5	167	2.05	4.50	40.5	222	25
4″ x 8″ x 2″	5.7	25.6	230	2.85	4.50	40.5	222	25
8″ x 16″ x 1¼″	14.3	16.1	145	7.15	1.13	10.2	889	99
8″ x 16″ x 1½″	16.8	18.9	170	8.40	1.13	10.2	889	99
8″ x 16″ x 2″	22.1	24.9	224	11.05	1.13	10.2	889	99
8″ x 16″ x 2½″	27.75	31.2	281	13.875	1.13	10.2	889	99
8″ x 16″ x 3″	32.25	36.3	327	16.125	1.13	10.2	889	99
Hexagonal Tiles	10.7	25.0	225	5.35	2.33	21.0	432	
Square Tiles	11.8	26.4	238	5.90	2.44	20.2	441	

— 347 —

TABLE XVI-43—REQUIREMENTS FOR U. S. STANDARD TESTING SIEVES AND APPROXIMATE EQUIVALENTS OF SQUARE AND ROUND OPENINGS

U. S. STANDARD SIEVES

STANDARD REQUIREMENTS FOR CERTAIN SIZES

Size of Sieve Designation	Sieve Opening mm.	Sieve Opening In. (Approximate Equivalents)	Permissible Variations in Average Opening, Percent	Permissible Variations in Maximum Opening, Percent	Wire Diameter mm.	Wire Diameter In. (Approximate Equivalents)
3 in.	76.2	3.00	±2	+3	4.8 to 8.1	0.190 to 0.320
2½ in.	63.5	2.50	±2	+3	4.4 to 7.1	0.175 to 0.280
2 in.	50.8	2.00	±2	+3	4.1 to 6.2	0.160 to 0.245
1½ in.	38.1	1.50	±2	+3	3.7 to 5.3	0.145 to 0.210
1¼ in.	31.7	1.25	±2	+3	3.5 to 4.8	0.140 to 0.190
1 in.	25.4	1.00	±3	+3	3.43 to 4.50	0.135 to 0.177
¾ in.	19.1	0.750	±3	+5	3.10 to 3.91	0.122 to 1.054
½ in.	12.7	0.500	±3	+5	2.39 to 3.10	0.094 to 0.122
⅜ in.	9.52	0.375	±3	+5	2.11 to 2.59	0.083 to 0.102
¼ in (No.3)	6.35	0.250	±3	+5	1.60 to 2.11	0.063 to 0.083
No. 4	4.76	0.187	±3	+10	1.14 to 1.68	0.045 to 0.066
No. 8	2.38	0.0937	±3	+10	0.74 to 1.10	0.0291 to 0.0433
No. 10	2.00	0.0787	±3	+10	0.68 to 1.00	0.0268 to 0.0394
No. 16	1.19	0.0469	±3	+10	0.50 to 0.70	0.0197 to 0.0276
No. 20	0.84	0.0331	±5	+15	0.38 to 0.55	0.0150 to 0.0217
No. 30	0.59	0.0232	±5	+15	0.29 to 0.42	0.0114 to 0.0165

No. 40........	0.42	±5	+25	0.23 to 0.33	0.0091 to 0.0130
No. 50........	0.297	±5	+25	0.170 to 0.253	0.0067 to 0.0100
No. 80........	0.177	±6	+40	0.114 to 0.154	0.0045 to 0.0061
No. 100.......	0.149	±7	+40	0.096 to 0.125	0.0038 to 0.0049
No. 200.......	0.074		+60	0.045 to 0.061	0.0018 to 0.0024
	0.0165				
	0.0117				
	0.0070				
	0.0059				
	0.0029				

APPROXIMATE EQUIVALENTS OF SQUARE AND ROUND OPENINGS

Inches		Inches	
Square	Round	Square	Round
3	3½	⅞	1
2½	3	¾	⅞
2⅛	2½	⅝	¾
2	2⅜	½	⅝
1¾	2	⅜	½
1½	1¾	5/16	⅜
1¼	1½	¼	5/16
1	1¼	3/16 (No. 4)	¼

TABLE XVI-44—APPROXIMATE PROCEDURE FOR TRANSFORMING "PASSING-RETAINED" SPECIFICATION TO AN EQUIVALENT "TOTAL PERCENT PASSING" SPECIFICATION

Assumed "Passing-Retained" Specification					Step 1		Step 2		Step 3		Step 4	
Passing	Retained	Percent Total Material		Sieve Size	Cumulative Percent Passing, Fine to Coarse Sizes		Cumulative Percent Retained, Coarse to Fine Sizes		Cumulative Percent Passing, Coarse to Fine Sizes		Equivalent Specification on "Total Percent Passing" Basis*	
					Min.	Max.	Min.	Max.	Min.	Max.		
Col. No. 1	Col. No. 2	Col. No. 3	Col. No. 4	Col. No. 5	Col. No. 6	Col. No. 7	Col. No. 8	Col. No. 9	Col. No. 10	Col. No. 11	Col. No. 12	Col. No. 13
1½ in.	1 in.	0	18	1½ in.	63	100+	0	18	100	82	—	100
1 in.	¾ in.	4	11	1 in.	63	100+	4	29	96	71	82	96
¾ in.	½ in.	5	12	¾ in.	59	100+	9	41	91	59	71	91
½ in.	⅜ in.	3	9	½ in.	54	93	12	50	88	50	59	84
⅜ in.	#4	9	13	⅜ in.	51	84	21	63	79	37	51	71
#4	#8	10	14	#4	42	71	31	77	69	23	42	57
#8	#16	8	12	#8	32	57	39	89	61	11	32	45
				#16	24	45					24	—

Column 2	Column 3	Column 4	Column 5	Column 6	Column 7	Column 8	Column 9	Column 10	Column 11	Column 12	Column 13
#16	7	—11	#30	17	34	46	100+	54	0	17	34
#30	6	—10	#50	11	24	52	100+	48	0	11	24
#50	5	—9	#100	6	15	57	100+	43	0	6	15
#100	4	—8	#200	2	7	61	100+	39		2	7
#200	2	—7									

Notes: COLUMN 5 is the same as *Column 2* repeated for convenience and clarity

COLUMN 6 is derived by *adding* the values in *Column 3* from *Fine to Coarse*

COLUMN 7 is derived by *adding* the values in *Column 4* from *Fine to Coarse*

COLUMN 8 is derived by *adding* the values in *Column 3* from *Coarse to Fine*

COLUMN 9 is derived by *adding* the values in *Column 4* from *Coarse to Fine*

COLUMN 10 is derived by *subtracting* the values in *Column 8* from 100 (i.e. *Column 10* = 100 − *Column 8*)

COLUMN 11 is derived by *subtracting* the values in *Column 9* from 100 (i.e. *Column 11* = 100 − *Column 9*)

The values for COLUMN 12 are obtained by selecting whichever value is the *larger* from either *Column 6* or *Column 11*
(i.e. *Column 12* = *Maximum* value from *Column 6* and *Column 11*).

The values for COLUMN 13 are obtained by selecting whichever value is the *smaller* from either *Column 7* or *Column 10*
(i.e. *Column 13* = *Minimum* value from *Column 7* and *Column 10*).

Where more or fewer screen sizes are used, Columns 3, 4 and 5 would be changed accordingly.

Generally, rounded figures are used as specification limits in Columns 3 and 4 and in Columns 12 and 13. The figures used in this table were selected to indicate more clearly the method.

"It will be noted that a very narrow specification by the "Passing and Retained" method gives a much wider specification by the "Total Percent Passing" method. This ability of the "Total Percent Passing" method to provide a narrow close control on the gradation, with reasonable margins on the screen sizes, is an important advantage of this method.

APPENDIX A

Evaluation of Materials

A.01 EXPLORATIONS AND BORINGS. — The materials investigation should include a sufficient number of borings to permit identification of the various soil types likely to be encountered both in the area of the proposed pavement and in the adjacent areas where material may be borrowed. A preliminary investigation which takes full advantage of any existing open ditches or cuts and the use of aerial photography will indicate the general areas of each soil type and make possible the strategic location of the boring sites so that the maximum information may be obtained from the least number of borings. The borings should be carried at least to the full depth of frost penetration or, where a cut is contemplated, to a depth of 6 feet below the grade line of the proposed subgrade. Borings in borrow areas should be carried well below the anticipated depth of borrow. The data obtained from these borings should be sufficient to develop soil profiles and to identify the principal soils in the area. Detailed tests should then be made of material obtained from large-size test pits or borings in areas representative of each soil type. The types of tests required are dependent upon the method of evaluation selected. The *Soils Manual,* Manual Series No. 10, published by The Asphalt Institute, contains details of the soil survey, sampling, and required tests for evaluation.

INDEX

INDEX

Test methods commonly specified, 53

Emulsion slurry
Definition and use, 160
Machine, Figure VIII-10, 160

Equipment, asphalt construction, 96-116

Erosion control, asphalt, for beaches, flood channels, lake shores, river banks and streams, 241-250

Extraction tests for asphalt paving mixtures, 49-50
Recovery of asphalt, 50

F

Farm uses, Figure XV-7, 275
Advantages, 273
Caution, 275
Construction, 273
Base, subbase, 274
Drainage, 274
Pavement type, 276
Subgrade, 273
Surface course, 274
Surface sand dressing, 275
Thickness of pavement, Table XVI-1, 274

Fine aggregate
Definition, 10
Specifications, 67, 68

Fine-graded aggregate defined, 10

Flash point tests
Asphalt cement, 20
Cleveland open cup, Figure III-4, 21
Pensky-Martens, Figure III-5, 22
liquid asphalts
Medium-curing and rapid curing asphalts, 26, Figure III-7, 27
Slow-curing asphalt, 29

Flexible pavement structures, defined, 12

Float test for slow-curing asphalt, Figure III-9, 29

Flood channel erosion control with asphalt, 241

Flux defined, 10

Fog seal
Definitions, 11, 159
Uses, 153, 159

Foundation, preparation for construction of asphalt pavements, 118-124
Compaction, 123
Construction control, 122
Drainage systems, 118, 119
Moisture control, 123
Old pavements used as bases, 124
Trench design, 120-122

Frost effects in asphalt pavement structures, 85

Full-depth asphalt pavement defined, 14

G

Gallons of asphalt required at various widths, and gallons per square yard
Per 100 linear feet, Table XVI-6, 301
Per mile, Table XVI-7, 302

Gilsonite defined, 10

Grade crossing, asphalt paved, 207

Grouting and capping rock and stone structures with asphalt, 246

H

Hard asphalt defined, 9

Hauling asphalt mix, 129

Heavy traffic
Criteria for test limits, Table IV-12, 71

THE ASPHALT INSTITUTE

EXECUTIVE OFFICES AND LABORATORIES

Asphalt Institute Building

College Park, Maryland 20740

MEMBERS OF THE ASPHALT INSTITUTE

(As of March 1, 1969)

The Asphalt Institute is an international, nonprofit association sponsored by members of the petroleum asphalt industry to serve both users and producers of asphaltic materials through programs of engineering service, research and education. Membership is limited to refiners of asphalt from crude petroleum. Institute members provide quality products and advocate quality construction and timely maintenance.

A total of 52 Members have headquarters offices in:

United States	38	Europe	6
Canada	7	Middle East	1

ALLIED MATERIALS CORPORATION
Oklahoma City

AMERICAN OIL COMPANY
Chicago

APCO OIL CORPORATION
Oklahoma City

ASHLAND OIL & REFINING COMPANY
Ashland, Kentucky

ATLANTIC RICHFIELD COMPANY
Atlantic Marketing Area—*Philadelphia*
Richfield Marketing Area—*Los Angeles*

BP CANADA LIMITED
Montreal, Quebec, Canada

BRITISH PETROLEUM COMPANY LTD.
London, England

BYERLYTE COMPANY OF KOPPERS COMPANY, INC.
Heath, Ohio

CHAMPLIN PETROLEUM COMPANY
Fort Worth, Texas

CHEVRON ASPHALT COMPANY
San Francisco and Baltimore

CHEVRON OIL EUROPE, INC.
New York

COMPANIA ESPANOLA DE PETROLEOS, S.A.
Madrid, Spain

CONTINENTAL OIL COMPANY
Houston

DOUGLAS OIL COMPANY OF CALIFORNIA
Los Angeles

EDGINGTON OIL COMPANY
Long Beach, California

ESSO STANDARD EASTERN, INC.
New York

FARMERS UNION CENTRAL EXCHANGE, INC.
Laurel, Montana

GREAT NORTHERN OIL COMPANY
St. Paul

GULF OIL CANADA LIMITED
Toronto, Ontario, Canada

Industrial Asphalt, Inc., Agent for
GULF OIL CORPORATION
Los Angeles

HUMBLE OIL & REFINING COMPANY
Houston

HUNT OIL COMPANY
Dallas

HUSKY OIL LTD.
Calgary, Alberta, Canada

HUSKY OIL COMPANY
Cody, Wyoming

IMPERIAL OIL LIMITED
Toronto, Ontario, Canada

KERR-McGEE CORPORATION
Oklahoma City

LEONARD REFINERIES, INC.
Alma, Michigan

LION OIL COMPANY
Hydrocarbons Division, Monsanto Company
El Dorado, Arkansas

MACMILLAN RING-FREE OIL CO., INC.
New York and El Dorado, Ark.

MARATHON OIL COMPANY
Findlay, Ohio

MOBIL OIL CORPORATION
New York

MOBIL OIL CORPORATION
International Division—*New York*

MURPHY OIL CORPORATION
El Dorado, Arkansas

NESTE OY
 Helsinki, Finland

NEWHALL REFINING CO., INC.
 Newhall, California

NORTHWESTERN REFINING COMPANY
 St. Paul Park, Minnesota

A. B. NYNAS-PETROLEUM
 Nynashamn, Sweden

PAZ OIL COMPANY LIMITED
 Haifa, Israel

PETROFINA CANADA LTD.
 Montreal, Quebec, Canada

PHILLIPS PETROLEUM COMPANY
 Bartlesville, Oklahoma

RAFFINERIE BELGE DE PETROLES, S.A.
 Antwerp, Belgium

SHELL CANADA LIMITED
 Toronto, Ontario, Canada

SHELL INTERNATIONAL PETROLEUM CO., LTD.
 London, England

SHELL OIL COMPANY
 New York

SINCLAIR OIL CORPORATION
 New York

SOUTHLAND OIL COMPANY
 Yazoo City, Mississippi

**STANDARD OIL COMPANY
 OF BRITISH COLUMBIA, LTD.**
 Vancouver, B.C., Canada

**THE STANDARD OIL COMPANY
 (An Ohio Corporation)**
 Cleveland

SUN OIL COMPANY
 Sunoco Division—*Philadelphia*
 DX Division—*Tulsa*

UNION OIL COMPANY OF CALIFORNIA
 Los Angeles
 Pure Oil Division—*Palatine, Ill.*

U. S. OIL AND REFINING COMPANY
 Los Angeles

WITCO CHEMICAL CORPORATION
 Golden Bear Division—*Los Angeles*
 Pioneer Division—*New York*

CONTRIBUTOR

ENVOY PETROLEUM CO.
 Long Beach, California

INSTITUTE ENGINEERING OFFICES
(As of March 1, 1969)

EASTERN DIVISION

WASHINGTON, D.C. 20006—1901 Pennsylvania Ave.. N.W.
Connecticut, Delaware, District of Columbia, Kentucky, Maine, Maryland, Massachusetts, New Hampshire, New Jersey, New York, Ohio, Pennsylvania, Rhode Island, Vermont, Virginia, West Virginia

BOSTON, MASS.—(Address: 599 North Ave., Wakefield 01880)
Connecticut, Maine, Massachusetts, New Hampshire, Rhode Island, Vermont

ALBANY, N. Y. 12206—50 Colvin Ave.
New York State (except New York City, Westchester County and Long Island)

NEW YORK, N. Y. 10020—1270 Ave. of the Americas
New York City, Westchester County, Long Island, New Jersey

HARRISBURG, PA. 17102—800 N. Second St.
Pennsylvania

RICHMOND, VA. 23219—Travelers Bldg.
Virginia

COLUMBUS, OHIO 43215—50 W. Broad St.
Ohio

LOUISVILLE, KY. 40207—4050 Westport Road
Kentucky, West Virginia

SOUTHERN DIVISION

NEW ORLEANS, LA. 70130—John Hancock Bldg.
Alabama, Arkansas, Florida, Georgia, Louisiana, Mississippi, New Mexico, North Carolina, Oklahoma, South Carolina, Tennessee, Texas

HOUSTON, TEXAS 77027—2400 West Loop South
Texas

OKLAHOMA CITY, OKLA. 73102—Kermac Bldg.
Oklahoma, Northern Texas

NORTH LITTLE ROCK, ARK. 72116—4507 John F. Kennedy Blvd.
Arkansas

SANTA FE, N. MEX. 87501—10 Radio Plaza
New Mexico, Western Texas

MONTGOMERY, ALA. 36104—79 Commerce St.
Alabama, Tennessee

ATLANTA, GA. 30326—3384 Peachtree Road
Georgia

TALLAHASSEE, FLA. 32303—Tallahassee Bldg.
Florida

RALEIGH, N. C. 27605—2016 Cameron St.
North Carolina, South Carolina

NORTHERN DIVISION

ST. PAUL, MINN. 55104—276 N. Snelling Ave.
Colorado, Idaho, Illinois, Indiana, Iowa, Kansas, Michigan, Minnesota, Missouri, Montana, Nebraska, North Dakota, South Dakota, Utah, Wisconsin, Wyoming

EAST LANSING, MICH. 48823—1019 Trowbridge Road
Michigan

INDIANAPOLIS, IND. 46205—4165 Millersville Road
Indiana

SPRINGFIELD, ILL. 62703—2604 S. Sixth St.
Illinois (except Chicago), St. Louis County, Missouri

CHICAGO, ILL. 60656—4950 N. Harlem Ave.
Metropolitan Chicago

MADISON, WISC. 53711—4333 Nakoma Rd.
Wisconsin

AMES, IOWA 50010—430 Fifth St.
Iowa

KANSAS CITY, MO. 64112—612 W. 47th St.
Kansas, Missouri (except St. Louis Co.)

JEFFERSON CITY, MO. 65101—616 Howard St.
Missouri (except St. Louis Co.)

OMAHA, NEBR. 68132—6901 Dodge St.
Nebraska

BISMARCK, N. DAK. 58501—206 N. First St.
North Dakota, South Dakota

DENVER, COLO. 80215—1401 Saulsbury
Colorado, Utah, Wyoming

HELENA, MONTANA 59601—Power Block
Idaho, Montana

PACIFIC COAST DIVISION

BERKELEY, CALIF. 94710—810 University Ave.
Alaska, Arizona, California, Hawaii, Nevada, Oregon, Washington

LOS ANGELES, CALIF. 90017—1709 W. 8th St.
Southern California

SACRAMENTO, CALIF. 95814—1107 9th St.
Central and Northern California, Nevada

PHOENIX, ARIZ. 85016—3625 N. 16th St.
Arizona

PORTLAND, ORE. 97225—4475 S.W. Scholls Ferry Rd.
Oregon

OLYMPIA, WASH. 98501—120 Union Avenue Building
Alaska, Washington

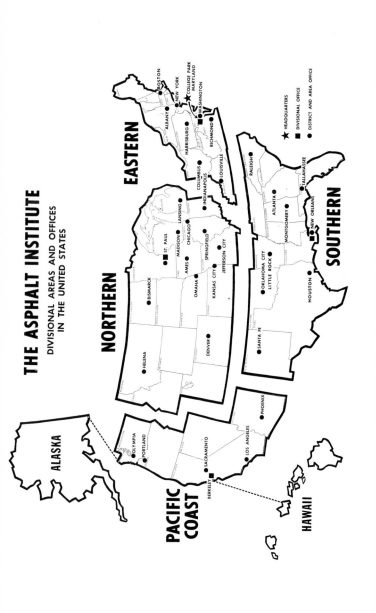

THE ASPHALT INSTITUTE

DIVISIONAL AREAS AND OFFICES
IN THE UNITED STATES

★ HEADQUARTERS
■ DIVISIONAL OFFICE
● DISTRICT AND AREA OFFICE

EASTERN

NORTHERN

SOUTHERN

PACIFIC COAST

ALASKA

HAWAII

BOSTON
NEW YORK
COLLEGE PARK MARYLAND
WASHINGTON
ALBANY
HARRISBURG
RICHMOND
COLUMBUS
INDIANAPOLIS
LOUISVILLE
RALEIGH
TALLAHASSEE
LANSING
ST. PAUL
MADISON
CHICAGO
AMES
SPRINGFIELD
OMAHA
JEFFERSON CITY
KANSAS CITY
ATLANTA
MONTGOMERY
NEW ORLEANS
BISMARCK
OKLAHOMA CITY
LITTLE ROCK
HOUSTON
HELENA
DENVER
SANTA FE
PHOENIX
OLYMPIA
PORTLAND
SACRAMENTO
BERKELEY
LOS ANGELES

NOTES

NOTES

NOTES

NOTES

NOTES

NOTES

NOTES

NOTES

NOTES

NOTES

NOTES

NOTES

L/15M/468